THE TROUBLED CALLING

Crisis in the Medical Establishment

THE TROUBLED CALLING

Crisis in the
Medical Establishment

SELIG GREENBERG

THE MACMILLAN COMPANY, NEW YORK
COLLIER-MACMILLAN LIMITED, LONDON

First Printing

The Macmillan Company, New York
Collier-Macmillan Canada Ltd., Toronto, Ontario

Library of Congress catalog card number: 65-17826

Acknowledgment is gratefully made to the following copyright holders for
permission to reprint from previously published materials:

The Journal of Medical Education published by The Association of American Medical Colleges and Dr. Osler L. Peterson for the excerpt from Part 2,
Volume 31, Number 12, December 1956. Copyright 1956 by The Journal of
Medical Education.

The Journal of Medical Education published by The Association of American Medical Colleges and Dr. Charles May for the excerpt from Volume
36, Number 1, January, 1961. Copyright 1961 by The Journal of Medical
Education.

The New England Journal of Medicine for the excerpts from "The Student
Looks at Drug Advertising," Number 259, 1958; "Medicine and Society"
by August Heckscher, Number 262, 1960; and "The Next Ten Years in
Medicine" by Dr. Caldwell B. Esselstyn, Number 266, 1962. Copyright 1958,
1960 and 1962 by The New England Journal of Medicine.

Printed in the United States of America

To Leon

ACKNOWLEDGMENTS

I HAVE drawn on so many published sources for material for this book and have interviewed so many physicians and other authorities in the health field who have generously helped me with information and advice that it would be impossible to try to list them. While the counsel of those whom I have consulted has been invaluable, they are in no way responsible for the conclusions, which are solely my own.

I am deeply grateful to the staffs of the John Hay and Biological Sciences Libraries at Brown University and the Library of the Rhode Island Medical Society for their unfailing courtesy and cooperation. I also am greatly indebted to the editors of the Providence (R.I.) *Journal-Bulletin* for granting me a leave of absence to do the research and writing. Above all, I owe a debt of gratitude to my wife, Miriam, for her encouragement, critical objectivity, and infinite forbearance.

CONTENTS

Preface   xi

1   The Doctor's Tarnished Image in an Age of Revolution   1

2   The Man Behind the Stethoscope   20

3   The Vanishing Family Physician   51

4   The Mystique of the Doctor-Patient Relationship   71

5   The Hospital: Focus of Conflict   98

6   The Crisis of Voluntary Health Insurance   129

7   Group Practice: Blueprint for the Future   166

8   Is American Medical Care the Best in the World?   196

9   The United States Faces a Mounting Shortage of
Medical Manpower   234

10   The Uses and Abuses of Drugs   274

11   Organized Medicine Fights for the *Status Quo*   321

12   Medicine's Widening Horizons and Responsibilities   347

TOWERING OVER the sprawling edifice of modern medicine is the uniquely potent figure of the doctor, who since time immemorial has held a special place in the hearts and minds of men. With all his newly acquired knowledge and skills, today's physician, like his predecessors, often evokes an aura of magic. A curious amalgam of the theoretical and the pragmatic, the idealistic and the expedient, he is engaged in a calling of extraordinary complexity and many incongruities in which all of us have a vital stake.

The practice of medicine is at the same time a way of earning a living, a compact with society, a science, and an art. Medical care is a commodity offered for sale to those who can afford it, and yet it also is primarily a personal service that the medical profession is—in theory, at any rate—dedicated to render to all those who need it. Despite its enormous progress, medicine remains an imprecise discipline, its dimensions varied, its quality difficult to measure, the elements making up its costs intricate.

Imperative for a better comprehension of the tangled interplay of forces in the American medical scene is a clearer picture of the exceptional character of the medical profession and of the doctor in his variety of roles—as a member of a tightly run guild fiercely resisting outside controls and clinging to a system of long and arduous teaching by apprenticeship; as a practitioner who, at his best, combines the clinician's intuitive art with the scientist's power of analysis and integration; as a healer performing both a realistic and a symbolic function in his relationships with his patients; as one who carries the load of a fearful and lonely responsibility and is often confronted by demands for understanding and compassion beyond his ability to meet; as a man torn by the clash between the priestly nature of his vocation and the economic considerations of his career, deeply troubled by the sweeping changes in the structure of health care and the need to readjust himself to a radically altered setting. Only through some insight into why doctors act the way they do, individually and collectively, can we hope to gain a more balanced view of the multitude of medical care problems now crowding for a solution.

A considerable portion of this study of the changing patterns of medical care and practice in the United States, therefore, is devoted to an examination of the processes that shape the medical profession, of its motivations and dilemmas, and of the formal as well as informal mechanisms through which it goes about its business. All these elements have a profound bearing on such crucial questions as how we can benefit more effectively from the harvest of new medical knowledge, whether and how our splintered medical services can somehow be put together again, how the essential personal relationship between doctor and patient can be preserved and enhanced in the face of all the forces tending to depersonalize it, and how the economic burden of medical care can be made more bearable.

This, one observer has aptly said, is "an age of fear and trembling," an era in which "cultures change radically, values are different, even diseases change."

Amid the constant flux in medicine and its social and economic setting and in a field surrounded with a vast amount of emotion, the temptation, inevitably, is to turn the complex grays of reality into stark black and white, to seek scapegoats, and to offer panaceas. So controversial have the issues of medical care become that neutrality itself is frequently suspect. But these issues, involving as they do the well-being of millions and the ultimate decisions of life and death, are far too momentous to be relinquished to the extremists of either the left or the right. Their solution can no more be entrusted to those who would rashly embark on perilous experiments than it can be left solely in the hands of those who have a vested interest in preserving the *status quo* and whose philosophy is that "everything's fine; don't rock the boat."

Painful though the process may be, the medical profession cannot evade the responsibility of adapting itself to the winds of social and scientific change. But a first and basic step toward the development of a more rational and effective system of health care must be an effort to separate fact from fancy, to clarify the problems and conflicts that beset the doctor in an age of revolution, to pinpoint the real issues so often obscured by slogans. It is to such an effort that this book is dedicated.

THE TROUBLED CALLING

Crisis in the Medical Establishment

CHAPTER ONE

The Doctor's Tarnished Image in an Age of Revolution

I

TWO THINGS can safely be said in summary of the state of American medicine today, and between them they tell a story of striking contrasts, of remarkable achievements and of promises yet to be fulfilled, of great successes and of perplexing failures.

On the one hand, medical science has scored prodigious advances in warding off death and opening up new vistas of healthier and longer life. Until barely two generations ago, medicine had little more than love and comforting to offer to the sick. Since then, countless lives have been saved and untold suffering spared through greater scientific progress than in all previous recorded history.

The other side of the coin, however, is a disheartening record of still unrealized potentialities. The dismal facts are that knowledge about how to prevent and cure disease has far outstripped its application, that medicine has infinitely more to give people than they are actually getting, that numerous health needs remain unmet in the richest country in the world, and that progress has been slow in the devising of the new and more efficient methods of organization urgently called for by the strikingly changing pattern of medical care.

This lag between the sociology and economics of medicine and its technology goes a long way toward explaining what must, on the face of it, appear to be a highly paradoxical situation.

Why does such a sense of profound discontent and unease hang over the American medical scene at the very time of medicine's greatest triumphs?

Why, at a time when doctors can do so much more for us than ever before, has the medical profession's prestige declined and the physician's traditional image as the compassionate healer become tarnished?

Why, at a time when medical services have never been in greater demand, has confidence in the profession's vaunted dedication to service materially weakened, and why is there so much grumbling not only about the high costs of medical care but, perhaps even more, about its growing impersonality and the alienation of doctors and patients?

Many elements figure in the answers to these questions, and there is no single, pat explanation.

There is no doubt that the organized medical profession has given far too little thought to the whirl of scientific as well as social, economic, and political change in which medicine has been caught up. The profession's clinging to a grossly outdated concept of rugged individualism has a great deal to do with the prevailing climate of unrest. While the average physician is conscientious and sincerely concerned about the welfare of his patients, there is little question that, on the whole, his role as economic man has been played badly. This is due not so much to the physician's rapacity as to the fact that he is in the incongruous position of being dedicated simultaneously to humanity and to the profit motive. Under the existing system of payment for each individual service, the doctor's need to get paid inevitably conflicts at times with the patient's need to get well. Collectively, the medical profession has been far more concerned with resisting the tide of change than with guiding it.

Basically, the host of bewildering problems now plaguing doctors and patients alike is fully as due to the revolution wrought by medical science. Its spectacular advances have profoundly affected the traditional arrangements under which medical services are rendered, organized, and paid for. In large measure, today's problems—notably the steadily mounting cost of medical care and the central dilemma of how medicine can be scientific and yet remain human—are the direct results of yesterday's successes. Medicine has yet to evolve ways of readjusting the conventional structure of its services to meet drastically changing demands.

With the conquest of the infectious diseases and the remarkable expansion of the human life-span, there has been a radical change in the pattern of illness itself and in the age makeup of the population of the United States. The long-term chronic ailments, which have emerged as the nation's foremost medical concern,

demand a far more exacting regimen of continuous and comprehensive care than the episodic treatment required by the short-
term acute infectious conditions. Longer life and a constantly
growing army of older people have led to striking alterations in
the social fabric of our society. Equally far-reaching are the economic implications of a rapidly rising proportion of children in
our population, owing to a surging birthrate and dramatic reductions in infant mortality.

With the increasing complexity of diagnostic and treatment
procedures, hospitals and other health services have grown into a
huge industry that depends on the recruitment and coordination
of thousands of people with technical skills and on heavy capital
investment in expensive equipment. Neither the price nor the
demand spiral shows any signs of leveling off. The great challenge, therefore, is to improve medicine's organizational efficiency and bring costs within the reach of the average person.
Only then will he be able to benefit from the kind of medical
care that we now have the scientific know-how to give but all too
often still fail to provide.

Equally challenging is the need for restoring the unity of
medical care. One of the great incongruities of modern medicine
is that while there has been a growing realization of the importance of the emotional elements in illness and of the need for
considering the patient within the context of his life history and
environment, the accelerating trend toward specialization and the
other effects of the complexity of medical science have been
working in the opposite direction, resulting in assembly-line care
and concentration on organic symptoms. Much has been gained in
the past few decades through the expansion of the frontiers of
medical knowledge, but something inordinately precious has been
lost in regard to the individual's deeper needs. Can the dismemberment of the patient by the fragmentation of medicine into
specialties be halted? Can he, as well as the doctor, be made
whole again? Can the widening gulf between technical proficiency and a concern for man's condition ever be bridged? The
least we can do is try.

As the standard of living and educational level of Americans
continue to rise and as they become more knowledgeable about
what up-to-date medical care can do for them, they expect more.
We no longer regard many disabilities as inevitable or accept the

idea that good medical care is a commodity to be made available only to those who can afford it. More and more, we have come to demand it as a basic human right, no less so than food, shelter, and clothing. Our per capita spending for medical purposes has more than doubled in the past thirty years, even after due allowance for rising prices, and will undoubtedly go up still further. The forward march of science has made medical services inherently more expensive. But we must insist on getting full value at the lowest possible price consistent with high quality of care. We have a right to expect—and should use political leverage, if necessary, to get it—more and better and reasonably priced care.

II

Medical care cost much less about a century ago and was worth much less.

In those days, life was infinitely more hazardous than it is today. Illness was much more prevalent and death far more rampant, particularly among children. Such scourges as scarlet fever, diphtheria, smallpox, whooping cough, and measles carried off the young by the tens of thousands every year. Typhoid fever, pneumonia, and tuberculosis were widespread and often fatal. Life expectancy at birth was little more than half what it now is. The death of women during childbirth was commonplace.

About a hundred years ago, a couple with twelve children could expect to raise six to adulthood. Epidemic diseases were the chief cause of child mortality. In 1900, death still claimed one out of every four boys and girls before they reached adolescence. Today, only eight out of every ten thousand children who have survived their first year fail to reach the age of twenty-four.

In the 1860's, diagnosis was mostly guesswork and treatment almost entirely symptomatic, being rarely able to get at the basic causes of illness. Treatment still consisted largely, as it had for centuries, in emetics, purges, bloodlettings, cuppings, blisterings, and poultices. With anesthesiology in its infancy, surgery remained a brutal ordeal and postsurgical infections a deadly menace.

About two or three generations ago, within the memory of millions of living Americans, the doctor with his battered black bag and such paraphernalia as he could carry in his saddlebag still constituted the sum total of the pitifully small arsenal of death-fighting weapons that medicine could muster. The patient's home was the hospital; the kitchen, the operating room. There were no X rays and no blood chemistry to detect the early and still curable stages of sickness. Laudanum and morphine were the most effective drugs available.

Scientific medicine, the product of industrial technology, did not really start coming of age until after the turn of the century —later than the general use of electricity. The telegraph had been invented by the time that anesthesia was first in common use, and aseptic surgery came in along with the automobile. It was not until about fifty years ago, as the late Dr. Lawrence J. Henderson of Harvard Medical School put it in a memorable comment, that a random patient taking a random disease to a random doctor stood better than a fifty-fifty chance of "benefiting from the encounter."

Since then, the progress of medicine represents one of the most brilliant chapters in the history of civilization. Increasingly adroit and more precise diagnostic tools have been developed to ferret out the secrets of formerly inaccessible areas of the body. The incredibly delicate operations being performed today would have been unimaginable a decade or two ago. The impact of the new drugs that have poured from the research laboratories since penicillin was first introduced in 1940 has been incalculable. Fully 90 per cent of the drugs being prescribed today were not available twenty years ago, and nearly half of them have come into the market only during the past decade. Steady advances have been made in the use of blood and blood fractions in transfusions. Provocative new insights into the emotional origin of bodily ailments have been provided by psychiatry. Improved physical rehabilitation methods, designed to restore lost functions and teach the handicapped to adjust to their impairments, are now saving many thousands from the bleak fate of lifelong invalidism.

More and more common are such surgical feats as the removal of entire lungs, the repair of congenital or acquired lesions of the heart, the resection of segments of the aorta and their replacement by vascular grafts or synthetic substitutes, and the transplanting of corneas from one eye to another.

High in the galaxy of new medications transforming the practice of medicine and spelling the difference between life and death for millions stand insulin, the sulfas, the antibiotics, liver extracts, various hormones, the anticoagulants, and agents for lowering or raising the blood pressure. Also far-reaching have been the effects of combinations of vitamins used to correct nutritional deficiencies and antihistamines used to relieve allergies. Immunization against polio is now possible, and a vaccine against measles appears to be well on the way. The tranquilizers have provided an important new tool in the field of mental illness and emotional disturbance. Other exciting possibilities are chemicals to arrest certain forms of cancer, solvents to remove cholesterol from the bloodstream, and new products to subjugate many still resistant viral diseases.

The great plagues of the past are no longer with us, many once common diseases have virtually vanished, and a number of maladies considered incurable not so long ago can now be cured. Even where cure is as yet impossible, the symptoms of many ailments can be alleviated and life extended. Better nutrition, housing, and working conditions have contributed materially to the generally improved health picture.

The death rate from all causes and for all ages has been nearly halved since 1900 and cut by 12 per cent in the past decade. Even more spectacular has been the drop in mortality from a number of infectious diseases. The tuberculosis death rate has fallen by 97 per cent since 1910. Deaths from influenza and pneumonia have decreased by 89 per cent since the introduction of the sulfa drugs in 1937. Mortality from acute nephritis and other kidney diseases has been reduced by 60 per cent. Appendicitis fatalities are now a rarity, even though a ruptured appendix was often a death sentence as recently as the 1930's. How mightily the odds of life against death have been turned in our favor may be gauged from this fact: if the mortality rates of 1900 had remained unchanged, there would have been 1,700,000 additional deaths in the United States in 1963 alone.

The dread that a child might be snatched by death has been lifted from millions of homes. The fear also has been taken out of childbirth. Since 1930, the loss of life among mothers during childbearing has been slashed from sixty-seven to only about three out of every ten thousand live births.

The steadily declining mortality rate has greatly lengthened the average duration of family life. Couples married in 1900 could expect, on the average, about thirty years of married life together before one of them died. Since then, the average length of married life has climbed to forty-three years. The chances of reaching a golden wedding anniversary have more than doubled for the typical couple since the turn of the century—from nineteen in a hundred to forty-two in a hundred.

Orphanhood has strikingly diminished as a social problem. In 1900, more than a quarter of the children born in this country faced the prospect of being orphaned by the time they reached the age of eighteen. In 1920, one child out of six was an orphan. Now the proportion is less than one in twenty. Whereas children who had lost both parents made up almost 2 per cent of the total child population in 1920, they currently represent only one-tenth of 1 per cent of all children under eighteen. A direct result has been the rapid disappearance of the dreary orphan asylums that were once such a notable feature of the social scene.

The average life expectancy of Americans has risen to the Biblical three score and ten, being, at birth, 67.3 years for a boy and 73.9 years for a girl. Twenty-three years have been added to the average life-span since 1900, almost as much as the human race accomplished in the preceding twenty centuries. This has extended both the working life and the retirement years of the average person and has opened the way for challenging opportunities as yet unrealized.

Longer life has inevitably meant a sharp increase in the incidence of the chronic diseases of old age. But scientists now think that many conditions lumped together as "degenerative" actually result from cumulative nutritional deficiencies and the after-effects of previous illnesses rather than from the aging process itself. While the ultimate appearance of chronic disorders cannot always be prevented, they can now often be delayed or mitigated.

The elimination or control of disabling childhood diseases not only has prolonged the average life-span but has removed some of the causes of old-age disability by reducing the serious impairments formerly left by these ailments in surviving patients. Increasingly becoming a thing of the past are the crippling mutilations of rickets and paralytic polio and the havoc of weak hearts, damaged kidneys, and impaired vision and hearing left by typhoid and scarlet fever, diphtheria, and measles. The control of whooping cough is eliminating bronchial conditions and their aftereffects. Penicillin, together with the general raising of the standard of living, which has cut down susceptibility to streptococcal infection, has provided a specific preventive against rheumatic fever, not so long ago a leading cause of heart disease.

Progress in medical science has proceeded at a geometric rather than an arithmetic pace. Among the advances chalked up during the past decade have been further refinement of the antibiotics and cortisone, major improvements in cardiac and thoracic surgery, the treatment of cerebral thrombosis with anticoagulants, and expanding knowledge of immunology and of the crucial role of blood compatibility.

As the results of today's laboratory investigations become part of clinical practice, some of the remaining incurable conditions will before long be added to the list of controllable diseases. Greatly intensified research on cancer and the heart and artery disorders holds out the promise of still further extension of the average life-span. We have barely begun to exploit the enormous potentialities for the prevention of illness through the fostering of sound health practices and the early detection of disease. Physicians are increasingly giving thought to a broader concept that views health not merely as the absence of disease but as a state of optimal physical, mental, and social well-being. The newly emerging goal of positive health takes into consideration not only the physiology of the body but also the wide variety of social, economic, and emotional factors that play a vital part in determining the level of the individual's overall efficiency.

The tremendous increase in research funds since the end of World War II and the profusion of new research tools, methods, and concepts are leading medical scientists to a much broader and deeper understanding of human biology than was ever dreamed of before. The use of radioactive isotopes and the development of new methods of molecular analysis and electronic measurement— along with startling advances in the fields of computation, microscopy, microchemistry, and tissue culture—are making possible more meaningful studies of cell genetics, function, and differentiation. This is producing a clearer view of the factors involved in normal and abnormal growth and in biological damage and repair. Significant strides are at the same time being made by psychology and psychiatry toward better comprehension of mental and emotional processes, the dynamics of personality, and the shaping of interpersonal relationships. New light on the bearing that the living and working environment has on health and disease is beginning to emerge from a variety of statistical and epidemiological studies. This concerted and unprecedented research effort is sure to pay further rich dividends in fuller and longer lives.

III

It is against this backdrop of brilliant accomplishment and of still greater victories looming on the horizon that we must view the serious deficiencies in our existing system of health care and the acute problems of readjustment posed by progress, within medicine itself and within the society it serves.

The *New England Journal of Medicine*, the most distinguished medical publication in the United States, said not so long ago that "medical practice is undergoing a metamorphosis, almost overwhelmed by the scientific advances that it has had to absorb, hard pressed by its economic problems, encumbered by its heavy weight of traditionalism, hampered by the very humaneness of its followers." Characteristically, the *Journal*, the official organ of the Massachusetts Medical Society, probably overstated the role of the medical profession's humanitarian motivations and understated that of the vested interests of mind and pocketbook opposing a rational reorganization of our health services.

There is a growing awareness, in and out of the medical profession, that the health care job being done today falls far short of what it could be with the knowledge, skills, and tools now at our command. Despite repeated assurances from the headquarters of the American Medical Association in Chicago that we have the best medical care in the world, there is ample evidence to the contrary.

Sober examination of the realities of the American medical scene shows that while, at its best, the quality of medical care in this country is unsurpassed, much of it is uneven and some of it quite poor; that adequate medical care is not now available in full measure to people of low and even medium incomes; that the poor, the aged, the mentally ill, and others who need medical care most generally receive the meagerest amount and poorest quality of services; and that we still carry a heavy burden of needless illness, suffering, disability, and premature death. For confirmation, take the statement of a prominent medical authority that "each year more people die of preventable diseases in this country than were lost in battle throughout all of World War II."

All too obvious in many sectors of our medical economy is a gross disparity between need and service. Since the volume of care given usually depends on ability to pay rather than on the severity of the disease, early symptoms are often ignored until they develop into serious illness. The frequent result is a residue of chronic impairments. There is no major disease whose toll could not be markedly reduced by more intensive application of currently known preventive and therapeutic measures.

For millions, patented nostrums—long known as the "poor man's medical care"—remain the first recourse in illness. These over-the-counter medications rarely treat more than the superficial symptoms. Even when they do no harm, they often delay the application of the proper therapy, sometimes until it is too late to be effective.

Equally disturbing is the widespread tendency in American medical practice toward promiscuous overmedication on the basis of symptoms rather than prescribing only after careful diagnostic work-up. Adequate diagnosis and the unraveling of the snarled skein of the patient's difficulties take time, precisely what the average busy practitioner lacks these days. The frequent result is the indiscriminate prescription of drugs, all too often under the impact of frenetic pharmaceutical promotion. This kind of symptomatic treatment usually does more for the doctor's than for the patient's well-being and peace of mind.

We have barely begun to tackle the tremendous but by no means hopeless problem created by the steadily mounting incidence (owing to the growing numbers of older people) of chronic diseases that are concomitants of longer life. The treatment of such long-term disorders as heart and artery disease, high blood pressure, diabetes, gastrointestinal conditions, arthritis, and rheumatism is much more complex and costly than that of the infectious ailments. Chronic illnessees require a lot of the physician's time and an intimate knowledge of the patient's background and environment. It requires sophisticated diagnostic procedures to detect and define such pathological conditions at the earliest possible moment and multidisciplinary skills for their treatment. It requires a substantial expansion of institutions for long-term care and an upgrading of their standards.

The condition of a large proportion of existing nursing homes, which, unlike hospitals, are mostly privately owned and operated for profit, is a scandal. Many of them are pitifully deficient in services needed for proper care and provide little more than shelter. The supervision of these homes must be tightened up to assure a more adequate level of care. The problem is one of quantity as well as quality: government estimates are that at least five hundred thousand additional nursing-home beds are needed.

We also have a long way to go in meeting the needs of patients with mental illnesses and emotional disturbances. At the present time, these patients occupy nearly half of the nation's hospital beds. There has been some raising of standards in recent years in the state mental hospitals. But the level of care they provide is still shockingly inadequate and primarily custodial rather than curative. This may be readily seen from the fact that the average of about $5.80 a day per patient now being spent in state and municipal psychiatric hospitals is about one-third of the expenditure in Federal institutions for the mentally ill. This statistic is even more shocking when compared with the average per patient per day expense of nearly $39 in general hospitals.

But while patients hospitalized for serious psychoses usually receive some degree of medical attention, only a small fraction of the hundreds of thousands suffering from significant psychoneuroses or from a variety of emotional disturbances are getting any at all.

In few areas of medical care is the operation of the American class system so crystal clear as it is in psychiatry. The close relationship in our vaunted democracy between family income and not only the volume but also the type of psychiatric care was reported in detail a few years ago in an enlightening study by a group of Yale University scientists. They found that economic and social status generally determines the diagnostic labels attached to mental illnesses and the choice of therapy. Lower-income patients are rarely able to receive private psychiatric treatment and are far more apt to wind up in the chronic wards of state mental hospitals, doomed to vegetate there for the rest of their lives.

"Separated from us," a prominent psychiatrist wrote recently, "are all the troubled people in villages and farms. Away from us are the wretched drunks and the youthful gangs in the wilderness of our cities. Removed from us are most of the poor, the criminal, the drug addicts. Though there are some low-cost clinics, their waiting lists are long, and we are all too easily and too often available to the select few of certain streets and certain neighborhoods."

Another field in which the role of class distinctions is sharply evident is that of dental care, where a huge backlog of unmet need exists for the great majority of Americans and particularly for the lower-income groups. The great gap between dental needs and services is shown by the findings of a U.S. Public Health Service study that more than one out of six Americans have never gone to a dentist in their lives, that about half the children in this country under the age of fifteen have yet to make their first visit to a dentist's office, and that about seventy million persons had not been to a dentist in three or more years. Only one out of every three Americans sees a dentist at all in the course of a year, and the proportion of those receiving reasonably adequate dental care is considerably below this ratio. There are two reasons for this deplorable state of affairs: the costliness of protracted dental care and the tendency of most people to look upon relief from a toothache as the principal province of dentistry, in total disregard of the fact that prevention of dental disease is one of the keys to good health. The rate of those who regularly consult a dentist is three times as high among the well-to-do as it is in low-income families.

There are mounting shortages of doctors, dentists, nurses, and auxiliary health personnel and a gross maldistribution of medical manpower in various sections of the country. The heaviest concentration of physicians is among those who have the most money to spend and not where the greatest health needs exist. The sellers' market in medical care, reflected in crowded waiting rooms and in the general reluctance to make home and night calls, is a heavy strain on overburdened doctors and a source of endless vexations for patients. There is little question that far too many physicians nowadays are working too hard and making too much money for their own good or for the good of their patients.

Excessive patient loads and the advances of medical science have made heavy inroads on the doctor's traditional role as a friend and counselor who takes the time to look beyond the purely physical symptoms and to meet the patient's frequently overwhelming need to get things off his chest. It has been predicted that computers may before long take over the job of making the diagnosis and outlining the course of treatment. But no computer will ever be able to provide the warmth, compassion, and personal magic that have always been among a good doctor's most essential qualities. Far from eliminating the need for these qualities, medical progress has greatly widened the scope of the physician's responsibilities.

The resentment of patients over a frequent lack of sufficient personal attention from their doctors, the costliness of medical care, and the fact that some physicians perform needless procedures and overcharge have led to widespread criticism of the medical profession as a whole. These and other trends in present-day medical practice, along with the posture of organized medicine, have brought about a growing estrangement between the profession and the people whom it serves and have drastically altered its public image.

Much of the aura of mysticism that has long surrounded the doctor has been dispelled, and the full glare of public scrutiny has been turned on him and his work, with unhappy results for all concerned. The traditional popular stereotype of the physician as an idealist dedicated to his calling and worthy of unquestioning confidence has, to a considerable degree, been replaced by an equally extravagant view of him as a reactionary and a money grabber who is more interested in a Cadillac and a mink coat for his wife than in the welfare of his patients.

This new image of the medical profession is patently over-simplified and unfair. Most doctors are conservative and fearful of change in the medical *status quo*. Some of them are unscrupulous or incompetent or both. But there unquestionably are thousands of physicians who care deeply for the well-being of their patients, who are considerate and competent, and whose backbreaking and often heartbreaking workday frequently runs from early in the morning until late at night.

There appear to be three major reasons for the general denigration of the doctor in the current American scale of values. For one thing, it is a natural reaction to the age-old tendency to overvalue doctors and to endow them with qualities akin to those associated with the priesthood. Because the physician's services are often performed under emotion-charged circumstances, he has always been either extravagantly praised or wildly damned for not being superhuman. People expect doctors to act with a kind of religious consecration. When forced to trust life itself to medical judgment, they are shocked to discover that physicians sometimes act with less than complete selflessness. The average person's growing sophistication with regard to medical matters, albeit superficial and largely drawn from newspaper and magazine reading, tends in itself to detract from his old unqualified admiration for the doctor as the sole possessor of arcane medical knowledge.

Another and even more important reason for the downgrading of the physician is the drastic effect of the scientific revolution in medicine on the traditional framework of medical care. What was once an individual and intensely personal service has been turned into a highly intellectualized discipline requiring complicated and costly professional arrangements. This has brought enormous benefits but also has served to impair in a great many ways the intimate links between doctor and patient and has left in its wake a long train of frustrations.

The changed public image of the medical profession also springs from a growing perception that there are grave weaknesses in the prevailing system of medical care and practice and that something better is needed. In the socially conscious climate of the 1960's, when by common consent the public interest is held to be paramount in many facets of our lives, a great number of Americans are losing patience with the medical profession's collective behavior and the inflexibility of its standpat leadership, with its failure to meet the challenge of changing times and its stubborn insistence that it alone knows what is good for the rest of us in the field of medical economics.

Medicine and its practice have been completely transformed within the lifetime of many of us. Not so long ago the economics of medical care was as simple as its technology of unaided perception and manual therapy. In those days, the physician not only could carry in his head the few rules of thumb that made up all the available medical knowledge but also was usually familiar with the patient's background and had a pretty good idea of what he could pay. The doctor's investment in training and equipment was small, and he could afford to give away his services or to receive payment in kind. So it was natural for him to carry on his practice as an independent entrepreneur.

The swift pace of scientific progress has changed a personal art into a multifaceted discipline. Today's physician is the product of long and expensive training and has at his command a bewildering store of information and tools. But the vastly greater effectiveness of medicine has increasingly deprived him of his ability to do the job by himself. Medical services now often require a wide range of highly differentiated professional and auxiliary skills.

In the simpler society of the past it was easy for the doctor to keep close to the patient's problems and anxieties. He rarely had to take a history, except for the immediate onset of the illness. He knew most of his patients as individual personalities and, even without articulating it, took their background into account in his diagnosis and treatment. But today's patients often come to the physician's office and to clinics and hospitals more or less as strangers. Their life experiences and beliefs and expectations, their special ways of feeling and reacting—all the things that are essential to correct diagnosis and treatment—are apt to be quite different from the doctor's. Complicating the situation has been the mechanical apparatus interpolated between doctor and patient. Getting a meaningful history and effectively applying its findings have become much more difficult tasks for the physician.

Specialization has greatly improved the quality of medical care, but it also has made it enormously more costly and has tended to disperse responsibility for the patient. What had formerly been a private relationship between two individuals has been reshaped into a large-scale industry involving some fifty medical specialties and subspecialties and more than sixty ancillary technical occupations.

As medicine has gained in effectiveness, Americans have been using more and more of its services. Thirty years ago, the average person saw a doctor twice a year. Today the annual average is five visits. In the same period, the annual hospital admission rate has increased from 56 per 1,000 population to 135 per 1,000, which means that at the present time, nearly one out of every seven Americans is hospitalized in the course of a year.

Medical care has become an increasingly important part of the American economy. More than 2,500,000 persons are now engaged in occupations directly related to maintaining the health of the American people as compared with only 1,000,000 in 1940 and 1,600,000 in 1950. As one of the nation's biggest and fastest growing industries, this vast enterprise clearly requires further coordination of its services, the pooling of skills and facilities, and a more equitable distribution of its products.

Drastic alterations are meanwhile also under way in the relationship between the producers and the consumers in medicine. The fact that three out of every four Americans now have some form of health insurance is bringing about a fundamental change in attitude toward the economics of medical care. More and more, arrangements for paying for at least some medical services are no longer made between individual physicians and patients who are sick and anxious. They are being made instead by groups of people who are well and capable of making up their minds soberly as to how they want to spend their money. No longer forced to bargain when they are flat on their backs, they are much less likely to accept the medical profession's claim to exclusive authority in an area in which it has no special competence.

Health insurance has proven to be a good deal more than merely a mechanism for spreading the risk of the cost of illness. It not only has generated new demand by removing some economic barriers to medical care but also has become a rallying point for the organization of consumers determined to get their money's worth. Significant comparative data on experience under various types of insurance arrangments are now becoming available for the first time and show that considerable savings are possible by organizing doctors to work in teams and by laying emphasis on preventive care and not only on the treatment of disease after it develops.

No such growth of prepayment as we have witnessed since the 1940's would have been possible without the advent of large-scale collective bargaining, with health insurance coverage as one of labor's most important fringe benefits. Management, which is now paying several billion dollars a year in health insurance premiums for its employees, has acquired a vital interest in medical economics. Labor's stake in health insurance is certain to be of even greater consequence. More than forty million workers and members of their families are enrolled under union-negotiated insurance contracts, and a number of labor leaders have emerged as knowledgeable and articulate spokesmen for the interests of consumers. Organized labor is increasingly realizing that its interest in health care must go beyond the traditional process of collective bargaining with employers and extend to the manner in which medical services are organized and provided.

Medicine's coming of age has coincided with a series of revolutionary changes in American society that have deeply affected every facet of health care. The population of the United States has increased since 1900 from 76,000,000 to about 195,000,000 and is expected to reach 233,000,000 by 1975. This is certain to aggravate the already critical scarcity of medical manpower. The oldest as well as the youngest age groups, both of which use considerably more medical services than do the middle groups, have grown much faster than the population as a whole. The number of men and women aged sixty-five and over has climbed from 3,100,000 at the turn of the century to about 18,000,000, or from 4 per cent to more than 9.3 per cent of the country's population, and is expected to total 22,000,000 by 1975. The baby boom that set in after World War II appears to have become a permanent feature of the American way of life, and there is reason to expect a continued heavy demand for the services of obstetricians and pediatricians.

There have been radical changes in the nation's income structure. In the last twenty years, the number of families with incomes of more than $5,000 a year has shot up from 5 per cent of American households to about half of them. This dramatic development has been offset by the decreasing value of the dollar; and for millions of families, the difficulty in meeting the costs of medical care remains acute. But the higher average level of personal income has been an important factor in the growth of the market for medical care.

Fifty years ago, city dwellers still made up less than half of the population of the United States. Now about three out of every four Americans live in urban and suburban areas, where the consumption of medical services is considerably higher than in rural communities. Generally, better nutrition and housing and greater leisure and opportunities for recreation make for better health. On the other hand, the stepped-up tempo of living, with its increased tensions, and a number of other hazards associated with our industrialized society are working in the opposite direction.

One of the basic dilemmas in the realm of health care is that scientific progress has multiplied the problems of medical economics almost as fast as it has solved some of the problems of therapy. Unfortunately, medical science has progressed much more rapidly than its social application. Still largely unresolved are the issues of how the abundant products of science can be more widely and economically utilized through more efficient organizational methods.

The conclusion is inescapable that medicine has in many respects outgrown its traditional arrangements for serving patients. But progress in devising new ways of providing health care and of paying for it has been slow. The creative scientific objectivity that has made possible medical miracles is yet to be matched by a similar outlook in reexamining and changing old ways or by a similar ingenuity in fashioning organizational innovations.

Everything that has happened in the progress of medicine points to the advantages of group practice—an arrangement under which doctors share offices, equipment, and patients—as a method of organization most conducive to quality and economy, particularly when it is combined with a program of comprehensive insurance. The urgency of such a team approach is underscored by the steadily proliferating body of medical knowledge and the costliness of up-to-date medical care.

But the medical profession has continued to cling to solo, fee-for-service practice, a form of piecework remuneration rendered obsolete by the fundamental changes in the character and cost of health services. Our medical care system remains almost entirely controlled by the suppliers and is marked by a wasteful lack of coordination. The fee-for-service method is a deterrent to preventive and timely medical attention. It makes for excessive costs and encourages needless services at the same time that it often denies care to those who need it but cannot pay for it. The autonomy of our voluntary hospitals, each of them a little empire unto itself, frequently verges on anarchy and leads to widespread duplication of expensive facilities and equipment. The most outstanding feature of the prevailing pattern is an almost total lack of anything like a rational system to assure the consumer that he will get the most out of his medical care dollar.

Another area in which urgent remedial action is needed is that of quality controls, where the ancient tradition of the marketplace, "Let the buyer beware," continues to prevail. The existing system of professional regulation is woefully inadequate and offers the public virtually no protection against unethical or incompetent practitioners. There are few enforceable standards of quality, and the supervision of professional performance outside hospitals is generally so weak as to be practically worthless. The medical profession not only has failed to establish adequate standards but is insisting that no one else attempt to do so.

The only hope for keeping down medical care costs lies in a more efficient organization of services, in wider use of less expensive facilities for ambulatory patients instead of hospitalization, and, ultimately, in much greater emphasis on the prevention and early detection of disease and its prompt treatment in order to avert, whenever possible, its development into serious illness. Medicine already has almost boundless potentialities for contributing to a more abundant state of human health, efficiency, and happiness. The American people, who have come to regard adequate medical care as a necessity and a right, are unlikely to continue to tolerate obstacles to the realization of these potentialities. In such a supreme area of concern as health and life itself, the consumers will inevitably have the last word.

CHAPTER TWO

The Man Behind the Stethoscope

I

IN THE EYE of the gathering storm is the doctor, a somewhat bewildered and reluctant warrior girding for dubious battle.

The purveyors of few other commodities or services are such a highly select breed as physicians generally are—so set apart by the heavy burden of responsibility that they carry and by the trust and faith that they engender; so familiar in their daily rounds with the essential conditions of life and its cardinal experiences, with birth and death, with fear and courage, with the physiognomy of pain and the yearning for compassion.

Few other professions make such demands of heart and mind on their practitioners as medicine does, require such a lengthy and formidably rigorous process of training, impose such a mold of clannish uniformity on their members, play such a variety of often incongruous roles, or have to contend in their tasks with such a wide margin of unpredictability.

And probably no other profession is, by and large, so receptive to scientific innovation and yet so narrow in its social and economic views, has such a split public and private personality, is so distressingly caught up in a vortex of sweeping change, is so sensitive to criticism and troubled by its impaired image in the era of its greatest technical achievements, and is so prosperous and yet so concerned about what the future may hold in store.

Although he is eons removed from the witch doctor with his mystic communion with the supernatural spirits, some of the attributes of today's physician are not so far different from those of the primitive medicine man. Faith in the physician's occult powers continues to play a role in the practice of medicine, despite its phenomenal scientific advances and the incredible electronic precision of its instrumentation. The doctor himself remains the most potent and frequently used drug we have. There still is magic, as there always was, in the physician's very presence in the sickroom, in his bedside manner, in the solace of the laying on of his healing hands. The doctor's principal job is to cure if possible, but it is also to relieve and to comfort. All of medicine's progress, all of its intricate skills and elaborate tools, have not eliminated and never will eliminate the patient's need for the warm responsiveness and understanding concern that are the hallmark of the healer.

The doctor is diagnostician, counselor, listener-to-troubles, allayer of anxiety, and educator. At its finest, his calling will always remain a synthesis of art and science—a subtle integration of diagnostic skills and total appraisal of the patient within his environment that is the essence of clinical wisdom. The rational and the intuitive, scientific analysis and sympathetic insight are blended in the practice of the physician's craft.

Since the beginning of time medicine and religion have gone hand and hand in their ministry of healing and reconciliation to help man meet the most profound issues of life and death. Medicine sprang from the church, and the functions of physician and priest were once indistinguishable. Out of this have evolved the standards of the doctor's professional integrity in his confidential relationship with his patients. Out of it has emerged the expectation of a single-minded, almost priestly consecration on the physician's part. And inherent in it also is the doctor's divided allegiance and basic dilemma. He must serve the sick, but he must also earn a living. His duty is a vocation without prescribed limits, but he also is pressed into a tightly structured system of utilitarian values upon which depends the advancement of his professional career.

Out of this welter of contradictions have grown a string of inner conflicts, a deep-seated clash between the medical profession's ingrained individualism and the inexorable trend of the times toward bureaucratic organization, and a set of fictions whose sole aim is to justify the conduct of physicians and to rationalize their special economic advantages.

In the profession's highly idealized catechism, the assumption is studiously maintained that medical practice continues to be a free-lance operation, that services are provided by wholly independent practitioners who are roughly equal in ability and competing in a free market, that the patient's right to pick his doctor freely is an indispensable ingredient of good medical care, that each physician serves what is substantially a cross section of the community, that medical services are readily available to all those who need them, that licensure is in itself permanent evidence of a doctor's competence, and that most people have family doctors upon whom they are dependent for medical advice and emotional support and with whom they enjoy the cherished doctor-patient relationship that is the cornerstone of the prevailing system of practice.

Most of these things are clearly at variance with the facts. While the rest are arguable, the weight of the evidence is heavily against them too. Scientific advances have made it impossible for any doctor to master the entire field of medicine, and physicians have increasingly become specialized and dependent upon one another and particularly upon hospitals. While the virtue of free competition is one of the medical profession's most fervently extolled articles of faith, competition in terms of price or product is actually stifled within the profession's internal structure, which exercises a pervasive influence on the bread-and-butter business of medical practice.

As an individual entrepreneur in a rigidly hierarchical profession, the doctor is often exposed to the attrition of compromise. Under his code of ethics, his professional obligation is to give his services to all those who need them. But the pecuniary pressures of his career often draw him to where the money is rather than to the area of greatest need.

Physicians vary greatly in intellectual endowment and in the ability to keep abreast of evolving medical knowledge. They vary in such invaluable assets as social connections and hospital appointments. They also vary widely in the class status of their clientele.

The practice of medicine is our most crucial and yet least regulated public utility. Aside from the laws against malpractice, patients have little protection against incompetent or unscrupulous physcians. The standards of professional performance and their enforcement are so inadequate that a license to practice medicine gives a man the right to do virtually anything regardless of his competence, short of an illegal abortion.

Patently specious is the contention that any departure from

the present system of practice would deprive patients of their "free choice" of doctor and thereby undermine the rapport between doctor and patient and lead to a serious deterioration of the quality of care.

Actually, the present haphazard method of uninformed choice of doctor is a serious impediment to good medical care. The average patient's freedom of choice is now severely limited by his ability to pay, by the number and caliber of doctors available wherever he happens to live, and, most of all, by his lack of competence to judge what a physician's technical qualifications are and whether he practices good or poor medicine. There is no freedom of choice of doctor at the Mayo or Lahey Clinics and at other institutions providing the best medical care in the United States. What patients need most is expert guidance in making the proper choice rather than freedom to make what often turns out to be the wrong choice.

As for the vaunted doctor-patient relationship, the most glittering jewel in the diadem of the solo practice of medicine, the facts are that numerous Americans have never had any such continuing and meaningful relationship and that overworked physicians are finding it increasingly difficult to give their patients the individual attention and personal concern so essential to effective medical care. It is hard to see, furthermore, why the affinity between doctor and patient should in any way be impaired by the adoption of a different method for transferring money from the patient's to the doctor's pocketbook. It is worse than meaningless for the medical profession to keep on acclaiming the merits of personalized attention while clinging to organizational patterns that make such attention less and less attainable.

II

From the day that they start medical school, and sometimes even long before then, students are cast into a unique professional mold. In the course of their training, the future doctors acquire not only a wide range of knowledge and skills but also a set of distinct values and behavior patterns and even a special vocabulary of their own. They learn by osmosis that there is a professional image to which they are expected to conform, and they inherit incompatible attitudes that are somehow made to seem a consistent guide to professional conduct. The end product is an unmistakable and, for the most part, strikingly persuasive stereotype.

Medical students are, to begin with, members of a select group. A student must meet rigorous intellectual and personal qualifications for admission to medical school; he must be able to meet at least part of the expense of the costliest and most arduous of all types of professional training; and he must be willing to postpone the start of self-supporting income, frequently until well into his thirties. Because of the inordinate cost and duration of medical education, most students are drawn from relatively well-to-do families. Fully 43 per cent of them now come from families in the top 12 per cent income brackets. Only one student in five comes from a family earning the median personal income. This fact in itself has had a not inconsiderable influence on the medical profession's conservatism and its increasing upper-status orientation.

Having relatives who are doctors often leads to an early awakening of interest in a medical career. It facilitates identification with the professional image and makes available the means and contacts helpful in vaulting the hurdle of admission to medical school. So it is not surprising that more than half of all medical students have relatives who are physicians and that 17 per cent of these have a parent who is a doctor. This, as well as the paucity of students from low-income families, contributes to the medical profession's cult of exclusiveness and its almost pathological fear of the possible leveling effects of greater numbers. The very use of the term "laity" to describe the general public underlines the profession's view of itself as a sort of secular holy order.

Medical education is strongly influenced by the mores of organized medicine and is to a considerable extent controlled by the medical profession. For this and other reasons, medical schools are not only institutions for training in the relevant scientific knowledge and in certain rules of conduct but are also sifting mechanisms. More so than in any other type of professional education, the candidates must survive a series of admission barriers and of anxiety and endurance tests during the course of training to demonstrate their fitness.

Not so long ago, between three and four qualified students were competing for each medical school opening. Both the number and the caliber of applicants have materially declined in recent years. But the selection process remains formidable, and one out of nearly every two applicants is still being turned down.

The intense competition has contributed to the generally high standards by permitting the medical schools to pick the cream of the crop. But the high selectivity also has its liabilities. It brings frustration to thousands of students every year and represents a tragic waste of many good candidates. It also has facilitated discrimination against racial and religious minorities and other restrictive practices designed to eliminate those considered undesirable.

Applicants are judged not only on the basis of their scholastic standing but also on their personality and character. These are, obviously, qualifications not subject to precise measurement and leave considerable room for the operation of prejudice against applicants whose sex, race, or creed differs from that of the examiners. Insistence on preserving quality, which is perfectly valid in itself, can also be used as a cover for other motives. There is substantial evidence that one such motive—in the past, at any rate—has been a deliberate desire by the medical profession to hold down the number of those entering its ranks in order to protect the level of its income. One educator has observed, probably with some exaggeration but more than a grain of truth, that "medicine is the only profession where the element of competition comes only at the beginning."

The future physician must master a truly staggering amount of factual information, along with a whole range of technical skills and professional attitudes. He must acquire knowledge in a broad spectrum of the natural sciences, ranging from anatomy and physiology to biochemistry and pharmacology. He must gain an understanding of the fundamentals of the human body's normal physical and psychological mechanisms and of the abnormal processes associated with disease. He must learn how to take histories from patients, how to make physical examinations and work up charts, and how to recognize some of the common patterns of illness. Much of his training takes place in laboratories and hospital wards and clinics and is accomplished mainly by working under expert supervision rather than by listening to lectures.

In this process, one of the few survivals of the apprenticeship system of the Middle Ages, the student develops judgment, discrimination, and self-reliance. He learns how to observe, how to reason about his observations, and how to integrate them into the picture of the total individual. He learns how to be disciplined and self-critical in the scientific appraisal of the evidence, acquiring at the same time a protective coloration of decisiveness to mask his uncertainties. If he is going to be a good doctor, he develops a high capacity for compassion and achieves simultaneously a detached attitude about human behavior. He learns how to bring insight and sympathetic understanding into the relationship with his patients without getting involved emotionally in their problems and becoming maudlin or moralistic.

All these faculties must ripen in the future physician under the almost daily impact of tragedy. He begins the study of the living with the dead. One of his first tasks, usually a traumatic experience, is the dissection of a cadaver to learn the structure of the human body at first hand. Thereafter, as the scene of his training shifts to the hospital, he repeatedly encounters pain, fear, despair, and death. Frequent exposure to the great crises of life gradually fosters in the student sufficient detachment to stand aside and view the human body as an entity devoid of spirit. Sometimes it forces him to develop a defensive armor of insensitivity.

The young doctor trains not only to know what to do when illness strikes but also to act decisively in the face of uncertainty. With all of medicine's progress, a physician's life is still full of imponderables and ambiguities. He often has to make broad judgments on the basis of incomplete data and must do the best he can with what is at hand. The practice of medicine, one authority has said, "is sometimes largely a matter of conjuring possibilities and probabilities." Because human life may depend on his tentative judgment, a doctor must learn to adopt a manner of certitude even when he feels unsure.

While the basic mission of the medical school is to teach

students to treat patients, one of its most important functions also is to instill by precept and example the distinctive traditions and values of medicine. In this process of socialization, the student unwittingly tries to emulate the teachers whom he admires and seeks to model himself consciously after the ideational prototype of the good doctor. He begins to realize that patients expect a certain style from physicians and that he must attempt to live up to these expectations. Step by step, he assimilates not only the profession's views but also its mannerisms. He and his classmates even acquire certain similarities in appearance and demeanor as time goes on.

The student's choice of a medical career is usually influenced, to start with, by his observation of how doctors act and how other people react to them. This cultural stereotype of the physician's role—or, more precisely, his multitude of roles—is broadened and refined in medical school and during the years of hospital internship and residency. The novice gradually develops a professional identity and self-image by learning what is expected of him and what he can expect of others. This is done not so much through a codified set of principles as by observing the behavior of instructors, nurses, and patients and getting a picture of the model doctor's conduct, values, and status. By the time that the newly certified physician is ready to hang out his shingle, he has absorbed much of the written and unwritten rules of the trade.

Interestingly enough, a number of studies have shown that, by and large, medical students lose a good deal of their idealism and tend to become more cynical as their schooling progresses. The percentage of those who feel that earning a substantial income is very important rises in successive school years. While humanitarianism is a predominant trait among first-year students, a considerable ratio of seniors have been found to express agreement with such statements as, "If you don't look out for yourself, nobody else will," and, "It is hard to get ahead without cutting corners." So apparent is this trend that some observers have characterized the distinction between the preclinical years of training in the basic sciences and the clinical years of hospital work as one between the "precynical" and "cynical" periods.

By the time that the medical student reaches his fourth year, these studies indicate, he is apt to have acquired an image of the doctor as rightfully authoritarian and a much less flattering one of the patient. The ideal physician is perceived as masculine, strong-willed, and dominant. Patients, on the other hand, are seen by many students as weak-willed, self-centered, and unreasonably demanding.

Another significant finding is that a disproportionate number of medical students suffer from personality maladjustments and emotional disturbances.

Why do many medical students lower the sights of their initial idealism, and what are the reasons for the high ratio of emotional instability among them? Does medicine attract a higher proportion of maladjusted individuals, or is there something in the medical school curriculum and environment that causes emotional insecurity and disenchantment?

Opinions vary on these points. Emotional stresses are unquestionably inherent in the whole process of medical education, with its repeated and premature exposure to harrowing experiences, its long grind, and the frustrations of a protracted period of economic dependency. Students are deeply affected by the initial experience of dissection and their attendance at autopsies. Day in and day out they have to contend with the shock of suffering, hopeless disease, and death. The bewildering mass of material to be mastered is likely to be frustrating and to deepen the student's sense of his own inadequacy. Full appreciation of what it means to be responsible for human life comes as a frightening realization to many students. Some of them find it difficult to adjust themselves to their differentness and to the inevitable conflicts between the lofty ideals of professional ethics and the realities of professional practice.

It is not easy to learn to bear the yoke of a career limited to sick and fretful people. It takes a rugged constitution and a well-adjusted personality to stand the physical strain of a doctor's long hours and the emotional strain of a job in which the routine may unexpectedly turn into tragedy. It takes integrity and fullness of heart, understanding and mercy not to become dogmatic or callous under the impact of continual crises and the emotional dependency of patients. Many doctors pass the test admirably. But others develop an omniscient manner and a patronizing insularity of view. The late Dr. Alan Gregg, a wise and perceptive student of medical affairs, liked to quote the remark of a colleague that "a physician is so surrounded by frightened patients, adoring families, and obsequious nurses that he will not brook criticism by God or man."

The serious decline in the quality of medical school applicants, along with a sharp drop in their number, is all the more ominous now, when the steadily growing complexity of medicine and the new insights into the social and emotional components of illness provided by the behavioral sciences call for students with the highest possible intellectual capacity and dedication.

The extreme length and heavy cost of medical education, along with the lure of competing careers in some of the physical sciences, are believed to be the major factors in the material reduction in the total number of candidates seeking admission to medical schools. At the same time, the ratio of mediocre applicants has shown a considerable increase. Since 1950, the proportion of students entering medical schools with a straight-A college average has slumped from 40 per cent to 15 per cent, and the ratio of dropouts because of poor academic standing has doubled, from 4 per cent to 8 per cent. Unless some way is found to reverse this alarming trend, it will inevitably be reflected in a poorer level of medical practice and research in the years to come.

A survey conducted by the Association of American Medical Colleges recently came up with the finding that medical students are "generally intelligent but not intellectual" and that 75 per cent of them read fewer than four nonmedical books a year and 40 per cent read fewer than two such books a year. Medical education has always been largely oriented toward preparation for a vocation instead of being broadly educational. Whatever interests in the humanities and social sciences that the student may have had in his undergraduate college years are usually dropped after he enters medical school. Training for medicine is so strenuous that it allows the student little time for anything else. It is, therefore, hardly surprising that the interests of most doctors are confined to their profession and that many of them are provincial in outlook, intolerant of criticism by outsiders, and indifferent to the changing needs of society, even in matters closely related to health.

Probably no two medical educators would agree on the precise qualities of character and intellect required for the making of a top-notch physician. But there is general agreement that the good doctor must be technically proficient and resourceful, that he must constantly keep pace with new developments in his field, that he must have the stamina to perform competently day in and day out, and that he must be dedicated to his craft, genuinely interested in people, and kind and forbearing to those who are weak and suffering and in need of help.

Quite a few physicians possess these qualities in full measure and are a credit to their high calling. Unfortunately, there are not nearly enough of them.

III

One of the most significant but least known facts about the medical profession is that its business of making a living is run behind the scenes pretty much along the lines of a feudal barony.

How do doctors get started in their practice? How do they go about recruiting their first patients and gradually expanding their clientele? Do they hang out their shingles and then just sit around waiting for the patients to start flocking in? Since they are forbidden by their formal code of ethics to advertise, do they build up their practice solely by word of mouth? And if they are specialists, which most successful physicians are, how do they go about getting referrals of patients from other doctors?

According to the profession's official apologia, medicine is a service to humanity rather than a trade, and whatever competition exists within it is resolved automatically and exclusively on the basis of individual merit. In medicine's ideological lexicon, there is no more hallowed principle than that of free enterprise. Officially, the profession is a democracy in which free-lance practitioners operate independently, and competence is the only consideration that matters.

Unfortunately, a good deal of this is just so much hogwash for the benefit of the yokels. Actually, the profession's inner workings and the way it goes about regulating its bread-and-butter business are implicit denials of its formal tenets of faith.

Enshrouded in fraternal mystery and quite different from the idealized fiction that the medical profession would like the general public to accept is an elaborate social machinery exercising a pervasive influence upon the day-to-day practice of medicine. The advancement of medical careers hinges primarily on the role that doctors play in this informal but potent internal structure. It depends on the physician's standing within this powerful guild framework, on his acceptance by the clique of his older and more influential colleagues, and on the degree to which he gains coveted admission into the hospital system, without which the successful practice of medicine is now virtually impossible. Competence is a pertinent qualification for getting ahead. But so is pull, measured by such yardsticks as social connections, personality, and ability to fit in.

Students of the operation of this shadowy fellowship describe it as the "inner fraternity" of medicine. Its unwritten canons of behavior supplement and in some respects even supersede those of the official code of ethics and of the constitutions of the county and state medical societies and of the American Medical Association.

While in theory the regulation of professional conduct is lodged in the formal organizational pyramid, its function in this area is relatively limited. The primary job of the official bodies is to do the profession's political lobbying and otherwise put up a front for it. Behind this façade, the "inner fraternity" operates to apportion the rewards of successful practice through a complex system of sponsorships and referrals. It is basically through this informal system of internal controls that recruits undergo their apprenticeship and are allocated positions in the professional and hospital hierarchy. Through it, patients are to a considerable extent distributed by referrals, competition is regulated, interlopers are excluded, effort is rewarded, and a rigid code of guild loyalties and face-saving devices is enforced. Only by adhering to the rules is a physician able to gain the recognition of his colleagues and to climb the successive rungs of the professional ladder. Anyone so foolhardy as to challenge the established order does so only at the peril of his career.

By far the most intensive study of the various stages of the medical career in an urban setting was made some years ago by Dr. Oswald Hall, who was then an instructor at Brown University and now is a professor of sociology at the University of

Toronto. Dr. Hall's findings, based on confidential interviews with a large number of Providence, Rhode Island, physicians and on an exhaustive examination of the hospital-staff selection system in that city, were later incorporated in his PhD dissertation at the University of Chicago. This unpublished thesis is a rich source of material on the real manner in which doctors go about the business of establishing successful practices. Competent opinion among physicians in Providence and elsewhere is that while there has been some relaxation in recent years in the racial barriers to professional advancement reported by Dr. Hall, the situation otherwise remains pretty much the same.

In substance, the *modus operandi* of the "inner fraternity" system documented by Dr. Hall in fascinating detail is not too far removed from the tightly controlled healing guilds of the time of Hippocrates, around 400 B.C. Now as then, the main objective is to see to it that those admitted to membership abide by the rules laid down by their elders, that the profession's operations are kept stable, and that unseemly and harmful competition is eliminated so that all concerned may share in the financial rewards according to their merits.

Granted an insight into the mechanisms of the practice of medicine such as few laymen have ever been able to obtain, Dr. Hall concluded that the profession constitutes "a closed system," that "admission is by sponsorship," and that access to patients as well as to hospital appointments is "narrowly restricted."

He decided that academic qualifications are far from being the only criteria for admission to medical school, that in each stage of his professional career the physician has to be "something of a promoter," that an inner circle of successful doctors exercises a powerful influence in securing crucially important hospital connections for its protégés, that as a physician's practice develops and as he proceeds to select a specialized clientele, "he may discourage his poorer patients and concentrate on serving those with higher incomes," and that "the code of medical ethics reflects a bygone era of independent practitioner-patient relationships and fails to control the present-day doctor-hospital relationships."

Dr. Hall draws an intriguing picture of "the lineaments of an institutional type of personality" all too familiar to anyone who has had sufficient experience with doctors. "There is devotion to work," he writes, "but to work related to a specific hospital system. The development of judgment is stressed, but judgment based on the advice of one's superior. . . . The valued traits are those which can be integrated into a firmly established system of medicine. It is assumed that the person who learns to play the role will be rewarded financially and by receiving institutional prestige; it is taken for granted that there may be some delay in receiving these rewards."

What it amounts to is that in order to get ahead, a doctor must learn to play the game, to stick to his assigned niche, and to wait patiently to move up. A man's ascent through the various levels of the professional hierarchy is, as Dr. Hall puts it, "partly by his ability and partly by his devotion to duty. 'Sticking to your knitting' is valued pretty highly. . . . Each successive appointment in the hierarchy is presumed to call forth a prolonged period of loyal service but not to whet the appetite for further immediate climbing."

The influences of the "inner fraternity" extend in four directions, Dr. Hall reports. "It influences the policies and practices of medical institutions. In large part it designates the doctors permitted to carry on specialized medicine. It functions to deflect superior clienteles toward its members. Finally it plays a major role in assigning status to the doctors of the community."

Not infrequently, the sponsorship process starts coming into play quite early, at the time that a young man or woman decides to apply for admission to medical school. This may be one of the reasons why children of physicians make up one out of every six medical students. Doctors' families not only are in a far better position than the average to afford the high cost of medical education but also are apt to have the connections that can prove of considerable help in gaining admission to a top-notch school. The same factor sometimes operates in obtaining desirable internship or residency spots in leading teaching hospitals. The standing of the medical school from which a physician graduates and the prestige of the hospital in which he receives his postgraduate training can have a material bearing on his future career.

It is true that since Dr. Hall made his study the number of available house-staff openings in hospitals has increased much more sharply than that of available candidates, so that interns and residents are now at a premium. This does not apply, however, to the best hospitals, where appointments are still eagerly sought by medical school graduates.

Interesting light on the criteria sometimes applied by hospitals in the selection of interns is shed by this comment by a prominent physician, quoted by Dr. Hall: "The main consideration is personality. That's an intangible sort of thing, but it means partly the ability to mix well, to be humble to the correct degree to superiors and to act the dignified but definitely superior part toward patients." While this particular doctor did not say so, it was perfectly obvious from many of Dr. Hall's interviews that the term "personality" is comprehensive enough to cover all sorts of bigotry and especially racial prejudice. A number of the physicians with whom he talked were virulently outspoken in their distaste for colleagues of Jewish and Italian extraction.

It must be borne in mind that hospitals, with their dominating role in medical practice, are more than centers for treating patients and training physicians and other health personnel. They also are the medical profession's most important mechanism for awarding status and the income that goes with it.

Doctors do not automatically become members of the hospital system after they complete their training. They are, in effect, invited into the system by the elders who control the process of staff selection. Such invitations are not extended merely on the basis of competence. Also taken into consideration are the possession of "proper" personal qualities. Nor does admission into the hospital system necessarily constitute incorporation into the "inner fraternity." Only those deemed to possess the right intangibles of personality are picked.

The prevailing system of medical practice is often stacked against the newcomer. Many young doctors encounter considerable difficulties in their efforts to get on the staff of the leading hospital in the community. Applications are sometimes held up for years, regardless of the candidate's qualifications, and occasionally are never acted upon. This is particularly true of surgeons, a specialty in which the competition and the remuneration are among the greatest in the profession. Young surgeons seeking to locate in a new community frequently run into an assortment of trials and tribulations. "Everyone acknowledges," an AMA committee reported after a lengthy investigation several years ago, "that in most cities the young surgical specialist must use finesse, diplomacy and careful self-promotion to wangle a hospital staff appointment."

The maintenance of high quality of service is not the only motive behind the so-called closed hospital-staff arrangement whereby admission of physicians to staff privileges has to be approved by a medical selection committee and the hospital's board of trustees. The desire to keep down competition may also be a factor.

It is mainly through the hospital that various openings essential to the furtherance of the young physician's career are provided. Through it, he obtains access to patients and the equipment needed to treat them. With the aid of a friendly department head, he can get a push in the right direction. Through the hospital he gradually becomes part of the referral and consulting fraternity, with its reciprocal favors. But he can hope to do so only by prudent observance of the rules and meticulous attention to the niceties of etiquette within the hierarchical pattern.

The period of internship and residency is in itself an invaluable opportunity for the neophyte to gain an insight into how the system works and to adjust accordingly. Here the new doctor is not only initiated into the actual care of patients but also learns a lot about the profession's mores, rituals, idiosyncrasies, and competitive techniques. Here, too, he is sized up by his elders, with results that may have a profound bearing on his future career. "I made a mistake and started off in a large hospital," one of the physicians interviewed by Dr. Hall said. "I got to see a large number of the kind of cases I was interested in. That was a blunder. I got to know cases instead of doctors."

Acquiring a desirable clientele, holding on to it, and improving it as time goes on—all these things take the sort of finesse and adroit manipulation that cannot be taught in medical school but must be picked up intuitively, with a timely lift now and then from members of the controlling elite.

As a rule, patients do not pick their doctors on anything like a rational basis, since they are not qualified to judge the relative competence of various physicians. Usually playing a role in such choices are a variety of extraneous preferences and biases, including a physician's popularity or his association with another successful doctor, that have little or nothing whatsoever to do with his qualifications.

To build up a specialized practice, a doctor needs referrals from colleagues. This means that he must have some way of repaying their favors, and he can do so best when he is a member of the inner circle. "Doctors in the fraternity are not likely to press patients to see a specific colleague," Dr. Hall comments. "They are more ready to name a half dozen, 'all equally good men.' This minimizes jealousy within the group by permitting the laws of chance to select the lucky colleague. Incidentally the patient is kept within the restricted circle of the fraternity."

General practitioners are often reluctant to send patients to specialists for fear of losing them. This is one of the reasons why doctors sometimes refer their patients to a specialist in a larger city or medical center instead of using a local man. A consultant's popularity is usually directly related to his readiness to return patients to the referring physician. On the whole, however, the professional etiquette is that the referred patient is the property of the first doctor and must be returned to him. To do otherwise, even at the patient's own request, may be construed as stealing a patient, one of the most heinous offenses in the code.

A more subtle reason for a physician's hesitation to refer a patient to a specialist may be his fear that this will undermine the patient's confidence in his own ability. The end result is that many doctors try to do themselves certain things that they are not qualified to do, and patients are thus deprived of the full potential of up-to-date medical services.

Referrals by general practitioners are pretty much of a one-way street, since specialists have no occasion to send patients in the opposite direction. But the process of reciprocal courtesies comes fully into play when one specialist sends his patients to another. Not only do these men do each other good turns, but the clientele is kept out of the reach of outsiders.

With the rapid Americanization of the descendants of immigrants, the tendency in recent years has been toward a more equitable distribution of honors within medical organizations. In many medical societies, it has become the custom to rotate top offices among men of various racial strains. But this process has been much slower within the "inner fraternity," which has a lot more influence on the mechanics of medical practice than the formal organizations do. To a large degree, the ruling cliques in most communities still comprise the practitioners who not only have the highest income and prestige but also are Protestants of native stock.

This coterie of men with similar social and educational backgrounds does not need any official titles to run the show. Its members wield power through their lucrative practices, often inherited or acquired from older physicians, and through their social status, their high standing in the specialist and hospital hierarchy, and their consequent strategic position to give their younger colleagues a hand in climbing up the ladder.

Built into the system over which the inner core presides are tried mechanisms for encouraging desirable initiates and relegating undesirable intruders to positions in which they are forced to compete on disadvantageous terms. There are established patterns of recruitment and promotion, of allocating patronage plums, and of legitimate succession. Newcomers have to go through the institutional apprenticeship with its required discipline. They have to demonstrate ability and live up to professional standards of performance. But professional competence in itself is not enough to qualify the candidate for the invaluable sponsorship at the right time and place.

To remain in good standing as a member of the ingroup, a physician must continue to conform to the established rules and usages in the conduct of his practice. It is considered extremely poor form, for instance, for a doctor to give the impression of showing off his skills. A physician's colleagues also are likely to resent it if he shows too much drive and if his practice grows too rapidly. Although lip service is paid to the ideal of free enterprise, unseemly competition is severely frowned upon by both the formal code of ethics and the informal complex of conventions and expectations.

State laws provide a variety of penalties for unethical practices by physicians, and medical societies have elaborate disciplinary procedures. But these are notoriously toothless and are rarely invoked, least of all for gross incompetence. Far more effective are the intangible but powerful pressures exerted within the profession itself against offending members. In the long run, it can prove deadly for a doctor to keep on stepping out of line.

IV

Of the two codes governing the conduct of members of the medical profession, the written one is, ironically, by far the most confusing.

The unwritten set of implicit values and understandings by which the profession runs its day-to-day practice makes sense to the average physician. It is conservative, curbs competition, and makes for stability. The men with the top income and prestige are recognized as the arbiters of the system and entrusted with dispensing the rewards and administering whatever chastisement may be called for. Professional standards of competence are maintained—to a degree, at any rate. The doctor has to adjust continually to a covert and intricate bureaucratic structure. But the customers are reasonably satisfied, or at least kept in check, and the membership has never had it so good financially. Cadillac advertisements and columns of advice on how to get still richer on the stock market have become prominent features of publications mainly circulated among doctors. While a front of idealism is studiously maintained for the laity, the profit motive is in full view within the family. The medical profession is now a conspicious, and at times even opulent, segment of our acquisitive and affluent society.

Much of the official code of medical ethics, on the other hand, is a lot of gobbledygook whose lofty enunciation of principle forces the profession into endless sophistry. Originally built around the Hippocratic oath of ancient times, the code is far more an idealized picture of what the profession would like outsiders to believe than an accurate guidebook to its inner workings. It covers a broad and contradictory list of precepts ranging all the way from the finest traditions of professional morality and self-discipline to monopolistic guild practices that are quite remote from any concept of ethics.

All too often, the code confuses manners with morals, medical etiquette with medical ethics, and attaches as great a penalty to the transgression of one as of the other. It involves economics much more than it does ethics. Nor does it always put the patient's welfare first. Its primary purpose, in fact, appears to be to protect one doctor against another—and not necessarily to the public's advantage.

While moral truths are immutable, the AMA has revised its official code of ethics five times since 1903. There is nothing wrong, of course, in updating a set of rules of conduct to conform with changing circumstances. But the successive revisions voted by the AMA seem to be public relations gimmicks more than anything else. Admonitions of ethical behavior are, moreover, futile unless the environment is conducive to it. Physicians, like everyone else, vary in moral fiber. Unfortunately, the existing framework of medical practice, in which most doctors are solo operators working without any supervision whatsoever, is not always designed to bolster moral standards.

Stripped of its verbiage, the code of ethics contains these major injunctions: uphold the honor and dignity of the profession; don't break the law; don't neglect your patients; call in a consultant if the case is difficult or otherwise warrants it; don't violate professional confidences; expose unscrupulous colleagues, but don't make any disparaging statements about other physicians; charge a fee commensurate with your services and the patient's ability to pay; don't pay or accept rebates or commissions for the referral of patients; don't permit anyone else to make a profit from your services; don't accept employment under conditions that may impair the full exercise of your medical judgment; don't advertise or otherwise solicit patients; don't steal patients from other doctors.

An extremely ticklish point within the profession—and one that can make a lot of difference to numerous patients—is what a doctor should do if he becomes aware of unethical conduct or incompetent treatment by a colleague. Should he tip off the patient or his family? Should he take it up with the offending physician? Should he complain to the medical society? So surrounded by circumlocutions and pitfalls is this delicate subject that he usually does nothing.

The 1949 revision of the code urged physicians "to expose, without fear or favor, incompetent or corrupt, dishonest or unethical conduct on the part of members of the profession." But a significant change in wording was made in the latest and abbreviated version of the code voted by the AMA House of Delegates in 1957. The latest version still calls on doctors to make available to every patient "a full measure of services and devotion" and says that "the medical profession should safeguard the public and itself against physicians deficient in moral character or professional competence." Direct reference to lack of competence is omitted, however, from the exhortation that practitioners "should expose, without hesitation, illegal or unethical conduct of fellow members of the profession."

But regardless of the precise wording of the code, it has long been held axiomatic in the profession that a doctor's duty to respect the reputation of his colleagues and not to discredit them, particularly among laymen, is fully as important as his obligation to safeguard high standards of practice. When the two responsibilities conflict, the second is much more likely to be overlooked.

There are a variety of reasons for this distressing situation. Most physicians are intensely reluctant to pass judgment on their fellows and prefer to keep their eyes shut to incompetence and rascality in order to avoid trouble. Guild loyalty is an ironclad rule, and it can be extremely dangerous for a doctor to gain a reputation among his peers as a captious critic. There is no more flagrant breach of the rules than to deprive a colleague of a patient by saying something uncomplimentary about his performance. A physician accused of washing dirty professional linen in public may discover that his patient referrals are rapidly drying up. Mutual back scratching and face-saving are much more prudent.

Time and again, medical society spokesmen have publicly taken the position that exposure of unethical practitioners is bad because it reflects upon the majority of ethical members of the profession. "By the same logic," a San Francisco newspaper commented on this line of reasoning, "no fraudulent banker ever should be exposed because it would 'destroy the confidence' of people in banks. No crook in city politics ever should be exposed because it would 'destroy the confidence' of the people in city government. No corrupt judge ever should be exposed because it would 'destroy the confidence' of the people in the judicial processes."

There have been cases in which physicians have been officially censured by medical societies for daring to bring out into the open instances of unscrupulous conduct by some of their colleagues. But doing something about gross negligence or incompetence is another story. The excuse usually offered by medical societies is that both under state laws and under their own bylaws, it is extremely difficult, if not impossible, to proceed against offenders in such cases. The fact that medical societies are self-governing bodies and that their bylaws can be changed is seldom mentioned.

While doctors are occasionally not above discussing the derelictions of some of their colleagues in private, this is rarely done in public. Such fraternal reticence does not always extend, however, beyond the borders of the United States. An illuminating insight into how physicians sometimes go about covering up the incompetence of their fellows was provided a few years ago in the Philippines, which has long been under American tutelage and presumably thus has absorbed some of our folkways. In a talk at the annual meeting of the Philippine Medical Association, later published in the association's journal under the title "Saving the Faces of Physicians," Dr. Timoteo Alday declared that all doctors make mistakes sooner or later and that "for the sake of ethics and long-continued friendship, errors in diagnosis, prognosis and management should be covered." Dr. Alday then proceeded to list, by way of example, a number of cases in which this was done. Among them were the case of a surgeon who had left a roll of gauze in a patient's abdomen, another case in which a woman diagnosed as suffering from stomach cancer was actually found to have a floating kidney, an instance in which acute appendicitis was diagnosed as typhoid fever, others in which acute appendicitis was diagnosed as peptic ulcer or acute gastritis and lobar pneumonia was diagnosed as perforated peptic ulcer, and a case in which a boy had died of typhoid fever the day after the attending doctor had "given a very good prognosis in order to convince the family not to call another physician."

There is no intention here to equate the competence of American and Filipino physicians, although it is pertinent to note that in recent years, graduates of Philippine medical schools have made up the largest group among the thousands of foreign-trained doctors serving as interns or residents in our hospitals. Dr. Alday's candid talk is quoted merely as an example of the lengths to which the professional cabal can be carried: "There are," he said, "many errors of physicians, and as you can see, we can always save each other, for we are dealing with individuals who do not know medicine, and we can take advantage of their ignorance. We must not take advantage of the errors of our colleagues and try to put down our brothers in the medical field. We must be ethical and gain professional prestige with a clear conscience."

What it all adds up to is that the term "ethical" is highly flexible; that the code of medical ethics usually lacks teeth when it comes to protecting the patient; that points of ethics are sometimes stretched to have patients visit the physician more often than is strictly necessary and to allow for dubious treatments, unnecessary surgery, and fee splitting; and that physicians in a self-indulgent society are sometimes confused about their ethical duties and about the distinction between making money and trying to make sick people well again.

On the other hand, the medical profession is not above using the code of ethics to shut up its more outspoken members and to punish those who stray from the party line.

The alacrity with which the code's provision against advertising is enforced has led one observer to remark that "a doctor is in greater danger of losing his professional society membership for unethical advertising than he is for butchering a patient." So prevalent, furthermore, is the concept of the profession as a secret fraternal order in which all are vulnerable without mutual protection that little distinction is made between advertising and information of public interest. The result, in effect, is a tight censorship on all public utterances by physicians.

The code of ethics also can be a powerful weapon for sanctions against doctors who undertake to practice under economic arrangements of which organized medicine disapproves. It has been used on numerous occasions to discipline physicians joining group-practice insurance plans. Such reprisals have taken the form of blacklists, boycotts, and outright expulsion from medical societies. The latter penalty means automatic loss of hospital priv-ileges, of the right to accreditation by specialty boards, and of the opportunity to take out malpractice insurance at a reduced premium.

But the misuse of the code of ethics and the punishment for medical heresy are not the only difficulties. The trouble goes much deeper. For one thing, it lies in the sort of incentives that the prevailing system of medical practice holds out to the doctor. Inevitably, the system of charging a separate fee for each service sometimes has a deleterious effect in obscuring the line between the necessary and the unnecessary visit, in fostering needless surgery and other procedures, and in discouraging referral of patients by one physician to another of greater competence in the particular field involved.

Then there is the influence of the social and economic envi-ronment. In a society in which getting ahead as fast as possible is the ideal and a man's status is measured by the car he drives and the country club he belongs to, the doctor is often tempted to put such values first. He is apt to feel that he has worked harder and sacrificed more than most people and deserves to be rewarded accordingly. Matters are not helped by the closed-shop aspects of the medical profession, by the growing view of medicine as a business rather than as a craft with a high content of social dedi-cation, and by the increasingly tight supply of physicians. Under these circumstances, it is not surprising that the young doctor's paramount goal often is to recoup his educational investment and to move on quickly to the status symbols of the split-level house, the high-priced automobile, and the Caribbean cruise. The setting has a profound impact not only on the doctor's integrity but also on the level of his competence and on the character of care rendered.

In a recent talk, a distinguished physician summed up the situ-ation this way:

"The important things in medical practice today are not just the doctor's training, knowledge, and conscience. Equally important is the framework within which he prac-tices. And this framework is based on the fact that the doc-tor's remuneration is directly dependent on the number and size of procedures he performs. The more of them he does, the more money he makes.

"At what point does a doctor decide that he's seeing too many patients, that he's getting too tired, that he can't do a good job? What are the criteria—in terms of activity and performance? As long as compensation is based on the type and frequency of procedures, the doctor has to fight off the tendency to put the emphasis there. It's a tough temptation, and it may warp judgment.

"As far as evaluating the quality of one's work and keeping up to date, the important thing to bear in mind is that no one can do it himself. It takes the day-to-day interplay with one's peers on an organized basis. This is done in the last two years of the physician's medical school education and during his internship and residency. Then it stops.

"Group-practice prepayment removes both the fee-for-service deterrent to good medicine and the professional isolation of the solo practitioner. It is true that this isolation is counteracted for many physicians by the work they do in hospitals—which, by the way, provide the doctors at public expense with an indispensable workshop, with the necessary tools, to a degree which doesn't hold true of any other profession. But much of the most significant medical service takes place in the home and in the office, where the original diagnosis is made.

"There is no getting away from the fact that the element of the patient's ability to pay is all-important and that it leads to many compromises. Often the investigation recommended is very much tailored to the patient's ability to pay, not only in the direction of overdoing but even more so in the direction of underdoing. The doctor's judgment is based on the question whether the patient can afford many procedures. This inevitably affects the quality of medical service. In group-practice prepayment, you not only eliminate this factor of ability to pay, but you get continuous responsibility for comprehensive care, without which there can be no good medicine."

V

The belief that laymen are totally ignorant about medicine, including its economics, and that it is futile to argue with them about it dies hard among doctors. But as patients have grown more sophisticated and vocal and physicians less secure on their Olympian heights, some tentative attempts to break down the communication barrier have become more common of late. The results to date, judging from all reports, have not been too auspicious.

The average doctor's tight schedule rarely leaves time these days for idle chatter. But smarting as he does under the rising tide of criticism of the medical profession, he is apt to try to get across something of its side of the story whenever the opportunity arises. The burden of his argument is likely to be that physicians undergo a long and costly process of training and do not start earning their living until much later in life than any other professional group, that the overwhelming majority of them do a conscientious and able job, that they work harder than most of us and are at the beck and call of sick and demanding people at all hours of the day and night, that they continue to provide a good deal of free service to those unable to pay, that they are fully entitled to an adequate income, and that they are being unjustly vilified by those who would rashly tear down the finest system of medical care in the world. Does the patient really want "socialized medicine"? Does he want the kind of assembly-line medicine prevalent in countries where the government has taken over full control? Does he want bungling and scheming bureaucrats to take charge of the intensely personal field of medical care? Does he want these bureaucrats to keep on interfering with medical judgment?

The patient may be irritated by the doctor's complacency, by his trite sloganeering, and by his curious blend of patronizing disdain and plaintive self-pity. But the patient, too, is in a quandary. Despite the mounting disenchantment with the medical profession, there is good reason to believe that the average patient respects his personal physician and is genuinely fond of him. The thoughtful layman is in no need of preachment about the vital importance of personalized medical care and of an intimate doctor-patient relationship. But he is deeply troubled by the medical profession's collective stance and by a lot of other things in medicine.

The layman wonders why medical care should cost so much and worries about how he will pay his family's medical and hospital bills. He is concerned about the splintering of medical services, the costly and often frustrating shunting from one specialist to another, the growing tendency to fob off patients with another jab of the needle, another laboratory test, and still another prescription. He is troubled by hasty and superficial treatment and by the fact that the doctor is frequently too busy and abrupt to listen to his fears and anxieties. He resents the narrow economic self-interest so clearly evident behind the profession's lofty rhetoric and its vapid pretensions that the profit motive does not operate in medicine.

At times, the layman may be unreasonable and demand much more than he can rightfully expect of the doctor under the conditions of present-day medical practice. What the patient really wants when he feels helpless and afraid is that rare and delicate ingredient—tender loving care. But is it fair to ask the overworked physician to play not only the role of healer but also that of social worker and father confessor? Does it make sense to put on him the burden of the end results of economic injustice and social maladjustment?

At social gatherings, doctors, when they mellow a bit and are sure of being out of earshot of their more dogmatic colleagues, occasionally concede that not everything is for the best in the world's best medical care system and that the job they are doing sometimes falls short of what it could and should be. But even then a full meeting of minds is seldom achieved. The conversation is liable to wind up with mutual recriminations and the clear implication that laymen are thickheaded and do not really know what they are talking about when it comes to medicine.

The average physician's condescension, his blindness to the full implications of the scientific and socioeconomic revolution, his assumption that the medical profession always knows what is best for people in the whole domain of health care, his need to keep the practice of medicine on an esoteric level, his highly idealized picture of himself—all these things are symptoms of his deep-seated maladjustment in a setting so radically different from the one he knew, or imagined he knew, when he first came out of medical school.

Beset by many inner conflicts, the doctor understandably tends to take refuge in fantasies of a golden age when medical care was no more than a dialogue between two human beings, unencumbered by a far-flung institutional superstructure. He seeks to perpetuate a past that never really existed for most sick people. He clings to a grossly outdated concept of benevolent authoritarianism and remains profoundly distrustful of any initiatives emanating from outside the profession.

There is grave peril for the medical profession in this sullen flight from reality and growing estrangement from the community. By its old-guard inflexibility and its increasing identification with ultraconservatism, it is in danger of bringing about the very thing it dreads most—full government control of medical services.

More than half a century ago, when the human relationships and economics of medicine were far simpler than they now are, the late Sir William Osler, one of the giants of medicine in this hemisphere, warned his colleagues against "a serene satisfaction with the *status quo* and a fatuous objection to change." On the face of it, reluctance to accept change appears to be a glaring inconsistency in a profession whose work keeps on changing all the time. The great tradition in medicine is not to be satisfied with things as they are, but to keep on searching for better ways of coping with disease. Why should physicians, so alert to scientific innovation, be so antiquated in their approach to the economics of medicine? Moreover, why should a profession whose members are individually, by and large, responsible, intelligent, and hard-working citizens be in the organizational aggregate so self-seeking and hidebound? One answer is that it is a familiar tendency on the part of professions and institutions to resist change lest their vested interests be imperiled. Professions respond slowly and defensively to the demands of a dynamic society. Their traditional interest in the improvement of standards is, to a large degree, but a corollary to their anxiety to preserve status and prerogatives.

Superimposed on this natural characteristic is a set of predicaments peculiar to medicine. One of the oldest of professions, its members are predominantly individualistic and conservative and deeply at variance with the collectivist trend of the times. Having invested a great deal of time and effort and money in their professional training, they feel that they are entitled to a commensurate standard of living. After a long apprenticeship, they are naturally determined to hang on to their lucrative privileges.

But the tension between the doctor's conservatism and the inexorable drift toward increased organization and social controls is not merely a matter of pecuniary self-interest. The average physician is a rugged individualist, conditioned by generations of public respect and confidence. He has become accustomed to believe that he is the sole judge of his own capabilities and limitations and of the fairness of the fees he charges. The idea of restraints imposed from outside the professional realm is repugnant to him. As a confirmed solo operator, he finds distasteful the fetters of the institutional orbit into which he is increasingly being drawn. While theoretically dedicated to the proposition that medical care should be readily available to all those who need it, he resents imposition of this concept by legal fiat. He is, furthermore, wary by necessity. Being responsible for life itself, he is trained not to accept any new ideas until their value has been amply proven.

Regardless of whether the medical profession's resistance to change is viewed as selfish and reactionary or is more charitably interpreted as a painful adjustment to the inevitable, there is no denying that it is marked by a long chain of perplexities. Are medical services a commodity to be sold only to those who can buy them, or are they a universal right? Must the doctor under all circumstances do the best he knows how for a patient, or should he limit his performance to what the patient can pay for? Where should the line be drawn between medicine as a public service and as a means of earning a living, between the dedicated professional man and the enterprising businessman?

Many physicians are keenly aware of these conflicts, and so, increasingly, are their patients. The unavoidable consequences are bewilderment, guilt feelings, and resentments. While doctors believe that their fees are fully justified, patients are inclined to regard some charges as exorbitant and to feel that the profession is, as a rule, overpaid. The public, which cannot quite rid itself of the traditional association of the medical profession with the priesthood, expects the doctor to subordinate his self-interest to the needs of the sick. But is this expectation wholly fair? In a culture of conspicuous consumption, where money is the sole measure of success and the trend is toward ever-shorter working hours and greater leisure, is it realistic to hold the physician alone to a course of altruism?

The doctor is clearly in an incongruous position in our society and is often torn between conflicting incentives. Partly, at least, the profession's predicament is of its own making. Having helped to build up an idealized image of itself, it is now paying the price of disillusion. Very often the patient goes through a process of disenchantment when he gets the doctor's bill. It may seem an unreasonable attitude to take, but it is deeply rooted in the emotion with which people have always invested the doctor-patient relationship and stems from a feeling that the ministry of healing is sometimes tainted by a rather crass grab for the dollar.

Increasingly, the medical profession has two images—the one it likes to project and the one it actually registers in the public mind. The fact that neither image fully corresponds to the reality is not nearly so important as the implications of the clash between them. There is profound danger in this conflict, to doctors and patients alike, in an age of great insecurity, when the patient's need for reassurance is often pressing and the doctor's understanding of disease tends to outpace his understanding of the patient.

The physician's conventional image must be readjusted to the drastically changed realities if it is not to continue degenerating into little more than a public relations stereotype. It can be readjusted only by greater responsiveness to the imperatives of social and economic developments. Such readjustment calls for the realization that a policy of evasion and obstructionism is particularly shortsighted in an area so sensitive as the right of people to adequate health care. It can best be achieved by a wider recognition that, no matter what form the organization of medical practice ultimately takes, the greatest satisfaction for the right kind of doctor will always be in the intangible rewards of his craft.

It is high time for the medical profession to realize that no amount of publicity can offset its consistent record of having to be dragged, kicking and screaming, into the twentieth century. All the publicity gimmicks in the world cannot erase the picture of inadequate personal attention and superficial treatment, of reluctance to see patients outside office hours, of an increased spirit of commercialism, and of mossback opposition to proposals for improving the distribution and raising the standards of medical care. No amount of manipulation of the facts can sell an unsatisfactory product for very long. What medicine needs is not better publicity but better morality.

CHAPTER THREE

The Vanishing Family Physician

I

THE DOCTORS are not the only ones who often hark back nostalgically to a golden age when medical care was strictly a one-to-one affair and its problems were infinitely simpler than they are today. So, very frequently, do the patients.

By now firmly enshrined in our folklore is the picture of the old-time family doctor. This homely paragon and repository of all knowledge carried the full complement of necessary equipment in his little black bag, was always on call when needed, and brought understanding along with surcease from pain, solving all problems with genial reassurance and a dose of quinine or a purgative. Compassionate and indefatigable, the old doc of yesteryear shared the common experiences of his patients and was beloved friend and counselor to the whole family. He had grown up with many of his patients, had brought their children into the world, and had watched them develop. He thought nothing of spending hours at the bedside, often keeping an all-night vigil with the parents of a desperately ill child. And his bill was invariably modest and scaled in accordance with ability to pay.

Like all legends, the romantic image of the warmhearted family physician of the horse-and-buggy days, when there was one doctor for all illnesses of a lifetime, is a blend of fact and fancy. At best, the doctor's arsenal of weapons against disease was pathetically small, and he could offer little more than hope and the laying on of his gentle hands. At worst, he was a quack.

There were no crowded waiting rooms in those days, no hurried and preoccupied physicians, no skyrocketing hospital charges. But neither were there any antibiotics, anesthesia, or surgical asepsis. There was no problem of the splintering of medicine into specialties, each with its own severely limited sphere. Nor were there any anticoagulants or exchange transfusions. Patients had to be cast in a heroic mold, and the shattering impact of death was far more common at all ages than it now is. But what is significant about our wistful hankering for the old-time doctor, the symbol of paternalistic devotion, is that scientific progress has left a serious void that we must somehow try to fill.

Somehow along the line, the passing of the physician of grandfather's day has endangered a priceless curative ingredient —the patient's feeling that the doctor has a personal concern for him, that he is interested and willing to listen, that he treats people and not just diseases. Instruments are indispensable, but they have no heart. Penicillin shots can be miraculously effective, but they are no substitute for compassionate understanding. The tragedy is that there is almost no one in the aloof and omniscient hierarchy of the present piecemeal practice of medicine whose assignment it is to fill this key role.

The patient wants up-to-date medical care. He is grateful for the skilled services of a urologist or otolaryngologist, of an orthopedic or cardiac surgeon, and of a host of other specialists when he needs them. But, above all else, he feels a deeply rooted need for a personal physician. He wants a doctor, with all the boundless connotations of that term. More than ever, the patient needs a personal physician to provide continued care and guidance and to integrate the regimen recommended by the specialists. Leading medical authorities are in agreement that the role of such a personal doctor is fully feasible provided that it is adapted to modern conditions.

With the dwindling number of competent general practitioners and the growing predominance of specialization, the traditional channel and sequence of medical care are increasingly imperiled. By choice or necessity, many patients already are bypassing general practitioners and are seeking directly the services of specialists. Competent opinion is that this is a far from desirable procedure, medically as well as economically. It not only is wasteful to go to a specialist for initial advice about some vague condition but also is often both frustrating and costly. This is all the more true if the patient, who has no natural gift of self-diagnosis and usually has considerable difficulty in orienting himself in the thicket of specialization, happens to consult the wrong specialist.

A specialist has been described as "a person who knows more and more about less and less." Being insecure about anything outside his limited orbit, he is apt to be overly suspicious and to order a series of expensive tests right off the bat. In the case of such a common and obscure complaint as persistent headaches, for instance, the patient is likely to wind up with a neurological consultation and an encephalogram and still be no better off. Most patients with vague gastric distress usually can obtain relief from an antispasmodic drug, along with some reassurance. But they are virtually certain to end up with a big bill for X rays if they directly consult a gastroenterologist.

Even more serious is the specialist's propensity to overlook the entity that a patient, or even a specific illness, represents. The trend in the specialties is to regard as irrelevant anything but the particular matter under scrutiny. This ignores the fact that a human being is far more than the sum of his symptoms and that no illness is free of emotional components that may sometimes be considerably more important than the illness itself. It is perhaps no mere coincidence that the continued fragmentation of the patient, the increasingly impersonal and episodic treatment, the round of costly and unintegrated examinations and explorations, and the whole frustrating maze of institutional complexity have been accompanied by an upsurge of functional illness—disease for which there is no apparent organic cause—and a growing demand for psychiatric services.

Dr. T. F. Fox, editor of *The Lancet*, the admirable British medical journal, once said, "Whatever happens to medicine, the age-old demand of the person—the patient—for help has to be satisfied, by somebody. Somebody must listen to him." But does the doctor have the time to listen? Does he have the inclination to do so when the patient turns to him? In his preoccupation with the disease, does he tend more and more to overlook the environmental and emotional influences on the individual and to feel that this is somebody else's job? These are among the most overriding and perplexing problems in medicine today.

II

Fifty years ago, nearly all doctors were general practitioners and took care of every medical need. Today, nearly 70 per cent of all private practitioners, and a still higher proportion in large cities, are specialists in one of the fifty-odd branches of medicine.

Ten years after graduation from medical school, 70 per cent of the class of 1930 had entered general practice. Only 35 per cent of the class of 1950 followed that course. More than 80 per cent of the graduates now leaving medical school prefer to reap the higher income and shorter hours enjoyed by specialists. Thoughtful observers of the medical scene are looking with growing concern at the prospect of the virtual extinction of the general practitioner and an even more lopsided profession.

Of all doctors, none leads a more hectic pace or works under greater handicaps than does the generalist, who has been rapidly relegated to a lower caste in the medical hierarchy. Usually overworked and underinformed, often denied hospital privileges, facing a virtually insurmountable task in trying to keep up with new scientific developments, these doctors see too many patients and cannot give them nearly enough time. The disquieting truth, according to reliable professional opinion, is that few general practitioners fully measure up to present-day standards of competence. Excluded to a large degree from the mainstream of medicine, many of them become progressively less equipped as time goes on. There are no controls on their practice similar to those imposed on specialists, who are subject to hospital-staff standards. The result is that the scope of work undertaken by the general physician is limited only by his personal assessment of his own limitations. He is jack-of-all-trades and master of none.

Despite the decline in their proportion, general practitioners remain the backbone of our medical care system. The entire system is jeopardized if the average general physician, the first line of defense against illness, becomes inadequate and practices slapdash medicine. Well over half of all Americans continue to depend on general practitioners for most of their care. In thousands of smaller communities, such physicians are responsible for virtually all diagnosis and treatment in the broad and basic area of internal medicine and for the bulk of obstetric and pediatric care and general surgery. In the larger cities, the lower-income groups also get most of their medical services from general practitioners. Since the better urban hospitals limit their staffs to specialists, the class distinction is blurred when the patient is hospitalized. But outside of hospital work, the clientele of specialists is largely concentrated in the upper-income brackets. Those unable to pay often have to get along with second-rate medicine.

There is no more valuable member of the medical team than the well-trained generalist. He is the one to whom the patient turns first for assistance and guidance when he is in physical or mental distress. He is the one who makes the initial diagnosis, provides the required treatment, and decides whether the appropriate specialist is to be called in. No matter how many specialists serve the patient over the years, the family physician is in the best position to have the most intimate knowledge of the individual and retains overall responsibility for his health. His relationship with the patient has the best chance of developing into the mutual understanding and give-and-take that are essential for well-rounded medical care.

Here and there are some general practitioners who meet these requirements admirably. Competent, warmhearted, and dedicated, these physicians are superbly effective in the early recognition and treatment of disease. At their best, they are the living embodiment of the myth of the omniscient old-time family doctor. They have the additional advantage of the basal metabolism test, X rays, the fluoroscope, the electrocardiograph, and the other diagnostic tools that are now part of the generalist's equipment or readily at his disposal. They can usually bring the resources of modern medicine even to the most isolated places.

But study after study has shown that many general practitioners fall far short of these standards. They have shown that numerous family doctors work in isolation, deprived of the professional stimulus and supervision provided by staff membership in a good hospital, and depend upon volume rather than quality. These practitioners rarely have office assistants or laboratory facilities worthy of the name. They develop a technique of snap diagnosis that allows them to see, but not really to examine, anywhere from twenty to forty patients in the course of an afternoon. The treatment they give is uniformly superficial. They resort promiscuously to the use of drugs, without regard to the patient's real needs or the possible side effects of the medication. They seldom seek the advice of specialists because they construe admission of the need for a consultant as a confession of inadequacy and fear that they will never see the patient again.

Sooner or later, many doctors have to make a choice between doing a proper job and carrying so heavy a patient load that sound diagnosis and treatment become physically impossible.

Despite all the advances made by medicine, a complete physical examination and an accurate medical history of the patient remain the best means of arriving at a correct diagnosis. But since these essential procedures are time-consuming, many physicians resort to symptomatic treatment. They listen to enough of the patient's story to make a show of interest, go through some of the motions of doing a physical examination, and prescribe largely on the basis of obvious symptoms. A patient with a chronic cough, for instance, is dismissed with a prescription for a cough medicine. Liver injections, hormones, and a variety of other drugs are handed out in cases where X rays or culture smears may disclose malignant tumors or other serious conditions calling for prompt surgery.

A truly devastating commentary on the state of general practice in a country that often brags of having the finest medical care in the world was furnished by the findings of an investigation jointly undertaken several years ago by the Rockefeller Foundation and the Division of Health Affairs of the University of North Carolina. Eighty-eight North Carolina general practitioners were picked at random as a representative sample for the intensive study, which took nearly two years and was conducted with the cooperation of the state medical society. Special teams observed the work of these physicians throughout their daily routines in their offices, on hospital rounds, and on house calls. The doctors were then graded according to the quality of their work.

The findings were "tremendous variation in the quality of medical care" and a high proportion of poor performance. Some of the physicians, the report on the study said, "obtained thorough histories and performed careful, competent physical examinations of each patient. The laboratory, which was usually manned by a trained technician, was used skillfully as an adjunct to the practice." But the poor doctors, who made up nearly half of the total, "practiced from their desk chairs. . . . Histories were almost non-existent, and the few questions asked were often irrelevant. Patients were seldom undressed or laid down for examination. Abdominal examinations were performed with patients sitting in a chair. The lack of attention to the patient's safety was demonstrated by unsterile technique in performing veni-punctures [punctures of a vein] and hypodermic injections."

In 43 per cent of the cases, the doctors studied were observed using improperly sterilized instruments, with the consequent danger of transmission of serum jaundice. "The same instrument," it was reported, "was sometimes used repeatedly for successive patients, and inadequate sterilization was done between each use. An occasional physician used sterile instruments with unwashed hands, while others failed to wash their hands after obvious or presumptive contamination."

The physicians were scored on the basis of the things they did right, did wrong, or failed to do at all when they should have done them. They were then ranked in five classifications. The breakdown was: group 1 (uniformly poor), sixteen; group 2 (poor but not quite so bad as group 1), twenty-three; group 3 (intermediate or average), twenty-seven; group 4 (pretty good), fifteen; group 5 (outstanding), seven.

The methods of patient care used by the doctors ranked as "uniformly poor" were summarized as follows:

"They evinced almost uniformly a superficiality and lack of thoroughness in their approach to the clinical problems encountered in practice. In history taking, questions were few, usually disconnected and lacking in incisiveness. These gave little evidence that the physician was thinking in terms of probable diagnoses. They were not planned or designed to explore the function of specific organs or physiological units. The physical examination was usually sketchy, and it was frequently difficult to understand, in view of the patient's history, why one area was chosen for examination and another ignored. The laboratory tests performed by these physicians were few, often poorly performed and showed the same lack of direction. Under these conditions the indications for specific treatment were usually lacking or unclear, and the treatment ordered gave ample evidence of this uncertain state of affairs. Throughout the handling of each patient this lack of direction and purposefulness made it difficult for the observer to follow the physician's reasoning."

Fifty of the doctors were scored as "poor" on medical history taking, and only eight were scored as "very good." Some physicians, it was found, took histories that "gave little evidence of clinical knowledge or skill."

At the outset of the study, the report said, it was assumed that at least the majority of the doctors picked for the survey performed complete physical examinations on all new patients and all old patients who had not been seen recently. But the observing physicians discovered that "complete head-to-toe examination was the exception rather than the rule." Although it was felt that "disrobing for a physical examination is so necessary to its accomplishment that it may be regarded as laboring the obvious to raise the question," the study found that in 45 per cent of the cases, examinations were performed with the patient fully or almost completely dressed: "Physicians were observed attempting to perform auscultation of the heart or lungs [listening to sounds within the body either directly or through a stethoscope or other instrument] through several layers of clothing or dropping the stethoscope chest piece down through the open neck of the clothing in this attempt. Similarly, several physicians failed to recognize the impossibility of feeling a soft, rounded liver edge through several layers of heavy clothing."

"Percussion [tapping] of the chest is one of the examinations which has become symbolic of the doctor's work," the report said. In 60 per cent of the cases, this was not done at all, despite the fact that many of the patients were suffering from respiratory infections. In another 17 per cent, the chest was "thumped perfunctorily."

"Examination of the breasts of female patients is a simple, rapid procedure which one might expect to be extremely popular in view of the considerable publicity given to breast cancer at the present time," the report observed. But in 86 per cent of the cases, the breasts were not even "routinely examined."

In 74 per cent of the cases, the doctors either did not examine the patients' eyes at all as a means of detecting possible disease or limited such examination to an inspection of the mucous membrane of the inner surface of the eyelids.

Essential laboratory procedures also were found to be frequently neglected. No red-blood-cell count was done in 53 per cent of the cases, and no white-blood-cell count in 45 per cent. There was no bacteriological work done in 58 per cent of the cases.

"Indiscriminate" use of antibiotics was discovered to be a daily occurrence. Many of the doctors, the report said, did not realize that antibiotics are worthless against viral infections or "understand the values and limitations of these drugs. For instance, the belief that antibiotics are effective in treating the common cold was found to be widespread. Other physicians used these drugs on the assumption that they are harmless or might prevent complications. The demand by the patient or his family for a 'shot of penicillin' obviously increased the pressure on the physician."

In the treatment of anemia, medications described in the report as "shotgun preparations" were used in 85 per cent of the cases. In only 15 per cent was "the therapy related to the type of anemia."

The report had this to say about the treatment of hypertension (high blood pressure) in 57 per cent of the cases: "Assessment of hypertensive disease poor or limited to blood pressure determination only. Management not skilled, neglect of simple therapeutic procedures such as weight reduction, rest and salt restriction. Drugs poorly selected or administration unskilled."

In 67 per cent of the cases, the doctors failed to recognize obesity as a clinical problem or gave inadequate dietary advice to overweight patients. "Examples were found," it was reported, "where patients with diabetes or hypertension specifically asked the doctor about the relationship between these diseases and obesity, only to be assured by the doctor that none existed."

"Emotional problems," the report commented, "appear to constitute an enigma for the practicing physician. Many physicians completely failed to recognize these problems in their practices. Others, while recognizing the problems, were either indifferent to them or appeared to be made uncomfortable by patients with such problems. References to malingering, hypochondriacs, 'problem patients' or 'getting them out of the office quickly' were frequently heard." One of the members of the survey team remarked that "the common practice of treating pregnancy as a somewhat humorous situation might well increase a mother's difficulties in adjusting to an unplanned and sometimes unwanted pregnancy."

The report also had some enlightening comments about the average physician's difficulties in keeping up with new drugs and the avalance of medical literature. Many doctors, it observed, are increasingly coming to depend for information regarding medical progress on promotional material put out by the big pharmaceutical companies and on drug salesmen, who are known in the trade as "detail men." "It was apparent from observation and statements from physicians that their practices in regard to medication and therapy are influenced significantly by the information and products supplied by the drug salesman," the report declared, adding that this is a far from desirable state of affairs, "since the detail man's function is not to provide education but to sell pharmaceutical products."

The study found no direct correlation between the quality of medical care provided by a physician and his income. In fact, some of the poorer doctors earned more money than some of the better ones. "This is hardly surprising," the report observed, "in view of the fact that the lay public has few valid criteria for assessing a physician's competence."

The survey report emphasized that the physicians whose work was studied appeared to be typical of the run of general practitioners. "The training taken by these doctors," it said, "is similar to the training in a wide variety of hospitals in all parts of the United States. The physicians studied came from many medical schools and had exhibited all degrees of academic success, so there is no reason to assume an adverse selection. It can therefore be stated with considerable assurance that in terms of medical education and training the physicians who participated in this study are not evidently different from general practitioners at large."

Competent opinion is that the conditions found in North Carolina are widely prevalent in other states as well. "I was not at all surprised at the findings of the study," said a nationally known physician with many years of experience in medical practice, education, and administration. "I expect that, to a greater or lesser extent, this situation holds true generally. North Carolina is not a typical Southern state. It has a far higher standard of living than most states in the South and good medical schools and hospitals. North Carolina doctors are no different from doctors elsewhere. They're doing the best they know how. It's not a question of the individual; it's the system."

What should have provoked a storm of controversy and much soul-searching left the medical profession totally unruffled. The sole reaction of organized medicine was to ignore the illuminating report of the North Carolina inquiry, which was published as a special supplement to the *Journal of Medical Education*, the official publication of the Association of American Medical Colleges. Dr. John S. DeTar, former president of the American Academy of General Practice and one of the few prominent physicians to comment publicly on the matter, conceded that the criteria used in the study for judging performance "were thoroughly fair." And he added, "What's more, I suspect that similar studies of obstetricians, surgeons, and pediatricians would yield like results."

Under a system in which each doctor is to a large extent his own judge and jury and in which performance is wholly a matter of individual competence and personal conscience, the proportion of good and poor work being done must remain a matter of conjecture. Free enterprise in medicine may have its advantages, but it also means the freedom to be incompetent and to get away with it. For a variety of reasons, the temptation to do so is particularly strong in the field of general practice.

As patients have come to recognize the value of specialization, family physicians have been downgraded to the category of "just general practitioners." They have been disparaged to such a degree that many families, particularly on the higher-income level, are more and more turning to specialists in internal medicine for initial diagnosis and treatment. While the dividing line between a general practitioner and an internist is not always clearly defined, the latter undergoes a longer period of training and is qualified as a specialist in chest or gastrointestinal diseases. To saddle him with some of the trivia of family practice is a waste of talent and a luxury we can hardly afford at a time when highly trained physicians are in short supply.

The fragmentation of medicine and the rapid pace of its progress are making it increasingly difficult for the solo generalist to keep informed in any phase of his profession. The nature of the work of general practitioners, the New York Academy of Medicine has said, "calls for unusually broad knowledge, but they are most often so taken up with their practice—and generally isolated from hospitals and other medical centers—that they have little time for continued training. The result is that in all parts of the country, but particularly in the smaller and more isolated communities, there are general practitioners who still practice much the same medicine they learned in their student days."

As general practice becomes less and less attractive and as younger physicians are drawn into the specialties and lured to the cities by the promise of higher income and greater professional stimulation, there is an increasing preponderance of older—and less competent—doctors in the smaller and poorer communities. A study made some years ago showed that the ratio of physicians under forty-five years of age to the general population was eight times as great in areas with the highest per capita income as in those with the lowest average income. A recent survey in Maine disclosed that more than half of the small-town doctors in that state are over the age of fifty-six. The proportion of general practitioners is highest among doctors who are sixty or older. When these men retire or die, the void is often being filled by newly licensed graduates of substandard foreign medical schools who cannot make the grade in the specialties.

A good family doctor can play a key role in the prevention of mental illness. As the first to be consulted and as the one most familiar with the patient's family background and occupational environment, he is in a position to detect incipient emotional disorders and to try to alleviate conditions that are harmful to mental health. But as can be readily seen from the findings of the North Carolina study, this is precisely what many general practitioners fail to do. They have neither the time nor the grounding in the basic elements of psychiatry to do more than to dismiss vague complaints with prescriptions for tonics or tranquilizers.

The incongruity is that the physician who covers the widest area of practice receives the shortest period of preparation. The usual single year of rotating internship, in which the medical graduate is exposed to brief periods of practical training in a number of fields, is clearly inadequate. The American Academy of General Practice, which was established in 1947 as a counterpart to the specialty boards, favors two years of rotating internship for physicians who are planning to become generalists. But the growing body of medical knowledge is outmoding even this approach, aside from the fact that after two years of internship, some of the graduates change their minds and decide to go instead into further specialty training.

The American Academy of General Practice, with about twenty-three thousand members, is now engaged in a concerted effort to raise standards. Its members are required to obtain credit for 150 hours of postgraduate study every three years to remain in good standing. It has been pushing, so far with little success, for hospital privileges for generalists and for the establishment of departments of general practice in medical schools. But the academy is fighting a rearguard action in trying to stem the tide of specialization. While some of its aims are laudable, its primary motivation is obviously to protect lucrative practices and to bolster prestige. The academy still insists that the general practitioner's competence extends to whatever he feels he is capable of doing. This is a pretty big order and keeps the door wide open for poor medical care.

III

The specialties are undoubtedly on a much higher level than is general practice. Nor is there any question that while specialization is probably being overdone, it has greatly improved the standards of medical care and enhanced its effectiveness. But specialization also has its liabilities. It has splintered medical services into narrow segments and limited the field of professional vision; it has enormously complicated the organization and economics of medical care; it has depreciated general practice and made it much more difficult to provide continuity of care; and it often leads to undue emphasis on isolated organic symptoms and excessive use of laboratory procedures that do not necessarily promote sounder judgment.

"Specialization," one authority has said, "is a more certain guarantee that one knows little outside his own field than that he is really expert within it."

The more specialization proliferates, the greater is the danger that there will be x varieties of specialists to diagnose and treat x varieties of disease but no single doctor to take care of the patient as a physiological and psychological entity. By training and experience, the specialist tends to concentrate on the symptoms with which he is most familiar and to overlook other causes of illness that may be fully as important. His approach is often impersonal and episodic. Preoccupation with narrowly defined medical problems dims the view of the multiple origins frequently figuring in disease. It also robs the patient of the unifying management and stable and affectionate relationship that can sometimes be more beneficial than the most potent drugs.

The spawning of the specialties is closely tied up with the greater concentration of medical services within the hospital and has accelerated the trend toward increasing, sometimes needless, hospitalization. In view of the skyrocketing of hospital costs and the mounting incidence of chronic conditions, there is a crying need for the development of alternatives to expensive hospitalization. But the specialists, who find the publicly subsidized hospital a most convenient and profitable adjunct to their practice, have shown little enthusiasm for the development of more economical measures such as outpatient diagnostic clinics and the care of long-term patients in nursing homes or in their own homes whenever possible. Nor have they displayed much interest in mass-screening programs and other measures for the prevention of disease and its detection in incipient stages. By the very nature of the specialist's work (most patients come to him only after their disorders are well advanced), his approach is primarily curative rather than preventive.

To become a certified specialist, a physician has to undergo anywhere from two to seven years of residency training after serving his internship. He must then pass an oral and written examination before a specialty board to establish his proficiency. Many specialists are in their thirties by the time they become fully qualified, and their long period of apprenticeship at nominal pay whets their appetite to regain their investment as soon as possible.

While the medical profession still presents a fairly solid front to the general public, its point of view is by now far from monolithic. The fact that many hospitals make their staff appointments contingent upon board certification has given the specialty boards a tremendous influence on the practice of medicine. With the division of the profession into about fifty specialties and subspecialties, divergent viewpoints have inceasingly come to the fore. Behind the façade of professional accord, there are frequent clashes of conflicting economic interests. The American College of Surgeons, for instance, has for years been engaged in a running battle with the AMA over the evils of fee splitting—in its most blatant form, this is a practice in which a specialist kicks back part of his fee to the general practitioner who referred the patient to him—and other ticklish issues. Stripped of foggy pretensions, the wrangle is largely over who gets what piece of the pie.

Specialization not only has set higher standards and closed many doors to those lacking board certification but also has created a system of status differentiation within medicine, with surgeons at the top and general practitioners at the very bottom of the pecking order. Although there are notable exceptions of successful specialists who come from poor families, the financial backing required for the protacted period of training tends to favor those from the upper economic and social strata. This accentuates the tendency of the specialist elite toward upper-class orientation.

Nearly half of all specialists are in the surgical field, which is the most remunerative. With one out of every fourteen Americans now undergoing an operation in the course of a year, thousands of surgeons are kept busy and prosperous. The huge volume of surgery and the fact that much of it involves elective rather than emergency procedures also provide a fertile field for abuse. While numerous lifesaving feats are daily performed by skilled and dedicated surgeons in operating rooms throughout the country, reputable authorities are on record that there is a staggering amount of needless and poor surgery and that some surgeons charge unconscionable fees.

Competence is not automatically assured by specialty-board and hospital requirements. Quite a few hospitals permit surgery by physicians without specialty qualifications. The bulk of inferior surgery is done by these surgeons-by-assertion, but specialists are not always blameless in this respect.

As is the case with medical licensure, specialty-board certification measures the candidate's knowledge and skills only at the start of his career. There is no provision for a periodic check to make sure that the diplomate stays on his toes. Human nature and the pressures of the average practice being what they are, backsliding is sometimes inevitable. But certification is good for a lifetime.

The better hospitals have established various mechanisms for policing the quality of staff performance, including a requirement for pathological examination of all tissue removed in operations, to make sure that no surgery is done on normal organs. In many hospitals, however, the job is done perfunctorily or not at all. Except in cases of flagrant misconduct, even the finest hospitals have to take it for granted, when renewing staff privileges, that board-certified specialists continue to be qualified.

The patient has a right to expect that the physician in whose hands he places his health, and possibly his life, is fully competent. He gets no such assurance under the present system.

IV

Medical progress has created two urgent needs that, on the face of it, appear to be contradictory but actually are not. Advances in the techniques of prevention, diagnosis, and treatment are steadily increasing the necessity for specialization and for teamwork. But at the same time, there is more need than ever before for the type of physician who not only can differentiate and take care of those needs that do not call for more specialized skills and apparatus but also can coordinate all the patient's medical requirements.

So vast has become the store of knowledge about the body's physical and biochemical structure and its countless and subtle individual variations, so complex the instrumentation, so great the array of new drugs with properties that often are potentially as hazardous as they are beneficial that no individual can possibly comprehend or utilize all these advances. The new tools are extraordinarily effective, but they present the physician with formidable problems. They call for highly specialized skills, for discriminating use, and for the collaboration of a wide range of disciplines.

But the greater the division of labor between the specialties, the more indispensable is some integrating mechanism. Such a unifying force is needed to correlate the services of the specialists and to take an overall view of the patient—not just as a collection of separate organs but as a complicated, troubled, groping, and utterly unique human being. Only a competent and perceptive family physician can perform this function. The science of medicine becomes a distant, frosty business when it is unwarmed by proper attention to the individual as well as to his disease.

Some of our present difficulties arise not so much from the growth of specialization, which as a natural consequence of expanding knowledge, as from a failure of integration. The main trouble does not stem from our plenitude of skills. It lies primarily in our failure to develop a viable organizational scheme to bring these skills to bear in the most telling manner for the benefit of the patient.

Far from being defunct, the now isolated and harried family physician must be assigned a role wherein he can function more effectively. This he can best do as a member of a group in which his vital sphere is clearly recognized, in which the required equipment is readily at hand, and in which he can freely call on a variety of specialists whenever necessary. Group practice, especially when operated in conjunction with a comprehensive insurance program, offers the most feasible framework for utilizing the general practitioner's great potentialities for health promotion and for basic diagnosis and therapy. Unlike solo practice, group practice sets the stage for a stimulating interplay of professional interests and provides an invaluable internal mechanism for a continuing appraisal of the quality of the doctor's work.

Only when he is allowed to work on an equal footing with his specialist colleagues and when the financial barrier to adequate care is to a large extent removed can the general physician come back into his own and regain his rightful place as the solid foundation of the structure of medical practice. Only thus can the dismemberment of the patient into separate diseases be halted and medicine made whole again. Only the interdisciplinary team approach provides the machinery for meshing general practice with the specialties for comprehensive care.

It is amply clear that medical care cannot be fragmentized into isolated elements without serious detriment to its quality and effectiveness. Diagnosis cannot be arbitrarily separated from treatment; surgery cannot be isolated from preoperative and postoperative care; hospitalization cannot be viewed as a thing entirely apart from care in the home, office, or clinic. Nor can they be completely isolated from the patient's family and group setting.

To do the most good, a medical care program should ensure and facilitate, through the collaboration of all the medical specialties, the patient's treatment throughout the full range of his actual and potential needs, physiological as well as psychological. This is admittedly something of an ideal and may be too much for a single generation to achieve. There is no question, however, that scientific medicine should be based upon the fullest and most exact knowledge of the patient that can be made available to the doctor. Until not so long ago, the knowledge most readily available for the supplementing of clinical judgment was drawn entirely from physiology. But medicine must keep in step with all the sciences that help make the patient comprehensible. The contributions of psychology and psychiatry to the understanding of psychosomatic phenomena are already indispensable. Additional light on the patient's interaction with his environment is being shed by research in the behavioral sciences, such as sociology and anthropology. Comprehensive medicine must be concerned with the whole spectrum of processes by which the human organism handles innumerable stimuli in such a way as to maintain a healthy equilibrium.

We clearly cannot even begin to approach this broad concept without a solution of the problem of how the needs for both specialist and personal care can be met. Much of the frustration and lack of adequate communication between doctor and patient so characteristic of today's medical care stems from this difficult problem. But it is not intrinsically insoluble.

A crucial question is whether general practice is dying a natural death or is being done to death by the prevailing patterns of medical education and practice with their overemphasis on specialization. There is considerable evidence that the latter is true.

The present medical school environment and hospital-staff policies are overwhelmingly steering young physicians into the specialties. Medical school faculties are dominated by specialists who, by precept and example, impress their students with the desirability of specialization. The graduate education of interns and residents in teaching hospitals is chiefly carried out by specialists. An important motivation in the decision to concentrate on one field of medicine is the sheer impossibility of achieving equal competence in all branches. But equally weighty reasons are considerations of income and prestige and the natural inclination of the young to base their choice of careers upon the success patterns of their elders.

It does not take medical students too long to become aware that specialization means higher economic rewards and professional status, that the general practitioner is looked down upon, and that there is no place for him in the hospital. As long as these inducements prevail, the more energetic and capable students will be attracted to specialty practice. This does more than merely perpetuate the existing disproportion within the professional ranks. When the young doctor bypasses general practice altogether to go directly into a specialty, he misses a precious opportunity for the insights that can best be gained through the most intimate contacts with patients.

The result is that the most promising students are siphoned off into the specialties and the rest are left to go into general practice. But is this a desirable procedure? Does a top-heavy array of specialists, overshadowing the cornerstone of services by general physicians, really make sense for the conservation of health?

"Who," Dr. George A. Silver has asked, "will see the patient in the first instance and determine if the complaint is minor or major? Who will refer cases to the specialists for more complex and precise diagnosis and treatment? Who will collate the reports as they come in? Who will adjust the precise 'scientific' reports or findings to the patient, that imprecise person of infinite variability? Who will be so intimately related to the family as to know the interpersonal problems, assess them in relationship to the complaints or symptoms, and provide the support and guidance that probably do more to determine the duration or severity of all illness than the specific teatment? Who will carry on the day-to-day psychosomatic practice?"

Obviously, these crucial functions can be carried out only by well-trained, broad-gauged generalists with some comprehension of the social, psychological, and preventive aspects of medicine. The training of such physicians is one of the most challenging tasks facing medical education. And it will take a far-reaching reorganization of medical practice to provide a meaningful niche for them.

In a more rational medical care system, excessive specialization will be curbed, provisions will be made for integrating the services of specialists, and the family doctor will be restored to his proper place in public and professional regard as the key figure on the health team. Since there are degrees of illness and of skill needed in handling them, he will resume his rightful role in the medical constellation and will guide his patients through the growing complexities of health care. By being freed of the burden of an overcrowded schedule, he will have time for thorough examination and history taking. He will depend on the acuity of his educated powers of observation even more than on gadgets to detect the danger signals of any possible deviation from the normal. A grounding in clinical psychiatry will enable him to evaluate and treat common emotional stresses that are often at the root of organic disease. Keenly aware of the potentialities of preventive medicine, the generalist will foster the concept of good health as distinguished from mere absence of disease and will guide his patients in keeping well and adjusted to their environment. Above all else, he will provide the continuity of care that is the keystone of good medicine.

There is nothing so comforting as the knowledge that when illness strikes, at any time of the day or night, there is a competent family medical adviser to turn to and that he will be ready to examine, to listen, to direct, and to follow through. The changes in our manner of living and in the ills that beset us have intensified the need for such a friend and counselor.

CHAPTER FOUR

The Mystique of the
Doctor-Patient Relationship

I

A CURIOUS AMBIVALENCE is coming to light in the feelings of many Americans toward doctors. A number of public opinion surveys in recent years have shown that most people have relatively little fault to find with their own doctors but have a much less favorable opinion of the medical profession as a whole. The majority of those interviewed said that they thought well of their own physicians. It was an altogether different story, however, when they were asked their views on doctors in general. This brought to the surface indications of widespread and deep-seated discontent, centered on the impersonality of present-day medical care even more so than on its costliness.

Major complaints were that physicians in general are "cold" and "impersonal," that they are too busy to listen and talk to their patients, that they charge too much and "won't come when called," that their examinations and treatment are often superficial, that they are too hasty in recommending expensive laboratory tests and surgery, that the patient has to wait too long even with an appointment and frequently feels "like a machine on an assembly line," and that being sent on a round of specialists usually means that no one really takes responsibility for what happens to the patient.

It is doubtful whether the average person is fully conscious of the extent of his need for attention when he is ill. But he expresses this need with the habitual protest that he would like more of the doctor's time. Typical comments are: "I'd like to be able to talk to the doctor more and to tell him more"; "I wish he would show as much interest in me as a human being as he does in my blood count and blood pressure"; "Sometimes I feel that he has to look at my card before he really knows who I am."

Interestingly enough, "takes his time" was given in the interviews as the most desirable trait in a doctor. This and "personal interest, sympathy, and kindness" even outranked the requirement that a physician be "up to date."

A considerable proportion of those questioned felt that most doctors try to cover up one another's mistakes, that they think they are always right, that they are clannish and consider themselves better than other people, that many physicians want to get rich quick, and that the medical profession is not nearly so selfless and devoted as it should be.

In every poll, most respondents consistently put their own doctors in a different category from the rest of the profession. In each classification of questions and answers, there was a significant differential in criticism along this line.

What are the reasons for this puzzling disparity? The AMA, which commissioned most of the polls, salves itself with the soothing notion that the average person's esteem for his personal physician is based on solid facts, while his harsher judgments of other people's doctors are largely the result of hearsay. But is this the only explanation? New insights into the dynamics of the doctor-patient relationship provided by psychological and psychiatric research indicate that the reasons why people tend to think differently of their own doctors than of the medical profession collectively are much more complicated.

One of the most tenable explanations is that the physician very often assumes the role of the powerful and beloved father in the patient's eyes and, like the father, can do no wrong. It thus becomes reassuring to think of one's own doctor as reliable and magnanimous and to have a less flattering view of other doctors.

A crucial point to bear in mind is that when people are sick and feel helpless and afraid, they tend to regress into childlike dependency. Under these circumstances, they usually welcome in their doctors the authoritarian qualities that they resent when they are healthy and want to be treated as adults. On the other hand, it is not uncommon for patients to transfer to their physicians some of the subconscious hostilities against parents that they have carried over from childhood.

People have always had mixed feelings about doctors. The physician is associated in their minds with suffering, illness, and death. But at the same time, he also stands for relief from pain

THE MYSTIQUE OF THE DOCTOR-PATIENT RELATIONSHIP   73

and the cure of disease. The conflicting sentiments evoked by these associations have been sharpened as medicine has become more effective and patients more knowledgeable and less docile. The irony is that the very things that have made the doctor's healing skills and tools so much more potent also have served to undermine the affection and regard in which he has traditionally been held. In the era of medicine's most brilliant accomplishments, doctors and patients are drifting apart; the medical profession has never been in greater danger of losing the people's faith.

Always regarded as a man of magic, the doctor has now become a scientific magician of whom much more is frequently expected than he can deliver. With the onrush of scientific developments, all too often exaggerated by the popular news media, many people fail to realize that medicine is still far from an exact science and expect a magic pill for every ill. The public has been educated to expect miracles, and the physician may be in danger of making an enemy and losing a patient if none is produced. Doctors are too busy these days to be overly concerned about the loss of a patient. But many physicians have an ingrained distaste for admitting that they do not know and are apt to feel that they must live up to a sort of superman role in order to keep their patients' confidence. This in itself is enough to set off a whole chain of misapprehensions.

Another irony is that the more intricate medical science becomes, the less mysterious it seems to the layman. Rightly or wrongly, patients are starting to feel that even technical matters relating to diagnosis and treatment are not wholly beyond their ken and that they are entitled to an explanation of what the doctor is doing and why he is doing it. No longer as obsequious toward doctors as they once were, they resent being treated as medical illiterates and want to be spoken to in understandable language. They are inclined to suspect that there may be quite a bit of clannish hocus-pocus in the rituals of medical mystery.

But probably most serious of all is a feeling of vague dissatisfaction with the doctor as a person and of growing impatience with him as a member of a profession whose struggle for the perpetuation of the existing order strikes many people as primarily a struggle for the perpetuation of a vested interest.

"Western man turned away from the priest to the doctor,"

one authority has said, and "now the inevitable disenchantment is taking place."

The patient may tell himself over and over again that medicine is basically a trade just like any other and that the doctor's need to make a living is naturally his first consideration. The patient nevertheless cannot help feeling disillusioned when the physician fails to live up to the ideal of selfless service that is so much part of our ethic. Where does altruism end and self-interest begin in medicine? Do the two necessarily have to conflict? It will take quite a few changes in the organization of medical care and practice to clear up the confusion and resolve the conflict.

Patients are not unaware of the clash between the medical profession's oft-proclaimed idealism and the harsh realities of life. In a society in which affluence is the principal yardstick of success, the layman may find the profession's preoccupation with the economics of its trade not altogether unreasonable. But what is an insult to his intelligence is the profession's fatuous pretension, undoubtedly motivated by its underlying guilt feeling, that the desire for money plays no role in its tenacious defense of the status quo. "It's possible that we spend too much time telling each other what great humanitarians we are," the late Dr. Elmer Hess, a former AMA president, once told his colleagues.

One observer has said that charging for medical services often leads to a "psychological trauma" on the part of both doctor and patient "because of the inherent feeling that it is no more right for a physician to make a charge than it is for a clergyman to send a bill for his prayer." While this is probably an overstatement, fees are unquestionably a major sore point between patients and doctors, embarrassing all around and a source of frequent misunderstanding. The physician may feel that to talk about such a mundane matter as money somehow detracts from his stature as a humanitarian. The patient, too, may consider it inappropriate to discuss a price beforehand and is duly shocked when he gets the bill. Being charged for help in his misfortune sometimes smacks to him of biological blackmail. This explains why the average person is all too ready to jump to the conclusion that medical fees are exorbitant, even though he knows that the cost of everything else he uses has gone up, and to feel that some physicians charge whatever the traffic will bear.

Removal of the cash-register element would undeniably have a beneficial effect on the doctor-patient relationship. But the patient's chagrin at being charged for what he may subconsciously feel should be an act of benevolence is only part of the picture. Fees are the one tangible transaction into which the patient can channel his disappointment with the doctor—the rankling feeling that he is being treated with condescension and denied his rightful share of sympathy and affection.

"The unhappy feelings that patients have about doctors," Dr. Lawrence Hinkle of Cornell University Medical College has said, "are not simply the result of crass behavior on the part of a few physicians. Perhaps it is true that some members of the medical profession have forgotten that with their special privileges, high status, and a good income go special responsibilities. But the discontent that patients feel about their treatment arises from something much deeper. It has its roots in the actual scientific inadequacy of the present piecemeal practice of medicine. Laboratory tests and limited procedures cannot replace a human understanding of the whole patient."

The patient wants someone who will make him feel well again. What he very often wants is not so much advice or treatment as someone who will listen to him about his troubles and understand how much he has to bear. He wants relief from psychological tension fully as much as from physical pain. He sometimes wants relief from unreasoning fears, the foremost of which is the fear of cancer. Many patients project their emotional frustrations into physical complaints and tend to magnify their symptoms as a means of escape from reality and of getting attention. The doctor needed by those who are ill or who think they are ill must not only be technically proficient but also have a genuine liking for people, a quick responsiveness to loneliness and the craving for reassurance and self-esteem, a tolerance for human failings, a compassion for suffering.

Dr. Thomas Findley of Tulane University School of Medicine tells the story of an apprentice physician who, a good many years ago, asked his mentor how to treat a case of scarlet fever. The older man reflected for a while before answering, "Well, the treatment of scarlet fever depends upon what is the matter with the patient."

"This was not a facetious remark," says Dr. Findley, "for the more experienced of the two well knew that the demands of one patient are uniquely different from those of all others. Illness is a threat to one's integrity, and the manner in which one mobilizes his defenses depends not only upon the nature of the pathologic stress, but also upon the quality of his emotional equipment. To the extent that this is meager, the dependency of the patient will increase and the clinical picture becomes diffuse and blurred."

Despite all of medicine's spectacular advances, recognition of the uniqueness of every patient is perhaps more essential today than it ever was. And so is possession by the doctor of that sensibility of heart which makes him feel for the distress of others.

The tragedy is that the chasm between physician and patient has been widened just when the insights of psychiatry are lending new emphasis to the need for viewing the sick person within the context of his past experience and his fears, compulsions, and aspirations. The breach has occurred at the very time when the hectic pace of living in our urban civilization imposes new strains on our adaptive capacities, when some of the major mechanisms of adjustment in our society have been weakened, and when the individual bewildered by his illness needs more rather than less personal attention.

The large family, a matchless emotional anchorage of complex and intimate interrelationships, is becoming a rarity. The proportion of people living in smaller communities, with their closer human ties and greater stability, has been sharply reduced. The authoritarian and reassuring influence of the church has declined. Many of our traditional standards of conduct have been undermined. The elements tending to induce anxiety are outstripping the available mechanisms for resolving it.

More than ever, there are men and women who have lost their roots, who are solitary in the bustle of our large cities and, feeling alone and abandoned, yearn for a chance to talk to someone freely, for sympathy and guidance. Since emotional stress is often accompanied by or is the cause of physical discomfort, it is only natural that such troubled people should look for medical advice. "In these initial stages," Dr. Michael Balint, a noted British psychiatrist, has said, "we do not know which is the more important of the two—the act of complaining itself or the particular complaint. It is here that the doctor's attitude becomes decisive."

But what happens if the doctor is too busy? What happens if he is preoccupied with organic symptoms, is too overworked to pay attention to nebulous complaints, or is inclined to be impatient with "neurotics"? How can physicians establish a meaningful personal relationship with patients who are rushed through what is, in effect, an assembly line? What happens when doctors are reluctant or unable to assume the responsibilities formerly split up among a variety of institutions? Some of the results may be plainly seen in the huge consumption of sedatives and tranquilizers, in the not uncommon resort to exorcism by surgery, and in the busy schedules of our all too few psychiatrists.

Competent estimates are that fully one-third of all those who seek medical treatment owe their distress or disability to functional disorders, for which there are no clear precipitating organic causes. In another third of the cases, the illness is believed to be complicated by emotional factors. In virtually every disease, there is an interaction of physiological and emotional elements. No sickness is, in fact, free of some degree of anxiety.

This alarming picture must be viewed within the context of the sober realities of American medical practice, especially in relation to the fact that the physician's income is directly connected to the number of patients he can manage to see. The average practitioner now works about sixty hours a week and sees more than twenty patients in the course of a day. Surveys indicate that one out of every three doctors puts in a seventy-hour week and sees more than thirty patients daily. One out of six works at least eighty hours a week and has a daily load of forty or more patients. It does not take too much arithmetic to calculate how much time a physician who is so overworked can give to each patient. A doctor who is forced to see too many patients necessarily comes to depend on superficial symptoms rather than on meticulous history taking, searching physical examination, and deliberate clinical judgment. He takes shortcuts in diagnosis and treatment and sometimes misses important symptoms. In short, he practices poor medicine.

The psychosomatic aspects of illness are neglected to an even greater degree when giving a patient extra time means that the physician has to sacrifice some of his income. Sufficient time is usually lacking for thoroughness and understanding—for asking the pertinent questions, for listening to what has been described as "the music as well as the words in what the patient says," for assembling an image of the patient's strengths and weaknesses, of the pattern of his reactions under stress, of his family, his job, and his view of the world. The effects of repeated frustration of the patient's deepest need to give vent to his feelings and to be listened to with sympathy can be fully as devastating as the neglect of physiological ailments. It is important to take the blood pressure, to palpate the abdomen, and to listen carefully to the heart. But it is just as important to listen to the patient and to try to understand what he feels.

The conflict between the patient's desperate need to unburden himself and the doctor's lack of time is not the only trouble. By the nature of his training, with its emphasis on the natural sciences and its neglect of the humanities and social sciences, the average physician feels far more at home in treating organic disease than in trying to cope with disorders that have emotional components. He also may be conscious of emotional inadequacies of his own and may prefer not to become entangled in the somewhat similar anxieties of other people. The ability to listen properly is, moreover, a difficult and subtle skill. It means that the doctor must not only master the technique of putting the patient at ease, so that he will speak freely, but also develop the even rarer ability to hear things that are left unspoken because the patient himself is barely aware of them. Not all physicians are able or willing to undertake such an assignment, even if the pressures of time were of no consideration.

A pertinent question to ask at this point is whether we have the right to turn to the doctor not only for relief from physical distress but also for salvation from the whole complex of frustrations and anxieties associated with daily living. Can the physician really be held accountable for not meeting this need as well as he might? Or do we expect too much of him? Regardless of how realistic or unrealistic our expectations are, their very existence presents the medical profession with a challenge that it cannot easily ignore. Throughout history, there have been mechanisms for the alleviation of tensions. In primitive society, these took the form of magic rituals. In our own times, reliance is increasingly placed on scientific competence.

Inevitably, vexations arise when, as is often the case, there are differences between the doctor's definition of his own job and the patient's conception of what it should be. Theoretically, at any rate, the average physician recognizes the need for an intimate relationship with his patients. But undertaking the role of combination therapist, father confessor, counselor, and comforter is another matter under the conditions of present-day practice and in view of the scientific complexity of medicine. The busy physician is apt to feel that he should not be burdened with functions that properly are the province of the church or of psychiatry.

The trouble frequently is that the patient still expects what the doctor is no longer equipped or prepared to give. Emotional support has always been one of the basic ingredients of the image of the healer. In the past, there was little else the physician had to offer. Now it is within his power to bring better health and longer life. But the patient's need for personal attention and sympathetic understanding is as acute as ever.

By virtue of his singular authority in ministering to the sick, the doctor has been endowed with powers bordering on the occult and has come to be regarded as the person to whom one could always go with the utmost confidence. Therein lies the medical profession's greatest strength and its Achilles' heel. For derogation is the natural result of disillusionment with those in whom we place boundless trust. As the traditional relationship between physician and patient has been disrupted and as discontent with the existing medical care system has mounted, the tendency has been to blame the doctor for everything, including some of the things that he is powerless to do anything about. Hostility and carping criticism are the reverse side of the coin of adulation.

Widely prevalent is the feeling that the medical profession has been inexcusably slow in responding to change and to the need for making the benefits of medicine more readily accessible to all, that much of the medical care we are getting is not as good as it should be, that its costs are excessively high, that doctors are often lacking in warmth and are sometimes callous, that they not infrequently overcharge and live too ostentatiously, that they selfishly arrogate to themselves the power of decision over all questions of medical economics, that they operate as a clique with its own rules and taboos and even a language of its own, that they protect their erring colleagues from punitive action and put loyalty to the clan above the public welfare.

Patients are not always unappreciative of the sterling qualities of some doctors, of their versatile competence, their grueling work loads, their sympathetic insights, their readiness to be on call whenever needed and to give of themselves freely. But many people are ignorant of the problems besetting the physician, confused about his precise role, and perplexed by the maladjustments of an age of revolution.

All of us grow up with an image of the doctor as a benevolent and omnipotent figure, possessed of abstruse knowledge and of the magic power to heal. Some of the awe and respect he elicits in childhood is carried over into adult life, making it difficult for the average person to find fault directly with his own physician. It is much easier to vent one's frustrations and resentments on a more nebulous target, condemning the medical profession as a whole. The intransigence of organized medicine and the progressive failure of communication between the profession and the public make such a transference all the more inviting and bode ill for future relations between physicians and patients.

II

"The secret of the care of the patient," the late Dr. Francis Weld Peabody told his students at Harvard Medical School about thirty-five years ago, "is in caring *for* the patient." Dr. Peabody laid down other memorable postulates in his lecture, which has since become a classic of medical literature. "The practice of medicine in its broadest sense," he said, "includes the whole relationship of the physician with his patient" and, despite its increasing reliance on the sciences, comprises "much that will remain outside the realm of any science." The clinical picture, he declared, "is not just a photograph of a man sick in bed; it is an impressionistic painting of the patient surrounded by his home, his work, his relations, his friends, his joys, sorrows, hopes, and fears."

Appropriately enough, the word "care" has many meanings in our language and stands for solicitude as well as for the technical services rendered by physicians.

"In whatsoever houses I enter," says the Hippocratic oath, the medical profession's credo, "I will enter to help the sick . . ." And, "I will keep pure and holy both my life and my art." Grandiloquent as these stern promises may sound, the doctor's task always has been and ever will be not only to relieve pain but also to allay anxiety. In the loneliness and terror of illness, the patient seeks deliverance from the fears of disability and death. He is pleading for reassurance and personal concern. What he really wants and needs is love.

To a striking degree, the theme of love and rejection keeps on recurring in soundings of the public's views on medical care. The patient's sense of unrequited love epitomizes medicine's crisis in human relations and the alienation of doctors and patients.

For a proper understanding of the patient's disenchantment and of the elusive ingredients of his relationship with the doctor, we must turn to two vital but frequently overlooked spheres. One of them is the psychology of illness and what sociologists refer to as the "sick role." The other is the doctor's dual position, in which a symbolic meaning is superimposed upon his realistic function.

Since time immemorial, sickness has had connotations going far beyond the physical disorder itself. In primitive society, the seriously ill were considered taboo and placed in segregation. This was more than merely a precursor of sanitary quarantine. It also was a measure of restraint. The intercession of supernatural powers was invoked not only for the recovery of the sick but also for the protection of the rest of the community against the evil that had befallen them. In our society, too, there are distinct mechanisms for dealing with the ill. Perhaps not quite so openly, these also have a twofold purpose and regulate the conduct of those who are ill no less than the attitudes of the well toward them. Along with a benevolent bearing, our social norms contain certain restrictions designed to shield the healthy from the excessive demands of the sick.

To a considerable extent, illness may be likened to a reversion to childhood. Both states are marked by helplessness and self-centered dependence upon those who are physically and psychologically stronger. In illness as in childhood, there is exemption from responsibilities. However, such exemption is to some degree limited in the case of the sick to guard against malingering, with the physician acting as the certifying agent. Otherwise, illness might offer too tantalizing an avenue of escape from adult obligations. The wide prevalence of psychosomatic ailments indicates, however, that there are various devices for circumventing these controls.

The more egocentric and emotionally insecure the patient is and the more constricted his interests become as they turn back on himself, the closer is the parallel with the weakness and inadequacy of the child and his need for the comforting tenderness of the all-powerful and loving parent. Like the child, he wants to be "babied" and looked after by someone who really cares, tends to be extremely sensitive, and is easily offended.

The rural family of the past, which was to a large degree a self-contained economic unit, was able to adjust itself fairly successfully to the strain of having to take care of the sick. Today's small urban family is much more vulnerable to the disruptive stresses imposed by such a task and has increasingly come to depend for relief upon the medical profession and such institutions as hospitals, nursing homes, and homes for the aged. Aside from their technical function, hospitals and their auxiliary institutions are significant safety devices for the pressures that the home is frequently no longer able to handle.

With the growing tendency to push the patient out of the home, a heavier share of the responsibility formerly borne by the family thus devolves upon the doctor. Regardless of whether he likes it or not, the physician often becomes involved in the private affairs of his patients. More and more, he is being asked to play the role of parent, priest, psychologist, social worker, and sometimes even vocational and marriage counselor.

In sickness, the subconscious wishes and fantasies that are the residue of childhood experiences are sometimes reactivated and projected onto the physician. The sick person sees himself as the child and the doctor as the parent, to whom are transferred the feelings he once had for his father and mother and who is expected to behave accordingly. For many patients, much of the power with which the physician is endowed derives from this source and is an adjunct to his professional knowledge and skill. But along with uncritical admiration, the doctor sometimes becomes the target of deep-seated resentments carried over from childhood. There are elements of both love and hate in this transference process, which can become particularly pronounced in the case of a patient's prolonged association with a physician.

With the neurotic patient's regression to dependency, the doctor is unrealistically overvalued and sometimes invested with magic omnipotence. Much is expected of him, but he is repaid with singular deference and respect for his authority. Through the patient's self-abasement, he receives much of the same emotional homage that was paid in primitive cultures to the medicine man.

The doctor draws some of his extraordinary powers of suggestion from the mystical elements in therapy that are born out of man's anguished groping for an escape from the pain of illness and the terrors of death. What started out as witchcraft still retains much of its symbolism. The doctor's influence is often still more powerful than the medication he prescribes, and at times he himself becomes the treatment. Unfortunately, the crucial drug that the physician represents has as yet no firmly fixed pharmacology as to dosage. Nor does the trend of scientific progress encourage this drug's most effective usage.

Very often, the interplay of doctor and patient is largely expressed through implied meanings and innuendoes, through what psychiatrists describe as the "extraverbal communication of ideas" rather than by way of concrete affirmation. Ideas can be conveyed not only directly but also inferentially—and sometimes be the very fact of their omission. For the skillful physician with some knowledge of psychotherapy, the patient's manner and gestures, his loquacity and lapses into silence provide vital clues to his inner life and to his unverbalized pleas for help.

In this emotion-charged setting, the small things that the doctor does and the things that he fails to do assume a symbolic meaning far overshadowing their factual significance. Much of the time, something seems to happen the moment the physician walks into the room. His very presence brings hope and lifts a load of concern from the patient and his family. The mere touch of his hands can bring respite. The act of venting anxieties and of allowing the doctor to invade the privacy of body and psyche enhances in the patient's eyes his occult role as an authoritative and protective figure.

The physician's laying on of hands draws its healing power from our need to be touched by those we love, a need going back to our earliest memories and intensified by illness. Just as a mother's kiss is able to bring relief to a child's injury, just as the king's touch was once believed to cure many ills, so does this gesture of affection bring momentary assurance that everything will be all right. When a patient struggling with anxiety is touched, it somehow gives him the feeling that his problem is being shared by the doctor. Aside from its technical purpose, the physical examination has a symbolic meaning. By giving his body over to scrutiny, the patient surrenders himself and puts his fate in the physician's hands.

Like the parent, the doctor can command obedience because he possesses knowledge of the utmost importance to the patient, knowledge that the latter does not have. But unlike most parents, he may sometimes exploit the relationship for his own benefit. Or he may subconsciously find the patient's submissive dependence so satisfying to his own inner needs that he continues to encourage a passive role long after the necessity for it has passed. Here there is a close parallel with the attitide of parents who find it difficult to loosen the apron strings when their children have grown.

Dr. Leandro M. Tocantis recently told students at Jefferson Medical College in Philadelphia that there are many occasions when "the disease requires no treatment but the patient does." It is rare, he said, when "the disease requires treatment but the patient does not."

As the role of personality and environment in the processes of health and disease is increasingly recognized, the focus in medicine is widening. Fully as important as the individual's organic impairment may be his habits, his relationship to his family and co-workers, and the numerous ways in which he adapts himself to the complexities of daily living and the conflicts they produce. Many people are ill because they come into conflict with their environment or with themselves.

Each of us, furthermore, lives in a multidimensional environment, made up of symbolic as well as realistic meanings and values. We not only exist as members of a social order and bearers of its cultural traditions but also live in private worlds of our own, wherein the significance of all experience is perceived and responded to in a highly personal fashion.

Under the impact of medicine's great laboratory period and its phenomenal progress in the physical sciences, the human organism was dissolved into its component parts. This has paid off enormous dividends in terms of increased knowledge about the body. But in the process the tendency has been to be preoccupied with the local pathology and to ignore the essential oneness of organic and psychic life. The intense interaction between body and mind, between the individual and his total setting, between man's biological mechanisms and his attributes as a social and ethical being, as well as the uniqueness of every patient, is yet to be fully recognized in daily practice.

Under the impetus of psychiatry, some advances have been made with the progressive elucidation of the mechanisms of psychosomatic disease. It is now generally recognized that treatment for a number of ailments—notably ulcers, a variety of other gastrointestinal conditions, high blood pressure, asthma, and certain allergies—must take into account emotional and social factors. The development of a functional disorder may be an individual's means of escaping a problem that he is unable to solve or finds too painful even to acknowledge. The doctor thereupon faces a twofold task—to treat the resulting illness and to help the patient handle the original problem. Relatively few physicians, unfortunately, have the time, bent, or ability to do so properly. For most doctors, the abnormality of a specific organ still overshadows the overall malfunctioning of the individual. They are still more interested in the trouble than in those who are troubled.

Not only is no illness free of psychological components, but these quite often become more important than the disease itself. The unreasoning fears that patients develop are frequently more unbearable than the ailments that triggered them. Under these circumstances, patients have an overwhelming need to talk to the doctor and to get a sympathetic hearing. The fact that they are now commonly denied this opportunity, which may be all that is required for insight and a fresh start, is one of the greatest indictments against the present state of American medical practice.

Illness is something we find it hard to cope with alone, and what we frequently need most of all is the assurance that someone understands our trouble and feels for us. Such sympathy is sometimes more appreciated than the actual advice, which may or may not be followed. But there is little time for listening and counseling when there are always other patients waiting or when the harassed doctor is trying to attend simultaneously to several patients. It is not uncommon for a patient to be referred from one specialist to another without once being given a chance to discuss his personal problems and to emerge as a person with a set of anxieties peculiar to him alone.

"I know," a wise physician once remarked, "that, if I listen long enough, the patient will tell me what is wrong with him." The dictionary defines the word "listening" as "making a conscious effort to hear; attending closely so as to hear." Obviously, the doctor cannot find out what is going on within the patient if he is in a hurry. Nor can it be done by rote. How to deal with a patient, Dr. Richard Asher has said, "cannot be taught like pharmacology. All the power of tongue and pen, and all the wisdom of textbook and lecture, can never teach a doctor the knowledge of when to probe and when to leave alone, when to chide and when to reassure, when to speak and when to keep silent. They are private mysteries with a different solution for every one of the million permutations of personality involved between a doctor and his patient."

The listening called for in the medical interview is a sort of secret dialogue in which there are no straightforward questions and answers. Obscure meanings become discernible only as both participants give of themselves. In this kind of colloquy, the patient often unwittingly furnishes the doctor with highly important leads. To the careful listener, an unconscious gesture or casual remark can convey fully as much as the things he hears with the stethoscope.

In the initial interview, an overwrought patient usually skirmishes with the doctor. The patient may mention a few inconsequential symptoms while he is sizing up the physician to determine whether he can be trusted with the real complaint. He may be talking of one thing while unintentionally conveying other things. The skillful auditor is able to tune in on this multichannel system of communication.

Giving a patient the feeling that he is being hurried is not the only way of avoiding having to listen. The physician may also do so by talking too much about extraneous matters, such as the weather, some sports event, or anything else that comes to mind. The end result is that the patient feels cheated and repulsed.

Nor is anything quite so dispiriting to an anxious patient as to be told that "there is nothing the matter with you; it's just your nerves." More often than not—and the patient usually senses it—this is the doctor's way of saying, "You're a neurotic, and I wish you'd go away and stop bothering me." Telling a patient after hasty examination that there is nothing wrong with him rarely reassures him and is likely to start him instead on a dismal trek from specialist to specialist and sometimes from operation to operation.

Dr. Walter C. Alvarez advised his colleagues a few years ago that "if you find that there is nothing wrong with the patient, your job is not done but should be just beginning." But the attitude of many physicians is that the distress of a patient without any clear organic pathology is self-inflicted and due largely to too vivid an imagination and that the best way to handle him is not to sympathize with him too much and to let him fend for himself, possibly with the aid of a tranquilizer. Some doctors have openly antagonistic attitudes toward emotional disturbances, which they tend to regard as a form of malingering. Their distaste for such disorders may stem not only from ignorance but from their own maladjustments and inner inadequacies.

A doctor's personality and quality of empathy have powerful curative properties. But the physician also can have an adverse effect upon the patient's outlook for recovery. Hostility in his manner and gestures, in the nuances of his voice, in the repertory of facial expressions—which speak louder and more convincingly than words—is quickly transmitted to the patient and can have traumatic results. A doctor can do just as much harm to a patient with his attitude and words as he can by prescribing the wrong medication.

How a physician feels about his patients depends to a considerable extent on how he feels about himself. To inspire them with confidence and hope, he must feel emotionally secure and be confident of his own ability and judgments. The maladjusted practitioner is a poor therapist. Having to deal with anxiety-laden situations only serves to increase his own anxiety and leads him to react with indifference or belligerence. Patients have an uncanny knack for sensing uncertainty or indecisiveness, even though it may be masked.

Dealing with unstable and anxious patients is a wearisome business and can easily strain one's stamina and temper. Through frequent exposure to the emotionalism of patients, doctors gradually build up protective defenses. They learn how to deal with other people's anxieties without excessive identification with the patient's problems and without becoming sentimental or sanctimonious. They develop the capacity to respond maturely to the great power that the situation sometimes gives them over patients, realizing the pitfalls inherent in it. This authority may otherwise be misused for the expression of the physician's own insecurities and need for dominance.

There are a great many reasons why people go to doctors, and the relief of pain is only one of them. The physician's role as friend, expert, and mentor is to allay fears, to rebuild confidence in the patient's own capacities, to restore faith in some scheme of values in which the patient can feel he has a place and a sense of dignity. All these tasks are in the great tradition of healing, and they call for knowledge and skill, for tolerance and perceptiveness, for a special faculty of patience and unhurriedness. "To give a patient the impression you could spare him an hour and yet to make him satisfied with five minutes is an invaluable gift," a sagacious doctor has said, "and of much more use than spending half an hour with him during which he is made to feel he is encroaching on your time."

The self-centered patient easily interprets the physician's preoccupied manner as indifference and can be deeply hurt by the barest inkling of neglect. He may be dying to seek an explanation but forgoes asking for fear of being brushed off. The shuffling of reports between glances at the clock while the patient is desperately trying to tell his story can make him feel dehumanized and rejected. Above all, the patient craves security and self-esteem. He wants to be reassured—and not necessarily by direct verbal communication—that the doctor will help him. He will forgive a lot—but never a lack of interest.

III

There are few more prized bromides in organized medicine than those that emphasize the sacredness of the doctor-patient relationship. But while all stops are pulled out in extolling its virtues, little is done to preserve it. In fact, the medical profession's stubborn clinging to obsolete organizational patterns does a great deal to jeopardize it.

"There are only a few things which touch so close to God, and the relationship between a doctor and his patient is one of them," said Dr. Edward R. Annis of Miami, the spellbinder who has emerged as the profession's top public spokesman, in a nationwide television broadcast against the Administration's medical care program for the aged. The mystical affinity between doctor and patient would be irreparably undermined, Dr. Annis asserted, by the plan for having Americans put aside money through social security taxes during their working years to pay for part of their medical care in their old age.

This is the familiar scare argument that is used by organized medicine whenever any change is proposed in the manner in which medical care is rendered and paid for. What is totally ignored is that profound changes have been wrought by scientific progress in the traditional doctor-patient relationship, that a large proportion of those in the lower-income groups have never had a personal physician, that the typical office visit of five or ten minutes can hardly be equated with personal attention, and that all too few people now enjoy the stable and intimate relationship with their doctors that makes for indispensable continuity and is a prerequisite of good medical care.

All the befuddlement of inane oratory cannot quite obscure the fact that the medical profession is using the largely mythical rapport between doctors and patients as a weapon in the battle to protect its lucrative privileges. How the interaction of physicians and patients can be readjusted and improved under the impact of the revolution in medical science is a formidably difficult question. But it is fatuous to try to stem the tide of change by maintaining that any departure from the *status quo* will automatically impair the doctor-patient relationship. And it is futile to seek to preserve a benevolent authoritarianism that is completely at odds with reality.

Aside from the basic requirement of competence, there is no ingredient on which the quality of medical care depends so much as on the kind of relationship that the patient establishes with his doctor. The more intricate medicine becomes and the greater the patient's bewilderment at what is happening to him, the more important are congeniality and mutual trust.

The social and cultural distance between physicians and patients has grown apace as a result of the formalizing effect of the progressive shift in the setting of treatment from home to office to hospital and the consequent interposition of receptionists, nurses, interns, residents, technicians, and elaborate instrumentation between doctor and patient. The change in the scene of treatment not only catapults the patient into a coldly impersonal environment but deprives the physician of the insights he was previously able to gain from observing the patient in his home and with his family. It is much more difficult to obtain a true picture of the kind of person the patient is within the few minutes allotted him in the office. And in confronting a doctor who is pretty much of a stranger the patient is liable to find it much harder to communicate adequately a sense of his difficulties in coping with the stresses of his daily life.

At one time a physician was expected to assume complete responsibility for his patient's welfare. But with the advent of specialists, the inevitable trend has been toward dilution of responsibility, which one authority has described as the "collusion of anonymity." Since the burden of responsibility is divided, no one, in the end, is fully accountable. This increasingly leads to a "nine to five" attitude in medicine: the patient in distress finds himself on his own after the physician's office hours.

The doctor was presumed to be always available when the bulk of his practice consisted in house calls, a system that provides the best means of really getting to know the patient. There are few things that can have such a miraculous effect in relieving tension as having the doctor come to the house when someone is sick. It is therefore hardly surprising that the reluctance of physicians to make house calls is a source of great public resentment.

Many patients feel that a doctor should be on call at any time, day or night. This is patently an unreasonable demand. But just as indefensible is the attitude of some doctors that, in the great majority of cases, house calls are unnecessary and that, except for emergencies, it will do the patient no harm to wait until he can be seen, and probably more effectively treated, in the office. Logical though this may sound, it fails to take into consideration the intangibles of emotion. The physician may know better when a distraught mother reports on the telephone late at night that her child is terribly ill. But the only thing he can do is go. House calls may be a nuisance from the standpoint of the physician's personal convenience and financial interest. But they are far from being uniformly capricious. A doctor worth his salt would rather make a dozen unnecessary house calls than miss one that is important.

Night calls are the medical profession's particular bugbear, and there are complaints that they are frequently made for trivial reasons. There are obvious psychological reasons why patients are so much more likely to send out distress signals after dark. For one thing, anxiety tends to increase with the coming of night when there is no improvement in the patient's condition and when he and his family become worried about the difficulty of getting a physician or druggist. There is, moreover, something fearsome for many people in darkness itself, which aggravates the dread of sickness and death. There are certain physical symptoms that quickly get a doctor out of bed after a hard day's work, only to find, more often than not, that they have been grossly exaggerated. This does not help him to maintain an unruffled professional air with the next day's patient load.

Another frequent sore point between doctors and patients is the tendency toward overmedication and the excessive use of laboratory procedures. These are no substitute for the conscientious attention to which the sick person feels he is entitled, and they not only contribute needlessly to the cost of medical care but very often subtract from its quality.

The laboratory can be invaluable in confirming the doctor's suspicions and in providing precise information. But laboratory findings that show relatively slight variations from the normal can be misleading without careful interpretation and thoughtful assessment of the individual. Preoccupation with the refinements of diagnosis and worship of the laboratory tend to lull the physician into uncritical inertness and lead to disregard of the patient as a human being.

Dr. Alex M. Burgess told members of the Rhode Island Medical Society at a recent annual meeting:

> "The eye that can read the colorimeter [an instrument for measuring hemoglobin content of the blood] and interpret the electrocardiogram often fails to notice physical asymmetry, visible peristalsis [contraction of the intestines], the minor variations in muscle spasm, and the like. The ear that hears the routine story of previous illnesses and operations often is unable to detect the tremor in the voice or the terror that the new experience of being a hospial patient may have engendered. Both in being able to realize that his unfortunate patient may be a fellow who needs a friend more than a sedative and to detect by the use of trained observation in preference to laboratory tests the real nature of his patient's condition, there has been a retrogression, a loss of competence, that is rather striking. One has only to watch the average recent graduate carry out a physical examination to realize that percussion, for example, is becoming a lost art; and dependence on the laboratory, X ray, and other aids has so undermined the confidence of many a young physician in his ability to see and hear and feel that without these mechanical aids, he hesitates to form an opinion."

This is not wholly the doctor's fault. Medical knowledge has become so vast and complex that before the student leaves medical school, he must acquire an understanding of a wide range of sciences, including biochemistry, physiology, biophysics, genetics, pharmacology, and even electronics. "By the time he is prepared to actually care for his first patient," a medical educator has said, "his view of the individual is considerably tempered by an array of molecules, enzymes, mitochondria, chromosomes, myocardial dynamics, and the like." The net effect is that he is primarily trained to look for and treat disease rather than to look after and treat the patient who has the disease.

To some degree at least, patients tend to sort themselves out according to the kind of doctor they intuitively want. Patients who have a deep-seated need to be told what to do gravitate toward domineering physicians, while others prefer more amiable and permissive practitioners. Doctors engage in a somewhat similar process of selection and, in one way or another, usually manage to get rid of patients whom they find objectionable. But despite this mutual winnowing process, which makes for greater compatibility, the social gap between physicians and patients has generally been widening.

Already preselected to some extent by social and economic status, doctors have been drifting away from association with their patients outside the sphere of health care. There are several reasons for this development. A marked shift into the upper-income brackets has fortified the snobbery of some doctors and promoted the use of their leverage as masters of a recondite science to control their patients. Social distance is a powerful weapon in maintaining authority. Some physicians believe that a degree of reserve is an essential ingredient in the therapeutic relationship between the sick and the well and that it is poor practice to extend the friendship with patients outside office hours. The medical profession's multiplying fears and conflicts may be another reason for its social exclusiveness. Doctors are increasingly seeing themselves as targets for unwarranted attacks by politicians, pressure groups, the press, and unscrupulous patients. They tend to feel that their excruciating responsibilities are unappreciated, and they are haunted by the specter of "socialized medicine." A natural reaction is to keep pretty much to themselves.

The patient's class status makes a considerable difference in his attitude and in his treatment by the physician. The upper-class patient is likely to be more detached and critical and to insist on being told the reasons for what the doctor is doing. Poorer patients, on the other hand, are apt to be more resigned and deferential. They are inured to discomfort and less likely to complain. But the gulf in social and cultural values enhances the chances of misunderstanding between lower-class patients and their physicians.

There are psychological as well as economic reasons for unpaid doctors' bills and for the greater inclination of lower-income patients to patronize chiropractors and other nonmedical healers. The chiropractor's table has with considerable aptness been described as "the poor man's couch." Practitioners of the healing cults are more folksy in their approach and thrive by listening and giving the impression that they are sincerely trying to help. Their stock in trade, aside from a variety of nostrums, is relief from the aloofness that is producing a deepening cleavage between doctors and patients.

IV

Far more significant than the medical profession's puerile reiteration of banalities and its futile efforts to perpetuate a largely imaginary past is a question central to the whole future of medicine: can doctors bring to bear in their practice the full weight of scientific techniques and still continue to care for their patients in medicine's high humanitarian tradition? Some of the most perceptive minds in the health field have of late turned their attention to this problem, and there appears to be some difference of opinion among them. The preponderant view, however, is that the science and art of medicine are not intrinsically incompatible and can be successfully fused with the proper skill and dedication. But the obstacles are manifold and perplexing.

There is relatively little difficulty if one's view of medical care is confined to the narrow sphere of combating bacterial infections and other pathological conditions and of relieving physical discomfort. From a purely technical point of view, the progress of medical science has been truly dazzling. The picture is much less encouraging if medicine is seen in its broader framework of helping the patient grapple with threats to his emotional as well as his organic equilibrium and of providing the counsel and support that will enable him not only to regain his health but also to use to the utmost his potentialities for work and social relationships. In this wider sphere, a good deal has been lost. Physicians still pay lip service to their profession's friend-and-adviser image but are finding it more and more difficult to live up to it. The mission of counseling has to a considerable degree been relinquished to the psychiatrists, of whom there are not nearly enough to go around.

Despite the patient's veneer of greater sophistication, the scientific complexities of medicine have passed far beyond his understanding. This is substantially true of all the scientific advances of our civilization, such as the incredible intricacies of sending a man into orbit and getting him back to earth. But to find totally unintelligible the things so intimately involving one's own fate and life is another matter. As the patient understands less and less, he feels more and more like an object and is deeply disconcerted by indifference to his own uniqueness in the natural order.

The more incomprehensible medical services are, the greater become the possibilities for conflict between the doctor's detached professional judgment and the patient's intensely personal concern. The patient's subjective understanding of what is wrong has become much less relevant, and may sometimes actually be an impediment, with the development of highly refined diagnostic techniques. The patient, furthermore, has yet to readjust himself to the realities of present-day medical practice, with its impersonal institutional setting and its emphasis on the physiological aspects of disease at the expense of the emotional components.

It is perfectly true that even the most impersonal doctor can now do a great deal more with a quick jab of the needle than the old-time family physician ever could with all his leisurely sympathy. There is room for argument that the far greater technical efficiency of today's doctors more than makes up for the deterioration of rapport between them and their patients. Some observers also question whether people generally still expect or require the same degree of personal intimacy and paternalism in their relations with their physicians as was the case several generations ago.

Nevertheless, the fact remains that most patients continue to want a lot more than just a proficient technician in their doctor. The average patient still wants a personal physician, while the average doctor is more and more interested in the technological skills of his craft. While medicine has increasingly been attracting students whose interests are primarily scientific rather than humanitarian, the patient still demands a single-minded and almost monastic devotion by the physician to the ministry of healing.

Many authorities are convinced that scientific rigor and humane understanding are indispensable and complementary aspects of medicine. They concede that relatively few individuals have the breadth of heart and mind to bring both qualities to their fullest flowering, but they feel that the ideal of a new and higher unity between technology and compassion is not beyond reach and should be vigorously pursued.

The biological portrait of the patient will never be complete without a combination of scientific and intuitive virtuosity that integrates all the diagnostic components to gain a total appraisal of the individual. While there is nothing subjective about the results of biochemical tests, the treatment indicated by them will always be enhanced by a personal approach. The science of medicine will always be enriched by the sympathetic insights of its art.

Inevitably, the patient will have to reconcile himself to some modification of his expectations. But the doctor, in his turn, must never forget that the effective practice of his calling requires the warmth of personal concern in applying scientific knowledge to the care of the individual patient.

A new kind of relationship between doctor and patient is gradually evolving out of the ferment of sweeping changes in the character and setting of medical care. While they frequently still feel rebuffed, patients are painfully learning to be somewhat less dependent on intimacy with the physician and more demanding of his technical skills. The newly emerging relationship is veering away from its old authoritarian base and toward a more educational approach. It is more democratic in the sense that the patient is becoming a more active participant in the treatment program for his own salvation. The shift, which calls for an effort at greater maturity, is not easy. The patient, perhaps no less than the physician, is reluctant to part with the comforting landmarks of the past. But he is growing up and learning, step by step, to attain a more equal status bordering on partnership. The doctor is still the dominant figure, but patients are developing the knack of talking back.

The frequent failure of communication between doctor and patient remains one of the great dilemmas of medicine, and an overriding challenge confronting the medical profession is to try to find the proper proportion between technology and under-standing. Here lies the key to the profession's public relations problem. The heart of the medical profession's image is the rela-tionship that exists between the individual physician and his patient. No amount of ballyhoo will suffice to improve that image unless doctors and patients are brought closer together again. The deplorable trend toward indiscriminate medication and the wholesale consumption of tranquilizers will be reversed only when the patient is given more of a chance to express his needs openly, to vent his hostility, and to replace his often childlike dependency with a more mature and supportive relationship with his doctor.

CHAPTER FIVE

The Hospital: Focus of Conflict

I

MORE THAN 25,200,000 Americans were admitted to general hospitals in 1963, and about half of them underwent surgery. The bill for short-term hospitalization, exclusive of the fees charged by surgeons, came to about $7 billion, the biggest single share of the nation's private outlay for medical care. This was more than five times the amount spent on hospital services in the United States as recently as 1946. Part of the spectacular increase is accounted for by the fact that there are now some 55,000,000 more Americans and many more hospital beds than there were in 1946. But the bulk of the rise is due to the steady climb of hospital rates, which in the past decade have soared at more than five times the rate of increase in the general cost of living.

In 1946, the average cost per hospital patient per day was $9.39. By 1963 it was up to $38.91. In 1946, the average patient stayed in the hospital for 9.1 days, and his bill was $85. The average stay has by now been reduced to 7.6 days, but the bill has jumped to about $300. Hospital room rates are now nearly six times what they were in 1935. They have increased more than three times as rapidly as the overall price of medical care services.

The end, moreover, is nowhere in sight. Experts are generally agreed that hospital costs will continue to go up at the rate of 5 to 10 per cent a year. A spokesman for the American Hospital Association has predicted that the average cost per patient per day may pass the $50 mark before the end of the sixties.

These telling statistics readily explain why there is no more explosive an issue in the entire controversial field of medical economics than that of runaway hospital costs. Americans are using hospitals to a far greater extent than ever before, and the steeper charges for such use are quickly reflected in higher premium rates for hospitalization insurance. With three out of every four persons now covered by some form of health insurance, hospital costs are no longer solely the problem of patients and their families. They are being underwritten by the healthy as well as the sick. Skyrocketing hospital costs and mounting insurance rates have brought a rising tide of public concern. There have been increasingly clamorous demands for greater efficiency in hospital operation and for reforms in the prevailing pattern of health insurance, one that encourages the excessive use of expensive facilities. There have been repeated warnings from responsible sources that the squeeze of spiraling costs may price voluntary insurance out of the market and force full government control of the whole complex of health services.

The cost figures in themselves tell only part of the story behind the profound crisis confronting the nation's hospitals—the bulwarks of our phenomenal medical progress—at the very time when they are advancing toward ever-greater miracles of healing and lifesaving. For the plight of the voluntary hospital system is not merely one of financing. Inextricably tied up with the question of costs is that of hospital function, in which the medical profession holds a pervasive position. The onrush of scientific advances had made imperative far-reaching changes in the responsibilities and goals of hospitals and in the manner in which they are run.

More so than in any other area of medical care, the problem of the technological revolution in medicine is coming to a head in the hospital. Here, more sharply than anywhere else, may be observed the clash between the challenging needs of today and tomorrow and the stubborn institutional resistance to change. This is the major arena of conflict in the swirl of organizational change in the health field.

The full importance of what happens in the hospital cannot be measured only by the fact that it now accounts for the expenditure of more than thirty cents out of every health care dollar as compared with only fourteen cents in 1930. As medicine has steadily grown more intricate, the hospital has become the keystone in the arch of the community's medical services. It is the strategic place where specialized skills and the elaborate tools for their application are concentrated, where doctors can see many kinds of patients and patients can be served by all kinds of physicians and auxiliary personnel, where medical practice and medical education meet, and where new research findings are narrowed down to focus on the individual patient. Upon the outcome of the battles currently raging within the walls of our hospitals and around them depends to a large degree the very future of the organization of medical care and practice in the United States.

There are many sound reasons for the continued rise in hospital operating costs. A U.S. Public Health Service official has summed them up with the cogent observation that "when we talk about the cost of medical care today as compared to the past, we're talking about the price of an electric washer-dryer compared to a washtub."

What is true of medical care in general applies with particular force to the hospitals, with their multiplicity of professional and technical skills and huge investment in costly facilities and equipment. There is no ready solution to the problem of the costliness of new and more effective medical procedures, infinitely more complicated surgery, and vastly more potent drugs. Such dramatic advances as open-heart operations, artifical kidneys, heart pacemaker units, cobalt-radiation treatment, and the use of radio-isotopes to pinpoint internal abnormalities are restoring patients to health sooner and more completely and, frequently, are saving lives that otherwise would be lost. They also are extremely expensive, especially in view of the fact that dozens of physicians, technicians, and nurses are sometimes required for a single patient. There is no getting away from the fact that good hospital care cannot be obtained cheaply.

Superimposed upon the cost dilemma inherent in medical progress—and enormously complicating it—have been a striking rise in the rate of hospitalization and a string of inefficiencies stemming from the character of the voluntary hospital. Thirty years ago, 56 out of every 1,000 Americans were admitted to general hospitals in the course of a year. Since then, the ratio of such admissions has climbed to 135 per 1,000. In the same period, the average length of hospital stay has been slashed by more than half. But because of the higher utilization, the annual number of days of hospital care per 1,000 population has increased from 860 to 1,020.

A variety of reasons, some of them fully valid and others highly questionable, have figured in the steady upward trend of hospitalization. The most obvious reason is that hospitals can do so much more for the sick than in the past and that the complex skills and apparatus of medical science can no longer be as effectively applied elsewhere. Only a couple of generations ago, hospitals were still dreary hostels for the poor and hopelessly ill; people were mainly sent there to die. Since then, the hospital has been transformed into the backbone and general headquarters of medical care. Now it is the place where people go to get well and where many of the procedures are elective or preventive. New medical sophistication has made hospital care an accepted component of the average American's standard of living.

Widespread insurance coverage has removed much of the economic deterrent to hospital care for those in the middle and low-income groups. The rapid increase in the number and proportion of older people has led to a much higher incidence of chronic diseases and therefore more frequent hospitalization. Many conditions of modern city living make for significantly higher hospital use than in rural areas. The large proportion of working wives means that often there is no one at home to take care of a sick husband or child. The high price of household or nursing help to care for the sick at home and the limited size of city apartments also force up the hospitalization rate.

The rising standard of living has at the same time brought a demand for more attractive hospital accommodations. Hospitals are expected to match the comforts of motels, and air conditioning, piped-in radio, television, and window draperies are commonplace. The new standards also call for a telephone at the bedside and some choice of menu. While the effect of these niceties on the patient's recovery is debatable, their effect on the hospital's unit costs is obvious.

A far more important issue than the need for frills is the question of whether the current high hospital admission rate is justified and whether there is misuse of costly hospital facilities for services that could be rendered much more economically elsewhere. There are conflicting views on this controversial point, to which we shall return in the next chapter. On balance, there appears to be substantial evidence of abuses in the use of expensive hospital beds. Some authorities feel that at least 20 per cent of patients in general hospitals do not belong there and could be cared for just as well in less expensive facilities. "To keep medical costs within reason," Dr. Basil MacLean, a former president of the Blue Cross Association, has said, "we must keep the patient vertical whenever possible. Once we put him between sheets, the bill begins to get out of hand."

There is no doubt that the prevailing structure of health insurance contributes materially to unnecessary resort to hospitalization. Its failure to give adequate coverage for diagnostic services and outpatient treatment provides built-in incentives for getting into a hospital bed merely to take advantage of insurance benefits. The lack of insurance provisions for visiting-nurse services at home also makes for needlessly prolonged hospital stays. Another cause of unnecessary admissions and excessively protracted stays is the lack of adequate nursing and convalescent homes for chronic patients and of mechanisms to help pay for such out-of-hospital care.

Two of the voluntary hospital's outstanding characteristics tend to aggravate the abuses made possible by the weaknesses of the insurance setup and are probably an even greater impediment to economy. One of them is the key role played by doctors in the functioning of hospitals and in the pyramiding of their costs. The other is the traditional and grossly outdated autonomy of the voluntary hospitals. Having grown at random rather than by design, they operate without any centralized planning or effective public controls and continue to expand in a hit-or-miss fashion that frequently makes for wasteful duplication of facilities and services.

The people who have the biggest say about how the voluntary hospital is run and about its costs are, for the most part, not hospital employees. They are private physicians who use publicly provided accommodations for their own practice without corresponding responsibilities. The public builds the voluntary hospitals and supports them—by paying hospital bills and Blue Cross and other insurance premiums, through taxes, and through philanthropy. But it is the doctors who, in large measure, call the tune on what the bill should amount to.

Major components of the hospital-cost picture are the frequency of hospitalization, the average length of stay, and the quantity of so-called ancillary services—such as various diagnostic tests, drugs, and medical and surgical supplies. Doctors control all these cost factors, which determine the level of hospitalization insurance premium rates. It is the attending physician and no one else who decides whether the patient should be sent to the hospital in the first place. It is he alone who determines how long the patient should stay. It is he who decides what the patient should get in terms of nursing care, medication, laboratory work, diet, and other services. It is the doctors who play a dominant role in determining what kind of new facilities are needed. Their influence has been generally used for the addition of bed capacity designed primarily for the acutely ill, which is most handy in their private business, rather than for the urgently needed expansion of more economical outpatient services and facilities for nursing and convalescent care.

"I'll tell you," said a hospital superintendent, "what very often runs up the costs of hospital care. It's things like excessive use of laboratory tests and X-ray examinations; costly drugs that aren't discontinued when the need for them ends; patients admitted for procedures that can be just as effectively and much more economically done on an outpatient basis; and patients who, for the doctor's convenience, are admitted a day earlier than they ought to be and discharged a day later. When all is said and done, the underlying fact remains that the hospital is completely at the mercy of the medical staff. Laymen have no choice but to accept the doctor's professional judgment."

"Physicians," commented another hospital executive, "are notoriously ignorant about hospital economics, even though they work and make much of their living here. Subconsciously or not, many of them seem to shut their minds to the cost factors for which they, more than anyone else, are responsible. They want laymen to raise the money, behave themselves, and not ask too many embarrassing questions."

Some patients misuse their insurance benefits by being hospitalized for diagnostic tests that could be done in the office or outpatient clinic but for which there is no coverage and by excessively protracted hospital stays during convalescence. Such abuses are, of course, impossible without the collusion of the attending physicians. Here we run into the blurred area of motivation. Some doctors may go along with their unscrupulous patients for fear of losing them to more accommodating physicians. Others rationalize their judgment in equivocal cases to give the patient the benefit of the doubt. Another possible reason for yielding to the whim of patients who want to rest in a hospital at the expense of Blue Cross is that physicians may feel that they will be more certain to collect their own bills if insurance covers part of the costs. As a rule, furthermore, doctors find it more convenient and profitable to have their patients hospitalized. A doctor may have to spend most of the morning seeing just four or five patients if he has to drive all over town to visit them. But he can see as many as twenty patients in the course of a morning if they are all in the hospital.

Legally, physicians are subject to the authority of the hospital's lay board of trustees, from whom they receive their staff appointments. But in actual practice the board's control over them is often tenuous. The doctor's anomalous position, in which he is at once a guest and a dominant figure in the hospital structure, leads to a confusing splintering of authority and frequent conflicts between medical prerogatives and administrative responsibility. The end result is that there are, in effect, two parallel lines of command—one for general hospital affairs and the other for medical treatment. Since the latter is the reason for the hospital's existence, the influence of the medical staff is usually paramount and inevitably extends to matters that are not strictly medical.

Medicine is probably the only profession whose practitioners are furnished with workshops at public expense. No physician is now able to provide all the varied and expensive apparatus he needs for the diagnosis and treatment of his patients. So the community has pooled its resources to furnish the required equipment for the physician. This not only makes possible the complex services required by present-day practice but has greatly extended the number of patients that a doctor can care for. It is estimated that the average member of a hospital medical staff is being provided, free of charge, with a capital investment of about $70,000. He has the free use of an institution whose maintenance, on the average, costs about $7,500 per bed a year.

This singular arrangement originated in the days when the bulk of hospital patients were indigent. The privilege of using the public investment in hospital facilities for their private practice was extended to doctors to remunerate them for the free services they rendered in the care of nonpaying patients. But the situation has drastically changed. Most patients are now covered by insurance, and public funds are used to pay at least in part for those who lack such coverage and are indigent. While the medical profession continues to boast about the free service given by its members, such service actually has dwindled to a small portion of the load carried by the average physician.

At the same time, there has been a radical alteration in the hospital's financial base. What was once an institution largely dependent on philanthropy now draws the lion's share of its support from paying patients, mostly through insurance benefits. But there has been no corresponding change in the composition of hospital governing boards. By and large, hospital trustees continue to be drawn from the upper social strata. They now generally represent former sources of income rather than the broad ranks of the consumer. Nor are lay controls on members of the medical staff commensurate with the staff's privileges. Although they use hospital facilities for their own profit without payment of rentals or overhead costs, physicians do not take kindly to the policing of the quality of their services and regard any efforts to control their fees as the rankest kind of heresy.

On top of the frustrating duality of authority is the haphazard manner in which hospitals are operated and expanded.

While hospitals are among the community's most valuable and costliest assets, there is no instrumentality for coordinating their activities in the interest of greater effectiveness and economy. Each hospital is a sovereign dominion and is usually more interested in its own perpetuation and growth than in the development of a balanced community health program. New hospitals are built and old ones expanded without any overall community planning and frequently without any regard for the volume and kind of facilities most needed. In some places there is an excess of hospital capacity, while in others there are serious shortages. There is a woeful lack of cooperation between hospitals, and they rarely take advantage of joint projects that could result in substantial savings.

Common sense calls for a division of labor among hospitals,

with each one concentrating on the things it can do best and most economically. But the trouble is that hospital managements generally suffer from an "edifice complex." For prestige purposes, they keep on pushing for more and bigger buildings and for every new piece of equipment invented. Or they are pushed in that direction by their medical staffs, who are concerned over the possible loss of patients who might have to be referred to other hospitals for some rare and elaborate procedures. The inevitable consequence is an extravagant duplication of expensive facilities and apparatus.

Such intricate and costly equipment as radioisotope laboratories, cobalt-radiation units, artificial heart-lung machines, artificial kidneys, and electroencephalographs can make the difference between life and death. But it is a waste of money for hospitals in the same community to duplicate, as is now frequently the case, such complicated apparatus. Unfortunately, no agency exists with the authority to force decisions in the public interest in this and other areas that affect the size of the hospital bill. The upshot is that hospital costs and charges keep climbing and health insurance premium rates go spiraling on.

Aside from the battles shaping up over the need for planning, integration, and tighter administrative authority over the activities of the medical staffs, there are other smoldering conflicts in the hospital field in which the consumers of medical care have a vital stake. Among them are the highly contentious issues of the salaried employment of physicians by hospitals, the expansion of hospital outpatient departments, the operation of hospital-based group-practice clinics, and the more effective tailoring of hospital facilities and services according to degrees of illness. The outcome of the little-publicized but bitter feuds now swirling around these issues will have a crucial bearing on costs and on the future patterns of health care.

The revolution in medicine is far from over, and hospitals have yet to fulfill their growing potential. Further scientific advances will unavoidably mean still costlier diagnostic and treatment procedures, more complex instrumentation, and additional and better-paid personnel. A continued rise in hospital costs thus appears inescapable. So it is all the more vital to eliminate the waste and lack of integration now common in the hospital field.

This will require a much higher degree of self-discipline by the medical profession and a far greater readiness on the part of hospitals to yield some of the privileges of their cherished autonomy than have so far been evident. The only alternative to voluntary planning is planning by governmental authority. If there are methods for operating hospitals more efficiently, as many authorities believe there are, the public will insist that it be done one way or another.

II

Although hospitalization is becoming a commonplace in American life, it is doubtful whether the average person has much of an inkling of how unique and complex an institution a hospital really is.

Wrapped into one in a hospital is a wide assortment of essential functions, of many of which the patient is rarely aware. Its multifold activities are focused on making it the place where the sick can get twenty-four hours of personal attention if they need it and where those in distress can go with the confident feeling that there are people who will know what to do. A hospital is a shelter, a place where pain is alleviated and afflictions are healed, a doctors' workshop, an educational center for tomorrow's medical practitioners and for auxiliary health personnel, a proving ground for medical research, a crucial pacesetter for raising the standards of medical care. It is a hotel, with many extra services thrown in. It is a restaurant providing food suited to special needs. It is a pharmacy and a laboratory for X-ray, pathological, and other diagnostic services. It is in the laundry business and can provide several changes of bed linens daily if necessary. Its standby power plant is ready to go into action at a moment's notice for emergency service if the regular source of power should fail. A hospital must stay in operation 168 hours a week, fifty-two weeks a year. Unlike the average commercial enterprise, it can never shut down, for human lives may be at stake.

After the patient is put to bed, he sees only a few of the people who will take care of him and usually has little idea of the massive size of the hospital team backing up the medical and nursing staffs. The scope of this team's job is indicated by the

fact that it includes some two hundred different job classifications, ranging all the way from cleaners, cooks, secretarial help,
and telephone operators to tissue technicians, radiologists, bacter-
iologists, and social workers.

Aside from caring for the sick, many of our hospitals devote
much of their energy and resources to clinical research and the
training of doctors, nurses, and a variety of technicians. No
medical school graduate is qualified to go into practice until he
has undergone a period of training in the hospital. Textbooks and
classroom instruction are essential, but it is only at the bedside
that theory can be put into practice and the science and art of
real patient care can be learned. No physician can keep fully
abreast of the steady stream of scientific developments without
the constant stimulation of working with his peers within the
hospital, which is his lifetime postgraduate school. Nor can the
preliminary findings coming out of research laboratories be trans-
lated into the tools of therapy until they have been tested in the
hospital. Here is where teaching is animated by an inquisitive
research spirit and the investigator's surmises are tested in the
laboratory of practice. The hospital also is increasingly emerging
as the pivotal center for community health, where the line of
demarcation between curative and preventive medicine is gradually dissolving.

At its best, the hospital of today is the focus and finest
product of the countless technological advances that have revolutionized medicine and brought us better health and longer life.
At the same time, hospitals have grown into huge business enterprises, with annual budgets that often run into millions of dollars.
Hospitals are now the fifth largest industry in the United States
from the standpoint of plant assets, expenditures, and number of
employees.

The sheer statistics of the hospital business are breathtaking.
A total of about $20 billion is invested in the nation's hospitals,
which have more than 1,700,000 beds. The hospitals have about
1,900,000 full-time employees, which is more than the steel and
automobile industries together employ, and operating costs of
nearly $11 billion a year. There were nearly 4,000,000 births in
hospitals last year. Short-term general hospitals provide 44 per
cent of the beds in all hospitals, but because their patient turn-

over is much greater than in publicly operated mental and tuberculosis hospitals, they accounted last year for more than 92 per cent of the admissions. Operating costs in general hospitals are much steeper than in institutions for long-term care. The cost per patient per day in voluntary short-term hospitals was nearly seven times as high last year as in state and municipal mental hospitals, where the care is mostly custodial.

But the mere statistics of the immense hospital establishment and of its managerial complexity can never convey the full story of its vibrant human function and of the manner in which it fuses the myriad elements of medicine into the priceless amalgam of care bestowed upon the sick. While hospitals have become one of our biggest businesses, they will never be a business in the ordinary sense of that term. As their costs keep on zooming, it is imperative that they be run in as businesslike a manner as possible. Business judgment in their operation will always have to be tempered, however, by a sense of social obligation, for their goal is better health and not financial gain.

Voluntary hospitals take care of all who require their services, those who can pay in full as well as those who can pay little or nothing. While the proportion of nonpaying patients has dropped sharply, and despite the spectacular rise in rates, many hospitals are still operating at a loss. On the average, hospitals last year collected from patients $2.13 per day less than it cost to care for them. The difference was made up from endowment income, gifts, and public subsidy.

Another drain on hospital finances is its standby, or readiness-to-serve, function. Not only must the full range of hospital services be maintained, regardless of the number of patients actually served on any particular day, but the staff and a certain proportion of facilities must be kept in constant readiness to handle emergencies. The hospital's lifesaving personnel and equipment have to be geared for instant action on an around-the-clock basis. No one can foretell what the rate of emergency admissions through the accident room will be on a given day. This means that costly beds often remain unused even though there is a waiting list of patients slated for elective procedures.

As productivity has risen, industry has been able to shorten its workweek. But hospitals, which must stay open from dawn to dawn, cannot shorten their week. To keep pace with the standard forty-hour week in the community, they have been forced to hire many additional employees to fill jobs on a three-shift basis. They also have been obliged to upgrade their lagging wage scales to bring them closer to those of private industry.

While raising its wage levels, industry has often managed to cut its labor costs through automation. But hospitals cannot substitute machines for people. No machine has yet been built to take a patient's temperature, give him an injection, or empty his bedpan. On the contrary, as new services proliferate and as improved equipment is constantly developed, more rather than fewer people are required to operate them. In 1946, voluntary short-term hospitals in the United States had, on the average, 148 employees for every 100 patients. By now the ratio of employees for each 100 patients has risen to 241.

Hospital payrolls have generally tripled in the past decade. Whereas in the automobile industry labor now accounts for only one-third of production costs, wages have shot up to about 70 per cent of hospital budgets. The ratio of employees to patients is expected to keep on rising, and hospital wage levels have still quite a way to go to catch up with those prevailing in industry.

Only about twenty cents of the hospital dollar is spent for household functions, which cover what might be described as hotellike services as well as food and laundry. This makes it amply clear why hospital rooms are so much more expensive than hotel rooms. Hotels have about thirty-five employees for every 100 guests, or only about one-seventh of the hospital ratio.

Around 1890, the average length of stay in a general hospital was fifty-two days. Since then, the average stay has been shortened by more than 85 per cent, owing not only to vastly more effective treatment but, in part, to the increase in the proportion of patients admitted for diagnostic studies and for conditions of short duration. Notable in the latter category has been the soaring obstetric use of hospitals. The proportion of births taking place in hospitals has nearly tripled in the past thirty years.

Hospital costs would be utterly beyond most people's reach without the downward curve of duration of stay. But the fact that patients now go home much sooner than they used to is not an unmixed blessing. Costs are not uniform throughout the duration of a patient's stay, and hospitals make up on convalescence for the high costs of intensive treatment in the first few days. The briefer stay deprives the hospital of much of this saving. The more rapid patient turnover also means that chances are greater that there will be vacant beds, which have to be staffed but produce no income. The economic drain of empty beds is especially severe in small hospitals, which are in the majority in our hospital system.

This brings us to one of the thorniest paradoxes in the hospital picture: costs are often needlessly inflated by both overuse and insufficient use of expensive facilities. On the one hand, patients are sometimes hospitalized for conditions that could be taken care of as well elsewhere and at much lower costs. On the other hand, hospital accommodations are not utilized as efficiently as they should be, with the result that one bed out of four is usually empty; and in some institutions, the average occupancy rate is considerably lower. Such a rate of low occupancy represents a staggering waste of staff and maintenance expenditures and leads to a correspondingly heavier proportion of overhead in per patient per day costs.

In 1960, the nation's general hospitals averaged only 74.7 per cent occupancy. This means that there was a daily average of some 160,000 unused beds and that in the course of the year more than 58,000,000 potential days of care were wasted. An empty hospital bed costs more than half as much to maintain as an occupied bed. On this basis, the annual cost of empty beds amounts to well over $900 million. They also represent close to $5 billion in idle capital funds.

It is neither possible nor desirable to utilize every bed in a hospital every day of the year, since some facilities must be held for unanticipated admissions and some services have to be kept separate for certain types of patients. But too many hospitals operate successfully with an average occupancy of more than 90 per cent of capacity to argue that most of the tremendous cost of maintaining unused beds is unavoidable. If hospitals had higher occupancy rates, unit costs would be reduced and the need for new construction materially lessened.

Fully 92 per cent of our general hospitals have fewer than three hundred beds each, 64 per cent have fewer than a hundred beds, and more than 40 per cent fewer than fifty beds. This aggravates the vacancy problem, because a hospital's occupancy ratio generally goes up with its size. While hospitals with more than three hundred beds average more than 80 per cent of occupancy, the ratios are only 60 per cent for institutions with a capacity of between twenty-five and forty-nine beds and 54.5 per cent for those with fewer than twenty-five beds.

The smaller the hospital, the more difficult it is for it to provide a high level of care and the greater are certain rigidities of use making for low occupancy. The problem, clearly, is to pool facilities so as to spread services over the largest possible number of beds. But here, as in all other areas of the hospital economy, we run into the prevailing uncoordinated and unregulated operation that stands in the way of greater efficiency. No one now has the authority to tell hospitals to do anything, short of requiring them to enforce the fire laws, to say nothing of getting units of inefficient size to merge.

Aside from the factor of size, there is the waste of costly resources involved in the sharp fluctuation in hospital usage by days of the week, by certain months of the year, and over holiday periods. In most hospitals, the patient count is down by about 15 per cent over weekends, and there is a roughly similar decline in average occupancy in the summer months. That this is in no way related to the greater incidence of illness during the winter is shown by the fact that many more beds remain unused over the December holiday season than in January. Sickness is, of course, no respecter of weekends and does not take off any holidays. But there are many conditions that would permit considerable latitude in the start of treatment or the scheduling of surgery.

Weekend and seasonal lulls pyramid costs; expensive equipment stands idle, while revenue falls off. In many hospitals, a large part of the staff goes home for the weekend on Friday afternoon, leaving operating rooms and laboratories unused for more than sixty hours, except for emergencies. There is little point in urging patients in elective cases to come in on weekends if they are going to lie there, burning up anywhere from $30 to $45 a day, until the X-ray technicians and blood chemists return on Monday morning. A recent study in New York showed that patients admitted on a Friday average two more days in the hospital than those admitted on a Tuesday.

Additional weekend staffing would naturally cost more money. But the extra expenditures would in the long run be more than offset by added revenue from increased patronage over weekends and by the savings resulting from reductions in length of stay. Seasonal lulls also could be remedied to some extent by more efficient staggering of vacation periods for the staff and better scheduling of elective admissions. The best way to keep down costs is to stabilize the hospital work load at a level most favorable for operating efficiency and to eliminate needless delays in the course of treatment that often prolong the patient's stay. Among the steps that can be helpful in this direction are preliminary diagnostic work-ups before admission whenever possible, performance of X-ray and laboratory tests that must be done in the hospital before rather than after patients are assigned beds, admission of elective cases at an early hour to expedite diagnostic tests and thereby possibly save an entire day of hospital stay, and better coordination in booking admissions for surgery to avoid keeping patients waiting for operating-room openings.

Admittedly, there is an innate contradiction between eliminating unnecessarily prolonged stays and trying to maintain a high occupancy ratio. If many patients are discharged sooner, there will presumably be still more unused beds. There is undoubtedly a conflict here between the interests of individual hospitals and of the community at large, which is one of the reasons why hospital managements sometimes drag their feet on instituting measures aimed at reducing needlessly protracted stays. There is no question that a vacant bed, which fails to bring in any income, is costly to the hospital. But from the standpoint of the community and of the level of Blue Cross premium rates, an empty bed represents a saving. What complicates the situation, however, is that in the end, the community has to make up hospital deficits through higher bills, philanthropy, or governmental subsidy.

This conflict of interest underscores the urgency of centralized planning to correlate hospital expansion with need on a community-wide basis, rather than solely on the basis of the ambitions of each hospital and of its medical staff, and thereby avoid the overbuilding of bed capacity designed primarily for the acutely ill. Unfortunately, the community has yet to exercise its unquestionable right to insist that needed beds be utilized optimally, that unneeded beds be eliminated, and that no new ones be added without careful prior assessment of whether they are essential.

There has been a tremendous expansion of hospital facilities in the United States during the past few decades, at a rate more than three times as high as the growth of the country's population. Under the impetus of Federal construction grants, obsolete facilities have been replaced on a large scale, and about 250,000 new general hospital beds have been added since 1948. In the last few years, the construction of hospitals and other health facilities has been running at an annual rate of close to $1 billion. The expansion has been, in general, a laudable development. Antiquated buildings have been razed, and additional bed space has been provided to keep pace with medical progress and mounting demand. But the helter-skelter enlargement of hospital plants also has some highly disturbing implications.

One of the results of the general lack of overall planning is that a community's hospital-bed supply is primarily determined by the level of its per capita income rather than by need and that whereas some areas have more hospital capacity than they can use, others have serious deficiencies. Another result of random expansion is that there is often an excess of facilities for the treatment of acute illness and a shortage of more suitable and more economic accommodations for the chronically ill. The consequence is that long-term patients, and particularly the aged, needlessly occupy expensive general hospital beds.

Competent opinion is that general hospital facilities are frequently not only poorly distributed but actually in excess of need. Excessive hospital space not only means needless capital spending but leads to low occupancy, duplication of services, and higher operating costs. It also tends to stimulate admissions for relatively trivial ailments and unnecessarily prolonged stays, especially since such abuses are encouraged by the benefit structure of hospitalization insurance.

"Inefficient use is principally a matter of the number of hospital beds available," Ray E. Brown, director of the graduate program in hospital administration at Duke University and a former president of the American Hospital Association, has said. "The fewer the beds, the greater the pressure on both the patient and his physician for more judicious use of the available hospital facilities. The only effective means of controlling hospital utilization is to control supply. A hospital bed that does not exist obviously cannot be used. A hospital bed that does exist has a tendency to be used."

It is not without significance that crowding of hospitals during World War II, when shortages of material and labor halted new construction, led to fruitful experiments with quicker ambulation and discharge of patients after surgery and childbirth. Doctors found that mothers could safely go home after five days in the hospital instead of ten. They discovered that patients could be discharged seven days after an appendectomy instead of thirteen and nine days after a hernia operation instead of seventeen. These discoveries have meant not only that hospitals can take care of more people than before but also that patients recuperate much faster.

Dr. Milton I. Roemer, director of research at Cornell University's Institute of Hospital Administration, has even come up with a new version of the principles enunciated by C. Northcote Parkinson that "work expands so as to fill the time available for its completion" and that "expenditure always rises to meet income." Dr. Roemer's thesis is that "utilization of hospital beds expands to fill beds as they are built." This theory is probably an overstatement. But it graphically points up some of the wasteful results of the drift and disorder now so characteristic of our voluntary hospital system.

III

The issues crowding for a showdown in the hospital field add up to a series of challenging questions.

To whom do the hospitals belong anyhow, and who is to regulate their operation and costs?

Are the hospitals the property of the autonomous and often competing community groups that originally founded them but no longer support them to any appreciable extent, or are they vital public assets that should be subject to full social control?

What are the proper functions of the modern hospital?

Should it be used as a pawn for professional rivalries and primarily as a place where doctors bring their patients and treat them with tools provided by public investment? Or should it instead be developed, as some of our finest hospitals already have been, into the center of the community's health care services, where the highest professional skills are brought together not only for treatment but also for education and research, where there is emphasis on teamwork and on preventive as well as curative care, where as much attention is devoted to ambulatory as to bed patients, and where the public interest comes first even though it may sometimes impinge on the interests of private practitioners?

These controversial questions and a string of related problems are certain to figure prominently in the rising storm over the reorganization of medical services into a more rational system to give the consumer his money's worth.

More than ever before, better medical care depends on the standards set by the hospital. It depends on the extension of the hospital's services to ambulatory patients, whom physicians now regard as their private preserve, and to preventive care, which the medical profession tends to neglect. Already the focal point of medical care, the hospital's role is certain to be still further enhanced by the doctor's growing dependence on his colleagues and on complex apparatus and by the wide range of skills and facilities required for the treatment of chronic disease, now our major medical problem. With proper organization and use of the team approach, the hospital's services can be not only of high quality but economical as well.

Tighter coordination of the private practice of medicine with the hospital's activities is essential for greater efficiency. But expansion of the hospital's functions is certain to intensify its conflict with the medical profession and to bring to a head the whole problem of doctor-hospital relationships. Hospital trustees, who continue to represent the philanthropy of the past, are predominantly conservative and have generally been reluctant to accept new challenges. They often rubber-stamp the recommendations of the medical staff, thereby allowing themselves to be the tools of a vested interest. But the very nature of the hospital's expanding services makes for increasing tensions between its lay management and the members of its medical staff. While these conflicts are usually masked by professional slogans, their base is invariably economic. The doctor's insecurity has grown as he has become increasingly dependent on facilities he does not own and on personnel he does not employ. What he is concerned about is not only interference with the traditional freedom of his practice but, most of all, possible restrictions on his earnings.

Underlying the growing contentiousness of doctor-hospital relationships is the fact that through its staff controls on the standards of performance, the hospital has, at its best, already become the most powerful police agent of the medical profession. Scientific developments are pushing it inexorably still further in the direction of becoming the profession's chief organizing force as well.

The doctor is an independent entrepreneur in the conduct of his office practice, where he can do pretty much as he pleases. But the hospital imposes a variety of restraints on him in return for the opportunity for the cost-free use of equipment, personnel, and administrative organization. In a good hospital, the patient is no longer the physician's exclusive property. Case records are subject to review, there is policing against unnecessary surgery, and incompetence and bungling are aired at clinical conferences. This may go against the grain of the profession's traditional freewheeling ways, but it improves the quality of medical care and sometimes also affects its quantity.

As the hospital's functions have broadened, the cry has mounted that it is encroaching on the prerogatives of doctors and engaging in the practice of medicine. Organized medicine has long opposed the right of hospitals to employ physicians on salary for some technical services, and the issue is certain to be progressively sharpened with the expansion of hospital outpatient departments. What the profession obviously fears is that the employment of some salaried specialists will be used by the hospitals as a precedent for invading all fields of practice.

For a number of years, doctors have tended to follow their paying patients by shifting their offices to more prosperous neighborhoods, away from the poorer areas with their greatest concentration of unmet medical needs. But the hospitals have not moved. Finding themselves in sections that have deteriorated into congested slums, some of our large urban hospitals have been forced into providing medical services for their neighborhoods through their outpatient clinics. This has been particularly true of teaching hospitals affiliated with medical schools. The schools are increasingly coming to feel that students not only must have hospital training but also should be exposed to the patient's home environment and are extending their services to some homes. While the doctors are content to leave patients who pay little or nothing at all to someone else, this development nevertheless adds fuel to their fears that the hospital will more and more emerge as the middleman between physician and patient.

The extremes to which these fears can be carried are shown by the bitter dispute between the medical profession and the hospitals over the so-called corporate practice of medicine. The feud has so far been centered on the employment of salaried physicians in hospital radiology, pathology, and anesthesiology departments. Since these specialty services require large outlays for equipment and do not involve the customary doctor-patient relationship, hospitals consider it logical to staff them as far as possible with salaried specialists. The custom also has been to use the profits from these departments to cover hospital operating deficits. This has incensed the medical profession and has brought charges that doctors are being exploited and that having to work on salary lowers their professional dignity and may impair their professional judgment. All of which is arrant nonsense. It is ludicrous to contend that physicians are ethical only under certain circumstances or that salaried employment in itself is apt to affect judgment. Some of the most prized scientific discoveries have been made by salaried physicians and allied scientists. What the struggle is basically about is not professional ethics but who will have direct access to the patient's pocketbook.

The wrangle over corporate practice in the narrowly technical hospital departments is merely a preview of the pitched battle yet to be fought over the large-scale extension of outpatient services and the establishment of hospital-based group-practice units.

As hospitals are gradually transformed into community health centers, it becomes ever clearer that with their concentration of skills and equipment they can provide more effective and more economical services to ambulatory patients, no less so than to bed patients, instead of having them go from the office of one specialist to that of another. But the expansion of outpatient departments is fiercely resisted by the doctors as a grave economic threat. Because of the adamant opposition of the medical profession, outpatient services have up to now been largely confined to the indigent. The profession's pecuniary interests cannot, however, stand much longer in the way of the march of the industrial revolution in medicine. In one way or another, the economics of medical practice will have to be reorganized to the advantage of the community and not just of the doctors.

A straw in the wind has been the growing tendency for physicians in recent years to move their offices into, or adjacent to, hospitals. A number of hospitals have erected special buildings for rental to their staff members. This is a step toward integrating the doctor more closely into the framework of the hospital and permits wider use of its diagnostic facilities by ambulatory patients.

Well-run outpatient clinics utilize manpower more efficiently than private practice does, tend to reduce resort to hospital beds, and can lower the total cost of medical care. Given the backing of insurance coverage, which they now lack, such clinics could not only perform a myriad of services for the walking sick but also become the focus of health promotion through timely preventive procedures. It is true that the very term "clinic" has the depressing connotations of charity services and instantly brings to mind hours of waiting on hard benches, dreary offices, and a lack of privacy. But hospital clinics do not have to be the sort of basement operation they have all too frequently been. There is no reason why they cannot be as well equipped and staffed as the hospital's inpatient facilities are, provided the insurance programs and enough doctors would agree to cooperate.

The logic of medical progress calls for making the hospital the pivot of a coherent system that not only serves the traditional function of bed care but also provides group-practice, ambulatory, rehabilitative, home-care, and preventive services. The separation of doctors' offices and the hospital, which leads to duplication of equipment and wasted time on the part of physician and patient alike, has been rendered obsolete by new knowledge and the changing pattern of disease. Ultimately, the hospital will be as concerned with keeping people out of the hospital as with the treatment and rehabilitation of those who are admitted.

IV

The urgency of the need for concerted action to keep down the overall hospitalization bill is underscored by the consensus of experts that both hospital costs and utilization will continue to go up. Unless the voluntary system tackles the job with reasonable dispatch and vigor, massive governmental intervention appears inescapable.

Hospitals must keep pace with the growing population, the rapid rate of technological progress, the need for still more employees, and the rising wage scales in industry. As the quality of the medical product keeps on improving, it will inevitably cost more. The trend toward greater use of hospitals is still being fed by a number of factors, outstanding among them the mounting incidence of chronic illness as people live longer. There has been a movement from the home to the hospital even for the last days of life. Deaths in general hospitals have increased in the past twenty years from 34 per cent to 48 per cent of all deaths.

Up to now, the sharp rise in hospital admissions has to a considerable degree been compensated for by the remarkable fall in the average length of stay. But the curve of the decline in the duration of stay is flattening out. The full impact of the shortened length of stay for maternity care and the acute diseases already has been realized. If a further steep climb in the use of hospital days and in pyramiding costs is to be averted, we shall have to look for alternatives to hospitalization, particularly in the chronic disease field.

Unfortunately, measures for offsetting the pressure of higher costs still remain largely unexplored. Such opportunities exist in steps to make sure that hospital beds are not used when care can be provided on an ambulatory basis or at home and to improve managerial efficiency. Under the latter heading come the maximum utilization of personnel and beds, a cooperative division of responsibility and sharing of expensive equipment among hospitals instead of letting each institution try to do everything, and the streamlining of physical plants to tailor them to the varying needs of patients instead of providing all patients with accommodations required only by those who are acutely ill. Helpful in the reduction of inpatient loads would be wider use of outpatient departments and greater reliance on nursing and convalescent homes and on organized home-care programs. Far too many elderly chronic patients who primarily need custodial rather than professional care are now occupying expensive general hospital beds because of lack of adequate facilities for them elsewhere.

Some cost factors, such as higher expenditures resulting from scientific advances and unavoidable higher spending for labor, are beyond the direct control of hospital authorities. But fully susceptible of remedial action are controls on admission and length of stay, on the duplication of facilities and services in a community, and on requirements for additional hospital beds. If hospital beds were used more judiciously, we would not need so many more of them. The best hope for coping with the upward spiral of hospital costs lies in more efficient methods of patient care and more effective coordination of the community's health resources. A major problem in the total cost of illness is how to keep people out of hospital beds, which must be considered the last resort in the chain of medical care.

There is general agreement in hospital circles on the need for community and regional planning and for more stringent cost- and quality-control measures. But getting started on any of these things is something else again. It is perfectly clear that before the opportunities for economy can be realized, ways will have to be found to remove roadblocks posed by vested interests, institutional inertia, and the effects of health insurance on hospital operations. Whether this can be done without the leverage of governmental power is still very much open to question.

Establishment of unified administrative controls within each hospital, to replace the present blurred division of authority between the lay management and the medical staff, must come before any effective collaboration among hospitals can be hoped for. But if this is feasible within the present pattern of medical practice is again highly questionable.

The operation and use of hospitals cannot be considered in a vacuum. They are profoundly affected by the nature of medical practice and the methods of financing of health care. There is little doubt, for instance, that the remarkable growth of hospitalization insurance, which now provides the greatest share of hospital income, has had both favorable and adverse effects on hospital operations. Insurance has brought hospital care within the reach of millions in the middle and low-income groups and has been a potent force in expanding the scope of services and improving the quality of personnel. But insurance also has led to overuse of hospitalization, some overbuilding of hospital plants, and a general relaxation of pressures for economy of operation.

The general policy of insurance programs to reimburse hospitals for their costs has reduced, if not wholly removed, incentives to keep expenditures at their lowest possible level. Insurance not only has stimulated demand but also has had a substantial impact on the distribution of medical care facilities. The exclusion of benefits for ambulatory and nursing-home care from prepayment coverage has led to pressure for the use of general hospital beds by patients who could get along with less costly care. At the same time, the lack of assurance of sufficient operating funds has deterred the development of adequate nursing homes, rehabilitation facilities, and home-care services.

Both the hospitals and the health insurance plans have yet to act upon the far-reaching implications of the new order of hospital economics. In the days when philanthropy provided the backbone of hospital finances, there may have been some justification for ignoring consumer attitudes. But although the consumer has now become the mainstay of the hospital economy through the mechanism of insurance, he still has little if any voice in the setting of hospital policies. Hospitals have continued to operate in their traditional manner, with decisions being made by small and usually self-perpetuating groups on the basis of their own evaluations of institutional needs. There has been a grievous failure to establish a community of real understanding between the hospitals and the consumers. And the tension between them has to no small degree been exacerbated by the fact that the customer's demands for service are consistently way ahead of his willingness to pay.

Blue Cross, in its turn, has all too often been inclined to confine its own role to that of a collection agency for the hospitals rather than functioning as an intermediary between the purchasers and suppliers of hospital care. Consumers are not adequately represented on most Blue Cross boards of directors, which are dominated by hospital representatives. Proposals by a number of state insurance commissioners and study groups that Blue Cross take a much more active interest in trying to curb the steady rise in hospital costs have been greeted with outright hostility by the hospitals and a conspicuous lack of enthusiasm on the part of the insurance plans.

Much also still remains to be done in the area of quality controls. While our best hospitals are equal to any in the world, fewer than four thousand of the nation's more than seven thousand hospitals meet the requirements of the Joint Commission on Accreditation of Hospitals, which is composed of representatives of the AMA, the American College of Surgeons, the American College of Physicians, and the American Hospital Association. The commission's requirements, which are a prerequisite for approval for internship and residency training, set certain standards for physical facilities, organization, program, and staffing. These standards are generally regarded as minimal and absolutely essential for adequate hospital performance. And yet about 600,000 of the more than 1,700,000 hospitals beds in the United States are unable to meet them. About 2,500,000 patients a year are treated in unaccredited hospitals, where the competence of the staff is often questionable and where there are no provisions for good record keeping, a certain percentage of autopsies, and other basic elements of quality control.

Even in some of the accredited hospitals, the safeguards against shoddy performance are far from foolproof. Approved hospitals have staff tissue committees for the evaluation and policing of surgery. All tissue removed by surgeons undergoes pathological examination, and practitioners found to have excised too many healthy organs are subject to disciplinary action. It is reported, however, that, in actual practice, tissue committees are not uncommonly something of a farce and that surgeons who are in the good graces of the ruling staff clique are rarely called on the carpet. The same thing is said to hold true of the utilization committees set up in some hospitals in recent years to check on unnecessary admissions and needlessly prolonged stays. Some of these committees, which have been organized in response to public concern over high hospital utilization and consequent Blue Cross premium boosts, are reported to exist largely on paper.

There are substantial possibilities for lowering the costs of medical care, in the opinion of many authorities, in the organization of group-practice units in association with hospitals to bring doctors closer to their tools of production and thereby obtain the benefits of greater efficiency and reduced overhead. The hospital —itself the outstanding example of integration in medicine, with its pooling of equipment and coordination of the knowledge and skills of the various specialties—provides the ideal setting for group practice. But this form of practice remains anathema to large segments of the medical profession. In this as in other areas, the hospital's potential for economy is frequently inhibited by the archaic piecework approach of the present organization of medical practice.

The pattern of private practice is in no small degree responsible for the cumbersome administrative structure of our hospitals and their elaborate staffing. The principal reason why the average American hospital has about 65 per cent more employees per 100 beds than its Swedish counterpart is that patients have different attending physicians. This means, among other things, that nurses have to prepare detailed reports on each patient's condition for doctors who are busy elsewhere much of the time and that pharmacies often have to keep in stock a wide range of drugs to satisfy each physician's wishes. Hospitals with full-time salaried medical staffs are able to get along with fewer nurses, technicians, and clerks and a much smaller selection of medications.

Although general hospitals now employ, on the average, well over two employees for each patient, the caliber of many of these employees leaves a good deal to be desired, and so, very frequently, do the standards of service. Elmo Roper reported several years ago, after a public opinion survey of attitudes toward hospitals in New York City, that "there is widespread and intense resentment against neglect, rudeness and impersonal treatment by hospital personnel. A bell unanswered in the night, a medical necessity thoughtlessly turned into a personal indignity, omitted explanations, a sterile efficiency that offends human sensibilities—

such experiences have made indelible impressions. They live on to color the public reaction to hospitals, even when not consciously remembered."

Countless thousands of patients have been irritated by the time-honored custom of being awakened in the bleak dawn to have their temperature taken and hands and face washed, only to be left waiting for anywhere from two to three hours for their breakfast, which quite often turns out to be cold. Patients are sometimes even awakened in the middle of the night to be given sleeping pills. These and other senseless practices, most of them dating back to the days when virtually all hospital patients were acutely ill, remain in effect largely for no other reason than that they have always been standard operating procedure. The hardest thing in the world for institutions is to change their set ways, logic and economy notwithstanding. The fact that the character of the patient population has radically changed and that many of the patients are able to take care of themselves a lot of the time has yet to dawn on most hospital managements.

Among the still largely unrealized opportunities for economy are in the areas of so-called progressive patient care and home care. The former, already instituted in a number of places, is a method of organizing the hospital so as to provide graduated services ranging from the intensive care of the critically ill to self-service care for ambulatory patients. Many patients do not need all the complex personal services and apparatus that the modern hospital is equipped to provide. The conventional system of putting all patients in hospital beds and offering them the same services regardless of their condition—even if they are in just for some tests—not only is far too costly but also is not calculated to improve their morale. Costs can be appreciably reduced by division of the hospital into zones of care. Under such an arrangement, convalescing patients or those who require only diagnostic services can do many things for themselves, such as light housekeeping and going to the cafeteria for their own meals, to the laboratory for tests, and to the clinic for a change of dressings.

Organized home care is an extension of hospital services into the community. Under programs in operation for a number of years in New York, Boston, and some other cities, patients with long-term illnesses of limited severity who do not need expensive institutional treatment are cared for at much lower cost at home with the aid of medical and nursing personnel provided by hospitals. If the home environment is suitable, the patient's relatives are taught how to perform certain simple tasks for him, and, if necessary, hospital equipment is brought right into the home for some procedures. Such home treatment not only can be furnished for about one-fifth of the cost that would be incurred in the hospital but also is often an improvement. Once a wife or daughter has been taught the techniques, she usually proves a superior nurse because of the affection she brings to the job. Supportive home conditions can do wonders for a patient's spirit.

While the existing home-care programs are still limited in scope, they already have demonstrated that by using visiting nurses, physical and occupational therapists, and housekeepers under medical supervision, they can relieve hospitals and other institutions of the burden of many chronic patients. The development of such programs would be greatly stimulated by the extension of Blue Cross benefits to home services as an alternative to prolonged hospital care. A number of experimental projects along this line have shown that extension of insured services beyond the walls of the general hospital can produce material savings.

Much the same thing holds true for nursing and convalescent homes. The neglect of these facilities, which have been left largely to proprietary operation and are often grossly inadequate, has greatly contributed to the uneconomic use of hospitals. Official estimates are that we now have only about one-quarter of the needed acceptable nursing-home accommodations. The shortage is certain to get the worse with the rising prevalence of chronic disease unless a large-scale program is soon undertaken for the construction and operation of such institutions under public auspices. Here, too, the extension of insurance coverage would be of inestimable help.

Nursing homes must, moreover, be removed from their stagnating isolation and brought into the mainstream of medical care through a functional relationship with hospitals so that there can be adequate professional supervision and a proper allocation of patients according to their need. Through close affiliation with hospitals, nursing homes could be used not only for the treatment and rehabilitation of the chronically ill but also as a sort of half-way house between the hospital and the home for recuperating patients.

Hospitals will have to redistribute their functions through community-wide and regional planning. Under such a realignment, big hospitals will largely confine their specialized skills and expensive equipment to complicated procedures and refer other patients to smaller hospitals and still less costly auxiliary facilities. The hospital will thus become the nerve center of a complex of supporting satellite institutions.

The need for redefinition of the hospital's role is based on a twofold premise: that economies can best be realized, on the one hand, by getting the greatest productivity out of hospital personnel and equipment and by lowering the unit costs through the expansion of ambulatory services and, on the other hand, by providing care elsewhere for those for whom inpatient services are not essential. Many of the leading experts in the health field feel that in the hospital of the future outpatient services will be at least of equal importance with inpatient facilities and that group practice will be the major pattern for both forms of care.

Some pioneering efforts in the direction of organized planning in the hospital field are under way in several states. But the surface of the possibilities of regional planning has barely been scratched. Regional coordination programs, usually built around a large medical center, include the sharing of diagnostic and clinical services by smaller hospitals in a certain geographic area, the referral of serious cases to the central hospital, the rotation of interns and residents, joint courses for nurses and other personnel, central purchasing of supplies, and assistance to physicians in smaller communities through consultations and refresher courses. Rural practitioners thereby become, in effect, members of a regional medical group and are able to benefit from a system of continuous professional education. The best-known example of effective regional coordination is operated by the Bingham Associates Fund through the New England Medical Center of Tufts Medical School in Boston and reaches out to fifty-six small hospitals in Maine and western Massachusetts. There is no question that such programs make for better and more economical medical care. The trouble is that they require not only the collaboration of hospitals but also the wholehearted participation of doctors, which is not always forthcoming within the present framework of practice.

The whole subject of hospital costs is increasingly generating concern and coming under public scrutiny as Blue Cross plans seek to justify their applications for successive rate increases before state insurance commissioners. The wastefulness of the excessive use of hospitals and of their haphazard operation and expansion is focusing attention on the need for better hospital management and clarification of the doctor's role in the hospital structure, for tighter controls on utilization, and for centralized planning that would take into consideration the overall community picture and possible alternatives to costly hospital-bed care. The time also has clearly come for a major shift in emphasis in the construction of health facilities, with much greater stress laid on providing more economical institutions for long-term care.

A basic flaw is the absence of any political instrumentality with significant decision-making power in the hospital field. This is in striking contrast with education, where the community's efforts are at all times under firm public control. Surely hospitals, with their huge investment and pervading role in our lives, are fully as important and should be subject to some form of effective public regulation to make sure that they are used wisely and in the interests of the community at large.

Costs will continue to climb, without an equivalent return in service and quality, if hospitals are allowed to persist in their extravagant practices, if they keep on expanding at random without the support of less expensive auxiliary facilities. Only sound planning and a close interrelationship of various medical services can produce the best possible quality of care for the most judicious use of the health dollar. It is doubtful whether much progress in this direction can be achieved as long as the power of decision rests mainly with those who stand most to gain from maintaining the *status quo*. But it is certainly worth trying. The only alternative to some form of public participation side by side with voluntary effort is full governmental control.

CHAPTER SIX

The Crisis of
Voluntary Health Insurance

I

ON THE FACE OF IT, there are few more impressive success stories than the spectacular growth of voluntary health insurance in the United States. There is probably no parallel in our history to the movement that, within the relatively brief period of little more than two decades, has brought at least some form of health insurance protection to three out of every four Americans. From modest beginnings in the years after the Depression, when the memories of crowded hospital charity wards and unpaid doctors' bills were still fresh in the minds of millions, the health insurance movement has grown into a mammoth force that has had a drastic impact on the economics of medical care.

In 1940, about 12,000,000 Americans had insurance coverage for part of their hospital expenses. Since then, the number of those insured for some of their medical costs has soared to more than 145,000,000. Health insurance premiums now exceed $8 billion a year, and benefit payments are running at the annual rate of nearly $7 billion. Sweeping changes in our economy have made possible this accomplishment, which is all the more remarkable in that no element of compulsion is attached to it. Of their own free will, the great majority of Americans have decided to relinquish part of their take-home pay to make certain that they will have some help in meeting their bills when illness strikes. More and more, they have become conscious of the benefits of medical care and stand ready to allocate an even larger share of their resources to pay for it.

But it is precisely in this greater health consciousnes of Americans and their growing awareness of the contrast between what modern medicine can do for them and what it is actually doing that we have to look for the causes of the critical predicament in which voluntary health insurance now finds itself. For behind the imposing façade of the achievements of voluntary prepayment lie a lamentable record of failure to rise to new challenges and a far-ranging crisis of cost and function. Grafted on a superannuated system of medical practice and hospital organization, the health insurance system is the victim of entrenched interests, its own timidity, and the continuing scientific revolution in medicine. It is increasingly caught in a squeeze of steadily rising prices for medical services and their uncontrolled use on the one hand and a mounting demand for more comprehensive benefits on the other. How the nonprofit insurance plans and the commerical carriers can meet the clamor for broader coverage without completely pricing themselves out of the reach of those who are mostly in need of prepayment protection is still far from clear. But there is no question that upon their success in solving this dilemma depends the preservation, with some essential modifications, of the existing organizational forms of medical care and practice in the United States.

Even in the area of enrollment, where its showing has been strongest, health insurance faces serious problems. About 50,000,-000 Americans still have no hospitalization insurance, which is the most predominant form of coverage. About 65,000,000 have no surgical expense insurance. Nearly 100,000,000 lack insurance protection against general medical expenses. Only about 35,000,000 have relatively broad insurance coverage against the costs of illness. Those without coverage of any kind are mostly the aged, the disabled, marginal farmers, migratory workers, and other low-income groups, all of whom have medical needs that are well above the average and are least able to pay for the services they require. The ratio of prepayment coverage among those with annual incomes of $7,000 or more is three and one-half times what it is for those earning less than $4,000 a year. In New York, it is about double what it is in Mississippi.

Health insurance enrollment experienced its most rapid growth in the 1940's under the impetus of a combination of circumstances. Foremost among them was the quickening pace of medical progress. As the costs of medical care began to climb in the wake of momentous scientific advances, the realization grew that the irregular and unpredictable financial burden of illness could best be spread by regular advance budgeting and the pooling of risks. There is a close parallel in this respect between the costs of medical and fire protection services. To ask the sick to bear the whole cost of their treatment, which under present conditions would bankrupt many of them, is not much fairer than to assess only those who have had fires in their homes or business places for the upkeep of the local fire department. In various ways, all of us, the well no less than the sick, benefit from good medical services. The need for assuring the stability of the medical economy was amply demonstrated during the Depression, when consumer expenditures for health care plummeted by one-third, hospitals were almost half empty, and physicians were unable to collect a large share of their bills.

Another impelling force of great significance was government action in banning wage increases during World War II. This deflected organized labor's demands into fringe benefits, mostly in the health field, which have since remained a matter of collective bargaining and have given the unions a vital stake in the organization and financing of medical care.

The medical profession, which to this day retains deep-seated misgivings about health insurance, was spurred into setting up prepayment plans of its own in the hope that this would avert legislation for compulsory insurance. Labor also had some strong reservations about joining the voluntary health insurance movement. But its motives were the exact reverse of the medical profession's. Labor came in reluctantly because the prospects for adoption of a government-operated program that it favored appeared dim. Labor's emergence as the principal champion of consumer interests in the health field is no accident. Many unions had their inception in mutual benefit associations that were formed to mitigate the expenses of illness and funerals.

The days of easy expansion of voluntary health insurance are over. But in order to head off large-scale governmental intervention, it must continue to expand, both in enrollment and in its benefit structure. At the moment, it is difficult to see how most of the existing enrollment gaps can be filled without the use of tax funds to help provide coverage for categories of the population, notably the aged, that are particularly poor insurance risks and are least able to afford the premium payments.

Fully as grave as the problem of extending prepayment protection to those who still lack it is the need for substantial improvements in the level of protection of those who already are insured. Here the issues are extremely abrasive, because they go to the very heart of the present organization of medical care. Benefit levels cannot be materially raised without an unremitting concern for the costs of care, which determine the price of insurance. This, in turn, requires sustained pressures for greater medical and hospital efficiency, which cannot be achieved without some far-reaching organizational reforms. The health insurance plans, which are closely tied up with the medical profession and the hospitals, have understandably shied away from facing up to these issues. But they clearly cannot have their cake and eat it too.

The inadequacies of voluntary health insurance are most graphically demonstrated by two highly disconcerting facts. The first is that while benefit provisions have progressively become more liberal, they still meet only about one-fourth of the medical bills of those who are insured. Prepayment has the best record in the field of hospital care, where it now meets about 60 per cent of the costs. Insurance pays 40 per cent of the costs of surgery, 30 per cent of the expenditures for the services of obstetricians, less than 10 per cent of physicians' out-of-hospital fees, and little or nothing for other services and supplies. This means that in the course of a year, patients have to pay out of pocket an additional $2.5 billion for hospitalization, $3.5 billion for doctors' services, $3.9 billion for drugs, and $4.5 billion for other health services, such as dental care, nursing-home care, and appliances. It is therefore hardly surprising that 15 per cent of American families wind up in debt each year in order to pay their medical and hospital bills.

The second perturbing fact is that the costs of both medical care and insurance have been rising much faster than the proportion defrayed by prepayment. While medical costs have been going up at the rate of 5 to 10 per cent a year, the ratio of such costs met by insurance has shown an average annual increase of less than 2 per cent. At the same time, insurance premium charges have been climbing during the past decade at the rate of 10 per cent a year under the impact of rising medical costs and increased utilization.

There is no indication of any reversal or even a slowing down of this disheartening trend, which keeps on depreciating the insured consumer's protection. Nor is any likely unless some far more forceful action is taken in the direction of cost controls than may reasonably be anticipated from the prepayment organizations as they are now constituted. In the meantime, repeated premium boosts are increasingly making insurance too expensive for those who need it most urgently.

But must we really resign ourselves to the treadmill of continuous price inflation and the wasteful use of expensive medical and hospital services? Is it inevitable that the price spiral should eat away the consumer's insurance benefit gains and prevent their extension to such essential areas as long-term illness, hospital outpatient services, dental costs, and prescribed drugs? Competent opinion is that this dismal prospect is not unavoidable. But the corrective lies in greater maturity and responsibility on the part of all concerned and in radical changes in the whole structure of medical care and health prepayment. The insurance plans will be unable to meet the mounting demands for more comprehensive coverage as long as they exercise so little control over the prices charged by doctors and hospitals and over improper utilization and none at all over the quality of care.

At the root of many of the troubles of the predominant insurance pattern are two fundamental defects—the concentration on coverage for the costs of surgery and other illness requiring hospitalization and the neglect of preventive and diagnostic services. Both approaches are unsound, from the medical no less than from the economic point of view. The net effect of these basic errors is that the prepayment system fails to provide any incentives for timely measures aimed at preventing disease or at catching it in its incipient stages and that it promotes excessive use of costly hospital facilities and other abuses that needlessly inflate the bill. Most of the insurance organizations have yet to learn the irrefutable lesson that prevention, diagnosis, treatment, and aftercare are one continuous process and that it is wiser and more economical to try to prevent illness than it is to pay through insurance claims for the end results of neglect.

The heavy financial burden of serious illness was documented about ten years ago in a study sponsored by the Health Information Foundation that showed that 11 per cent of American families had medical expenses of more than $500 a year. Medical prices have risen sharply in the past decade, and the high-cost figures are undoubtedly much higher now. In the year in which the survey was made, the payments in excess of $500 per family accounted for 43 per cent of the total spent for health services. In other words, a little more than one-tenth of the families had to pay more than two-fifths of the medical bill. The prevailing insurance benefit structure rarely offers anything approximating adequate help for victims of prolonged illness. All too often, prepayment now insures the doctor, by making it possible for him to collect from patients who in the past paid little or nothing, more than it does the patient.

Aside from meeting only a quarter of the overall bill, present insurance coverage is badly lopsided. It provides little protection or none at all for services performed outside the hospital, although expenses for these services still make up the bulk of medical costs. With the sole exception of surgery, its contribution toward physicians' fees is negligible. The costs of long-term physical or mental disease remain largely uncovered. Home and office calls, drugs and appliances, dental services, nursing-home care, home-nursing services, and a number of other medical care items have to be paid for directly by the great majority of insurance subscribers. What it amounts to is that most of the things deemed worthy of coverage when the patient is flat on his back in a hospital bed are considered outside the insurance framework when he is confined to bed at home or is still on his feet. It is small wonder, then, that this setup provides a ready inducement for getting between hospital sheets.

Good medical care means emphasis on prevention, early diagnosis, office supervision of illness, with provisions for proper consultation, adequate home care, and rehabilitation of the patient to teach him to live with his disabilities. All these things are now generally excluded from insurance benefit schedules. It is true that physicians' home and office calls are relatively inexpensive. But the cost of a number of such visits is likely to add up to a substantial amount, and there are often additional costs for laboratory tests and drugs that many people are unable to afford. The inevitable outcome is that early symptoms are frequently neglected; as a result, relatively minor complaints are allowed to develop into major ones.

Prompt diagnosis and care can abort many ailments before they become serious. They can control toxemia in pregnancy, keep diabetes from causing arteriosclerosis or gangrene, avert permanent damage to the heart or kidneys from streptococcal infection and even save lives by detecting malignancy when it is still treatable. Insurance coverage for diagnostic procedures would, in the long run, reduce the load of costly hospital admissions. It would admittedly also tend to bring in some additional patients with conditions that currently remain undiscovered. But there is all the difference in the world between the cost of necessary and unnecessary hospitalization.

The experience of several large independent prepayment plans employing salaried physicians on a group-practice basis has shown that it is feasible to provide coverage at a reasonable premium for a wide range of services now excluded by most insurance contracts. The main reason why the independent programs have been able to keep their costs within moderate bounds is that they pay their doctors according to the number of patients handled rather than for specific services. Group-practice prepayment also eliminates the financial deterrent to early disease detection. The main reason why preventive services are now so often neglected is that people tend to put off what they have to pay for until the need becomes urgent.

The key problem of insurance under the prevailing system of solo practice is one of how to maintain adequate controls over how the money is spent and over the quality of services. As long as the medical profession continues to resist effective checks on its fees and on the amount and quality of its services, the costs of truly comprehensive benefits will be prohibitive and out of most people's reach. No one has yet been able to devise means for preventing doctors from pyramiding their services under the system in which a fee is paid for each separate procedure.

The basic trouble appears to lie in trying to superimpose a modern concept of comprehensive health prepayment on the ramshackle structure of solo practice. Insurance is merely a mechanism for spreading risks and cannot in itself solve the problem of ballooning medical costs. On the contrary, by removing the economic barrier to utilization of services, it tends to generate demand and thus becomes an inflationary factor. The overall bill—not only in terms of dollars but also in terms of pain and of blighted or lost lives—can best be cut through intensive development of preventive medicine to reduce the incidence of illness, a more efficient organization of medical practice, and improved quality of medical services. The preservation of the traditional fee-for-service method under an expanded voluntary insurance system is possible only with a much greater degree of responsibility than the medical profession has yet displayed.

The story of the growing insurance crisis, in a nutshell, is that Americans are seeking medical care much more frequently and are finding that the devices they have organized to protect themselves against its costs are sadly inadequate. All too often, insured patients are shocked to discover that they lack coverage for many services, that prepayment meets only a fraction of the costs of covered procedures, that their doctors can charge them extra if their incomes are above a certain level, and that, under the archaic Robin Hood system of medical fees, some physicians actually hike their bills by counting insurance as an additional asset and thereby defeat its main purpose. The insured are dismayed to find that in the case of such serious illness as a heart attack or a stroke, their policies provide no protection whatsoever if treatment is outside a hospital. Oddly enough, their resentment is mostly aimed at Blue Cross and Blue Shield, the nonprofit plans, rather than at the commercial carriers, which on the whole do a much less creditable job. It is taken for granted that the latter are in business to make a profit and nothing else.

The voluntary approach is too deeply rooted in American practice to be easily abandoned. Even organized labor now shows little enthusiasm for a government-operated health insurance system if the job can be done more effectively and economically within the framework of voluntary prepayment. Otherwise, pressures for government intervention will become irresistible. Improvement of the voluntary system is the strongest possible measure that can be taken to assure substantial continuance of the present pattern of medical care in this country.

II

How much misuse of hospitalization is there, and to what extent can such abuses be laid directly at the door of the lack of balance in most voluntary health insurance programs? Although this has been one of the most heatedly debated issues in the health field for years, it is doubtful whether any precise answers will ever be available. There is no question that the predominant method of insurance, designed mainly to cover hospital care and geared to the solo pattern of practice, tends to encourage hospitalization. Some authorities nevertheless feel that it is an oversimplification to attribute all, or even the major part, of the greatly increased hospital utilization to loopholes in the insurance system.

How much hospital care is enough has never been definitely established. There are as yet no absolute criteria as to when a person should or should not be hospitalized; and to no small extent hospital care is as much a feature of the prevailing standard of living and of what patients have come to expect as it is the product of medical judgment. What was regarded as a normal hospital admission rate a generation ago is certainly no standard for today. More frequent hospitalization is fully warranted by the increased technological importance of the hospital in modern medical care, higher buying power, the steady rise in the numbers of older people, and the large backlog of previously unmet health needs. In fact, medical experts generally feel that most people do not go to the doctor as often as they should and that some of them would profit from hospital care but cannot afford it or fail to take advantage of it for some other reasons. The waste represented by unnecessary admissions is relatively small, these experts maintain, compared with the benefits derived from justified admissions that might otherwise have been thwarted by economic barriers.

But even when allowance is made for these factors, the preponderance of authoritative opinion, backed up by impressive evidence, is that there is substantial overuse of costly hospital facilities and that both the insurance benefit structure and the character of medical practice contribute to it materially.

The problem of insurance for hospital services is intimately linked up with the nature of prepayment for physicians' services.

When insurance coverage is largely restricted to hospital care and to physicians' services in the hospital, the inevitable temptation is to use inpatient hospital facilities for procedures that could be provided just as effectively and far more economically in the outpatient department or in the doctor's office. This is unavoidable if the patient must occupy a hospital bed to become eligible for benefits. Also figuring in the picture are the overbuilding of hospital beds in some places and the lack of adequate outpatient and nursing home facilities. There is no evidence of any great effort on the part of the medical profession or the hospitals to reduce needless hospitalization. Not only do some doctors find it advantageous to lend a hand in such abuses, but it is generally more convenient for them to have their patients hospitalized. And from a financial point of view, it is vitally important to a hospital to have as high an occupancy rate as possible.

Excessive hospital use is characteristic of voluntary health insurance in the United States. The original approach was that the function of health insurance, as in the case of commercial insurance, is to provide financial protection against the most costly and relatively infrequent events. The hospital bill loomed large as the most obvious item in this category, and it has remained to this day the cornerstone of health insurance. But the trouble is that the principles of casualty insurance, with their special devices for eliminating the small claims and inhibiting abuse of coverage, are totally inapplicable to the complicated contingencies of health care. Health insurance boosts rather than lowers costs in the long run by excluding preventive care and early diagnosis and by making accessible the costliest instead of the most economical forms of care.

Medical care problems require the application of social rather than commercial insurance principles, with the broadest possible pooling of risks and resources, with mechanisms that encourage subscribers to consult physicians about apparently minor symptoms whose early treatment may nip serious illness in the bud, and with proper attention to controls on the level of fees and the quality of services. Without these safeguards, health insurance not only becomes a vehicle of extravagance but militates against the fundamental requirements of good health care. The stress on hospital prepayment has, of necessity, resulted in an artificial increase in the demand for hospitalization in an attempt to stretch the available protection to cover part of the uninsured costs. This, in turn, has forced repeated hikes in hospital insurance premium rates.

The insured go to the hospital much more frequently than do the uninsured, and their overall use of days of hospital care is considerably higher.

A Health Information Foundation survey found that the insured have 140 admissions per 1,000 persons per year as compared with only 90 per 1,000 for the uninsured. The average length of time spent in the hospital by the insured tends to be lower because of the higher proportion of short-stay cases and the fact that admission for the uninsured is more likely to be put off until they are seriously ill. But in the aggregate, the insured average 1,000 hospital days a year per 1,000 persons as against 700 for those without insurance. This clearly makes a tremendous difference in the nation's overall hospital bill.

Even more striking is the higher surgical rate for the insured, which is nearly double that of the uninsured. Only one out of every twenty persons without health insurance undergoes surgery in the course of a year, such procedures being mostly of an emergency nature. But for the insured the rate is one out of every eleven, with a high proportion of elective surgery. A steep surgical ratio raises issues going well beyond its effect on insurance premium rates. Also involved here are the standards of medical ethics under the inducement of fees that are at least partly guaranteed by insurance and the consumer's inability to evaluate the quality of professional services or even the necessity for them. The placing of insurance price tags on practically any organ in the body that can be shaken loose sometimes leads to flagrant abuses.

The Health Information Foundation study discovered that while only 5 out of every 1,000 uninsured persons have their appendixes removed every year, the annual appendectomy rate for the insured is 11 per 1,000. This big difference cannot possibly be attributed to medical reasons alone. If it were, the death rate from ruptured appendixes among those without health insurance would be appalling.

Even more open to suspicion is the still greater differential in the tonsillectomy rate. Hospitalization rates for children up to the age of seventeen for tonsillectomies are 30 per 1,000 for the insured as compared with only 9 per 1,000 for the uninsured. The sharply higher tonsillectomy rate among the insured is particularly deplorable in view of the fact that the value of this operation and of surgery for the removal of adenoids in children is seriously questioned by reputable medical authorities, except in a restricted number of cases in which certain special conditions exist. Respiratory diseases decline as youngsters grow older, and the drop has been found to be exactly the same in children who did and in those who did not have tonsillectomies and adenoidectomies. A study made by Dr. Osler L. Peterson of Harvard Medical School shows that while one Blue Cross plan in the United States has a rate of 12.3 hospital admissions for tonsils and adenoids per 1,000 subscribers, the rates for such admissions are only 3.6 per 1,000 persons in England and 0.25 per 1,000 in Sweden. "Since the diagnostic criteria of what constitutes a diseased tonsil are notably fallible and the results of tonsilectomy-adenoidectomy performed as a treatment for repeated respiratory infection very debatable," Dr. Peterson has said, "I believe that the lower rates of Sweden and England represent more discriminating use of this operation." It is lamentable that the natural inclination of many surgeons to rush their patients into the operating room should be spurred by the bait of insurance payments.

Appendectomies are likewise notoriously susceptible of abuse. Pertinent is the experience in this area of the Welfare and Retirement Fund of the United Mine Workers of America, which until recently operated one of the nation's largest direct-service labor health plans. When the fund set up its own group-practice terms of salaried physicians, it managed to slash the rate of appendectomies for its beneficiaries by 59.4 per cent.

Devastating evidence of excessive hospital use and of the key role played in it by insurance has come from a number of studies. A survey of 12,102 consecutive cases in twenty-five hospitals made some years ago by the Michigan State Medical Society showed that out of a total of 76,238 days spent by these patients in hospital beds, 11,172 days were "unnecessary to the recovery, safety or reasonable comfort of the patient." While 14 per cent to the patients paying their own bills were found to have come to the hospital unnecessarily or to have stayed too long, this faulty use was attributed to 36 per cent of the patients who had Blue Cross coverage. One out of every eight such patients was hospitalized merely for laboratory or X-ray examinations, which were readily available in the outpatient departments of the same hospitals. A spokesman for the Michigan Blue Cross estimated, on the basis of these findings, that about 18 per cent of the insurance plan's premium income went down the drain for unnecessary services.

A more recent study of 5,750 patients in eighteen diagnostic categories discharged in the course of a year from forty-seven Michigan hospitals found that nearly one out of every ten patients had stayed longer than was medically warranted and put the total overstay for this group at 200,000 patient days. The report of this survey, made by the highly reputable University of Michigan Bureau of Hospital Administration, estimated that overstays in the state add up to some 500,000 days of needless hospital care each year and said that the annual bill "for unnecessary care in Michigan is probably close to $15,000,000." Not staying in the hospital long enough was found to be almost three times more common than staying too long when the patient paid the bill himself. But when the bill was paid wholly or in part by some other source, mostly by insurance, overstay was twice as common as leaving too soon. The report attributed most of the overstays to extramedical factors unrelated to the patient's condition. The most frequently mentioned causes were "physician's usual practice in such cases" and "no one at home to care for the patient."

An exhaustive review of the utilization of one thousand general hospital beds in Rochester, New York, made by fourteen teams of physicians, showed that 16.5 per cent of the beds were being used unnecessarily as far as medical reasons were concerned and that an additional 5 per cent could have been vacated if adequate long-term care facilities had been available. The doctors felt that outpatient care would have been sufficient in more than one-third of the cases of needless use of hospital beds; that in another third, nursing-home care would have been adequate; and that the remaining patients could just as well have been cared for at home. In a recent spot check made for the state of New York by other survey teams, admissions solely for the purpose of X-ray tests were found to be the most common abuse. "Excision of superficial lesions under local anesthesia" and "removal of casts which were too tight" were cited as other frequent examples of unwarranted hospitalization.

A study of ten thousand hospitalized Blue Cross subscribers in Pittsburgh came up with the conclusion that one out of every ten "would have been treated at home if his hospital bill had not been prepaid through Blue Cross." Another study of patients who had stayed thirty days or longer in four Boston hospitals and accounted for nearly one-third of the total patient days in these institutions found that 42 per cent, most of them elderly people, did not require continuing active treatment. These men and women were reported to be occupying hospital beds principally because of "unsuitability of the patient's home, reluctance of the family to accept the patient, and lack of other facilities and services." The superintendent of a hospital of more than two hundred beds in Rhode Island has said that between 30 to 40 per cent of the patients at his institution were there not for medical reasons but because they had nowhere else to go.

The length of time that patients are kept in hospitals for the same diseases varies widely, depending on the doctor's idiosyncrasies, the patient's preferences, and the rules of the particular hospital. Medicare, the government-financed program for medical care for wives and children of servicemen, several years ago reported "startling" regional differences in lengths of stay in civilian hospitals. The average length of stay for Medicare cases of all kinds ranged from 4.8 days on the West Coast to 6.9 days in New England. For appendectomies, the average ran from 5.1 days on the West Coast to 7.5 days in New England. Hospital stays for children were, on the average, 4 days on the West Coast and 5.7 days in New England. Brigadier General Floyd L. Wergeland, executive director of the Medicare program, estimated that its annual hospitalization costs would have been about $7 million higher if the New England pattern had prevailed throughout the country.

The finances of voluntary health insurance plans can be jeopardized by a difference of even a decimal point in the frequency of hospital admissions and average length of stay. In the small state of Rhode Island, an increase of about one-fourth of a day in the average duration of hospital stay recently boosted Blue Cross payments by more than $450,000 a year. The Philadelphia Blue Cross has estimated that it would save $3 million a year if the average stay of its hospitalized subscribers could be cut by half a day.

Aside from needless admissions and overstays, insurance claims are not infrequently overburdened by the ordering of excessive laboratory tests and by delays in discontinuing the administration of costly drugs when they are no longer needed. "When it comes to laboratory and X-ray work paid for by insurance," one hospital superintendent said, "some practicing physicians and many interns and residents shoot the works in the hope that one or two of the tests will make the diagnosis. Doctors who keep on ordering endless and pointless tests do so mainly to camouflage their own inadequacies. Unsure of themselves, they want to create the impression of being painstaking in their work. They also use batteries of random tests as a check on their own judgment. There would undoubtedly be an outcry from patients if they had to pay for it out of their own pockets. The same thing holds true of expensive medications. Not only do some physicians fail to stop them promptly when the need has passed, but they are rarely conscious of the wide differential in the costs of some brands with essentially the same properties."

All in all, the conclusion is inescapable that the insurance emphasis on hospitalization and the exclusion of coverage for ambulatory care have built-in incentives for chiseling and make for much higher costs than are medically necessary. Many hospital beds are occupied by patients sent in for diagnostic work-ups, which could be done just at well and less expensively outside. Much hospitalization, especially for chronic illness, is owing to poor home conditions and the lack of adequate provision for home-nursing and housekeeper services.

A basic fact to bear in mind is that not even the worst hypochondriac can be admitted to or remain in a hospital unless a doctor certifies that he needs treatment there. The physician alone determines whether hospital care should be provided at all and how long it should last. But the doctor is not a party to the hospitalization insurance contract. This imposes upon the medical profession a need for a high degree of self-discipline, which will have a crucial bearing on the future form of the financing of health care. Unfortunately, many doctors have a blind spot when it comes to hospital costs and tend to blame everyone but themselves for their continued upward course. They generally drag their feet on the tightening of controls on hospital utilization, regarding it as a delicate area that impinges directly on the profession's hallowed prerogatives.

Nor are hospital managements always completely blameless in this respect. Since the occupancy rate can make all the difference between red and black ink in the hospital's books, superintendents sometimes press physicians to keep beds filled. There is widespread suspicion in informed quarters that hospitals really welcome the mounting demand for their services, not only because it keeps down deficits but also because it provides justification for their urge for expansion.

At a time when so many health needs still remain unmet, it is inexcusable wastage to use needlessly many hospital beds which are primarily designed for the acutely ill and cost $25,000 each to build and about $39 a day to maintain. Why pay for expensive hospital care when the same services can be provided at home or in the office and when early diagnosis and sound medical management can obviate the necessity for hospitalization altogether? Why not build the mechanisms that will halt, or at least slow down, the steady inflation of the costs of medical care and keep them within the reach of the average person?

III

The remedies for the drain of excessive hospital use are pretty clear. But how to implement these remedies, given the present disposition of forces in the medical marketplace, is far from clear.

Several large group-practice prepayment plans have convincingly demonstrated that the need for inpatient hospital care can be materially reduced and overall costs kept at a reasonable level by providing coverage for services in the clinic, the doctor's office, or the patient's home and by paying physicians a salary rather than for each separate procedure. Principally responsible for higher costs under the more conventional form of health insurance are the lack of extensive coverage for out-of-hospital services, the tendency toward indemnity rather than service benefits, and the fee-for-service method of medical practice, which militates against preventive care and places a premium on keeping the patient sick rather than well.

The methods of paying and of prepaying for medical care have a significant bearing on the kind, quantity, and quality of services that people get. When doctors are paid on a piecework basis, the natural tendency is to put off consulting them until disorders become serious. The same thing happens when insurance is weighted in favor of acute illness and puts impediments in the way of preventive care. The question of whether, when, where, by whom, and even how medical services are performed is thus influenced by the present prepayment system.

On the whole, the increased use of health services made possible by insurance is a positive and welcome development. But there is a fundamental difference between greater utilization that meets essential health needs and is designed to prevent disease and higher utilization springing from misuse of the prepayment mechanism. Judging by this criterion, the prevailing system of medical practice and most insurance plans have serious inadequacies and must be substantially reorganized in the interests of better health care at the lowest possible cost.

The major challenges facing voluntary health insurance are the extension of coverage to the fifty million Americans still without it, a basic reorientation of the whole prepayment approach, and a broad expansion of benefits.

All these tasks involve enormously complicated problems that go to the very roots of the organization of medical care and practice. They raise such extremely controversial issues as the feasibility of comprehensive insurance benefits, the merits of paying doctors on a capitation basis or by salary versus the traditional fee-for-service system, and the advantages of group practice over solo practice. How can adequate health insurance be financed for those who cannot afford even the present form of prepayment? What will broader benefits cost, and how can they be paid for by those who already have some coverage? How can the quality of insured medical services be improved? Unless equitable answers can be found to these crucial questions, the extension of tax-supported medical care by piecemeal stages is unavoidable.

There are three main types of health insurance providing for cash indemnity, service, or comprehensive benefits. Aside from the method of coverage, the scope of protection offered varies widely. Only about five million persons now have fairly comprehensive insurance for most health services, including physicians' home and office calls. About 77 per cent of the population has coverage for at least part of the costs of hospital care. A close second is insurance against the costs of surgery. In third place is insurance for other physicians' services, primarily in the hospital.

Cash indemnity insurance undertakes to pay the subscriber specified amounts toward the costs of certain services, which meets only part of his hospital and doctors' bills. The size and range of the indemnities vary according to the premiums paid, but home and office care is rarely covered. This type of insurance is mostly sold by the commercial carriers, but the nonprofit Blue Cross and Blue Shield plans sometimes likewise provide only partial indemnities. The insurance companies also offer so-called major medical policies for high-cost illnesses. These generally reimburse about four-fifths of the costs, after the subscriber himself has paid the first $100, $200, or some other fixed "deductible" sum.

Under the service type of coverage, the subscribers are guaranteed certain services for which the insurance plans pay directly to hospitals and physicians. But this guarantee is beset by considerable qualifications. Under Blue Shield plans, which are controlled by medical societies, surgeons accept fixed fees from the insurance organization in full payment for their services only if the subscriber's income is below certain limits. Otherwise, the surgeon is entitled to make an extra charge. The income limits vary, but a sizable proportion of subscribers are subject to extra billing. Most Blue Cross plans provide full coverage, with some limitations, for hospital services. But some of them pay only a set daily rate, depending on the premium, toward the hospital bill.

The comprehensive plans cover much of the gamut of medical services, in and out of the hospital, and have their own staffs of doctors, usually practicing in groups that include the various specialties.

The medical profession prefers the cash indemnity approach

because it allows physicians to charge as much as they please and does not go very far in interposing intermediaries between them and their patients or in limiting their freedom of practice through a variety of regulations. Indemnity coverage does not offer doctors the same degree of assurance that they will collect payment for their bills as service benefits do, since the cash reimbursement is usually paid to the patient and not directly to the physician. But so strong is the profession's aversion to anything smacking of regimentation that its members would rather retain the right to charge as much as they want to and then take a chance on collecting some of their fees than relinquish any part of their vaunted independence. They are, moreover, concerned that the fixed service fees for subscribers within certain income limits may eventually become the going rates for everybody.

From the subscriber's point of view, indemnity insurance is the least satisfactory form of prepayment. Its uncertain protection is liable to leave him with substantial bills at the time of illness, particularly since some doctors raise their fees when they discover that their patients are insured. The financial incentives inherent in the indemnity system sometimes conflict with purely medical considerations and tend to inflate costs by encouraging unnecessary or questionable procedures. This is equally true of other forms of prepayment based on the fee-for-service method of remunerating physicians and is the principal reason why insurance is largely confined to services in the hospital, where at least some measure of control exists. As there is no mechanism for curbing the number of services that doctors may choose to render, the costs might otherwise prove prohibitive.

Service insurance gets away from the method of mere reimbursement for some of the costs of illness and comes closer to the concept of full responsibility for the maintenance of health. It assures the patient of some of the care he needs, regardless of what the doctor's charges are. When operated through group practice, it is able to place the emphasis where it belongs—on early diagnosis and treatment, on completeness of care, and on its quality. Comprehensive service benefits remove the financial deterrents to prompt use of medical care and tend to keep down costs by encouraging the maximum use of diagnostic and therapeutic procedures on an ambulatory basis.

But for the medical profession comprehensive health insurance is the road to the dreaded bugaboo of "socialized medicine." It lays the groundwork for so-called third-party intervention between doctor and patient, one of the strongest terms of opprobrium in the lexicon of organized medicine, and raises the specter of forced salaried employment and of ultimate bureaucratic controls on income and perhaps even on the exercise of professional judgment.

Protection against the economic hazards of illness is not the only problem. Nor does exposure of the patient to the physician ensure in itself that full value will be received. To reap the full benefits of up-to-date medicine, the patient also must have some assurance that the services for which insurance payments are claimed will be rendered by competent physicians under conditions of practice conducive to effective professional teamwork. No such assurance is available under most of the existing prepayment programs. Blue Shield and the commercial plans take no responsibility for the caliber of the doctors providing services to their subscribers. The same fees are set for the partially trained, inexperienced surgeon as for the most distinguished specialist. Most insurance plans not only pay as cheerfully for bad medical care as they do for good but also encourage poor care by making needless surgery and other procedures more lucrative through the guarantee of fees. The same rates are paid by Blue Cross to the unaccredited hospital as to the best teaching hospital.

The need for adequate quality controls goes beyond considerations of health alone, all-important though they are. The ultimate financial feasibility of health insurance also depends on them. The quality of medical services is intimately related to its quantity, which can quickly bankrupt a prepayment program if it is allowed to swell unchecked. If voluntary insurance is to meet its growing responsibilities, mechanisms will somehow have to be devised for insuring professional oversight of the standards of medical care.

On the whole, the private insurance companies have had a baleful effect on the course of prepayment health plans. The insurance industry, which was stimulated by the giant strides of Blue Cross and Blue Shield in the 1940's to expand its coverage in the health field and now surpasses them, is naturally interested in the most profitable prepayment plan rather than in the one that is most desirable medically. The sole purpose of commercial insurance is financial protection against certain costs of sickness—particularly hospitalization and major surgery, which are easier and administratively cheaper to insure than others. Using traditional insurance principles, which are completely inappropriate in health coverage, the commercial carriers have been able to forge ahead and to overtake the nonprofit plans with such devices as "deductibles" and differential premium pricing, whereby they have been able to pick off the better risks by offering them more favorable rates.

The danger of coinsurance, or "deductibles"—a method wherein the first $25 or $50 or some other fixed part of initial expenses is held back from coverage as a deterrent to unnecessary utilization—is that they are likely to deter preventive diagnosis and treatment. Throwing part of the burden on the patient merely constitutes a barrier to needed medical care. There is no demonstrated evidence that small medical claims are necessarily medically unimportant. Insurance exclusions reduce the level of the premium only in the sense that part of the charges is shifted back to the sick person. And by discouraging necessary medical attention, the overall cost is ultimately boosted.

Coinsurance also tends to inflate costs in other ways. If the schedule of a "major medical" policy sets payment as 80 per cent of the cost of the covered procedures, there may be a tendency, in time, for the doctor to fix his fees in terms of the patient's ability to pay out of his own pocket over and above the insurance reimbursement. Some physicians are similarly playing havoc with Blue Shield by raising their fees because the patient has insurance coverage. The net effect of such a maneuver is that the patient derives little benefit, if any at all, from his premium payments.

One of the biggest problems of the Blue Cross and Blue Shield plans is the competition of the experience-rating system used by the commercial carriers to establish their premium rates. In fact, the very survival of the nonprofit programs may depend on their ability to resolve the dilemma posed for them by this method of directly relating the level of a given group's premium to its record of utilization of health services. The commercial insurance companies prefer to sell medical coverage to groups of workers in industry, where the risks involved can be estimated with a fair degree of precision and benefits and premiums can be tailored accordingly. The Blues, on the other hand, have traditionally charged the same premium rates and offered the same schedule of benefits to all subscribers under a so-called community-rating method. Because of the burden of insuring older people, who are more adverse health risks, they have had to charge relatively higher premiums. This has increasingly put them at a competitive disadvantage and has more and more enabled the commercial carriers to siphon off the younger and better-risk age groups.

Caught in the squeeze between steadily rising hospital and surgical costs and consumer resistance to repeated boosts in premium rates and left with an increased proportion of older subscribers, many Blue Cross and Blue Shield plans have been forced in recent years to turn to experience rating and are thus also discriminating against the aged and other poor risks. This development violates the whole intent of uniform community-wide coverage to which the Blues have always been dedicated. The fundamental purpose of social insurance in the health field is to spread the financial hazards of illness on the widest possible basis by having the good risks help pay for the poor ones. But under experience rating, those who need care most are charged the most, even though they are often least able to afford it. By pricing prepayment protection beyond their reach, this approach has implications of the utmost gravity for the whole future of the voluntary health insurance movement. The nonprofit plans cannot hope to extend their coverage to those who are still entirely without it or to carry out the urgently needed expansion of benefits by adopting the practices of commercial insurance. If this trend continues, some form of governmental action to help insure the poorer risks will become the only feasible alternative.

Blue Cross, which to a large degree started as a move to bail out the hospitals and still is substantially controlled by them, is deeply in trouble throughout the country; its costs keep on rising, and this is forcing a succession of premium rate increases. It appears to have reached an enrollment plateau and is racked by serious inner conflicts. At the root of its quandary is its schizophrenic posture: it is a public service and yet must also be a business in order to survive in a competitive setting. Aside from the outcry against its premium boosts, the most baffling predicament of Blue Cross is that it is under constant pressure for more comprehensive coverage but is unwilling or unable to exercise the significant controls on hospital utilization and costs without which broader benefits would be wholly impracticable.

By the very character of their sponsorship, both Blue Cross and Blue Shield have been largely inhibited from taking advantage of the most promising potentialities of modern health care—those of preventive and rehabilitative medicine. Instead of a more subtle organization of health services on a continuing rather than an eposodic basis, instead of a more precise fitting of services and facilities to each patient's condition, their approach has been to channel all the sick into the costly general hospital. Consistently disregarded has been the whole spectrum of opportunities for more economical preventive practices, for facilities designed to meet the simpler needs of the ambulatory ill and convalescent, and for nursing-home and home care for the chronically ill.

Blue Cross could play a vital role as an active intermediary between the buyers and providers of hospital services instead of being a mere buffer and a collection agency for the hospitals. It could perform invaluable services in using its leverage to seek to improve hospital efficiency. It could seek to counteract the distorted ratio of inpatient hospital use by forceful promotion of outpatient coverage. It could make important contributions to more effective and economical care of long-term patients. But it has sadly failed to measure up to the responsibilities implicit in its pervasive influence in the whole field of the financing of hospital care and has been signally lacking in vigor in trying to control costs and the quality of services. From the consumer's point of view, its influence in recent years has been static and negative.

Blue Shield coverage is, in the main, confined to physicians' services in hospitals and principally to surgery. Its defects and problems are pretty much the same as those of Blue Cross and are further complicated by the fact that it is the creature of the medical profession and is firmly tied to the solo, fee-for-service practice of medicine. This makes any significant controls on the quantity and quality of services extremely difficult, if not impossible.

In varying degrees, the some seventy Blue Shield plans provide only cash indemnity payments toward physicians' bills for a considerable proportion of their subscribers. Moreover, there is rarely any vigorous policing to secure adherence by doctors to fixed fees under the income-ceiling provisions. Extra charges even for those falling within the income limits are reported to be not uncommon. The Blue Shield benefit structure does little to encourage seeing a doctor early, before the complaints become serious enough to require hospital care. There are gross inequities in its overemphasis on surgery to the neglect of general practice, internal medicine, and other specialties.

The Blue Shield fee schedule, which largely determines the level of its premium rates, is wholly under the control of the people who collect the fees. But although the insurance plan guarantees the doctors full payment of their fees even in the case of low-income patients who formerly paid little or nothing, they are in no mood for sacrifices. They have indignantly resisted suggestions for scaling down the fixed fees below normal charges. All too often they regard Blue Shield mainly as a mechanism for improving their collections rather than as a means of more effectively serving their patients.

The economic fate of the medical profession is irrevocably tied to health insurance. Prepayment plans are providing an increasingly large proportion of the average physician's income. Many doctors, especially surgeons, now draw well over half their income from insurance payments. "Health insurance is not going to be turned back," Jerome Pollack, former health plan negotiator for the United Automobile Workers of America and now professor of administrative medicine at Columbia University, has said. "The only alternative to its further expansion and improvement will be some other social method of financing and distributing costs. The burden will never again fall solely on the afflicted."

It is clearly in the medical profession's interest to do its utmost to help make voluntary prepayment work. But, to date, the record in this respect has been far from encouraging. The profession has yet to learn that it has no right to dominate health insurance programs and that its technical knowledge does not automatically confer upon it the franchise to decide all the social, economic, and administrative questions involved in their operation. It has yet to acknowledge that there have been radical changes in the relationship between consumers and producers in medicine and that what was good enough in the days when the provision of medical care was a simple transaction between an individual doctor and an individual patient is often no longer applicable. It has yet to accept the fact that the primary responsibility of physicians should be confined to professional services and that it is the prerogative of the large organized groups of laymen who contract for these services to negotiate on how they are going to spend their money. If the doctors fail to see the logic of the idea that Blue Shield, in which millions of people have a vital stake, cannot be exclusively controlled by those for whom it is a major source of income, it will ultimately be forced upon them.

The average physician still views health insurance, even when it is run by his own medical society, with considerable distaste. He never tires of grumbling about the red tape and the paper work. He dislikes the regulations and restraints inherent in any organized effort. If he is not a surgeon, he is apt to feel that the Blue Shield fee schedule is out of balance and is unfair to him. He is apprehensive that insurance may become an instrument for changing the traditional forms of medical practice and that the state or Federal government may before long step in and dictate the level of fees. He is concerned that the growing agitation for extension of coverage to outpatient services will further enhance the power of the hospital and cut into his own practice.

Fleecing patients for no other reason than that they happen to have insurance coverage has become a problem of expanding proportions. Some medical society spokesmen have condemned the practice, but there is no evidence of any concerted disciplinary action to combat it. Medical society grievance committees are notoriously lacking in teeth when it comes to proceeding against miscreant colleagues. The insurance companies have always been extremely reluctant to tangle with the medical profession, upon whose good will their profitable health underwriting business so vitally depends. But scandalous overcharges to some insured patients have increasingly put the forbearance of the commercial carriers under a severe strain.

Top figures in the insurance industry have in recent years openly expressed their exasperation and have made public some telling examples of unconscionable fee gouging. An official of the Equitable Life Assurance Society has reported, for instance, that one patient with an annual income of $6,000 a year was charged

$1,200 for dilation, curettage, and cauterization of the cervix, a relatively simple procedure. A patient who earned $3,000 a year received a bill for $1,500 for a gastrectomy. In a third case, a doctor actually attempted to collect the equivalent of a man's entire annual income for a single operation. The patient, whose income was $2,500 a year, was billed for $2,500 for a lobectomy, the removal of part of a diseased lobe of the lung.

Arthur G. Weaver, vice-president of the John Hancock Mutual Life Insurance Company, has bluntly warned that the use of a double standard of fees by many physicians, the higher of which applies to insured patients, and their tendency to over-prescribe and to order excessive X-ray and laboratory tests "may eventually defeat voluntary health insurance and the private practice of medicine." The insurance carriers have every reason to oppose governmental intrusion in the health field. But it is not inconceivable that they may some day be forced to join labor in advocating regulation of the medical monopoly if no other way is found to curb the threat of uncontrolled costs.

A ringing appeal to the medical profession to rise to "the challenge of assuming its proper role in demonstrating that voluntary programs for medical care can narrow the remaining gaps of care and costs" was issued in 1958 by the AMA's Commission on Medical Care Plans. The commission, which had spent four years studying the operations and problems of more than one hundred health insurance programs of various kinds throughout the nation, called on the profession to work for constant improvements in the character of prepayment coverage, to put less emphasis on expensive hospitalization, and to "discharge more vigorously its self-imposed responsibility for assuring the competency of physicians' services and their provision at a cost which people can afford." It stressed that "the existence of insurance should alleviate the economic burden for the individual and should not result in an increase in the customary or reasonable charge." It urged "a judicious, tolerant and progressive attitude" toward new developments in the medical care field and recognition of "the need for continued experimentation" with various mechanisms for the provision of health services of high quality at the lowest possible cost.

The AMA House of Delegates later approved the commission's report with an obvious lack of enthusiasm, and it has since been gathering dust, as have many other AMA study reports, which have mainly served as a substitute for action.

IV

The best that can be said about the AMA's bitter opposition to the proposed program for medical care for the aged financed through the social security system is that it is fully consistent with its record of unflagging resistance to anything that may conceivably impinge upon the highly profitable privileges of its members.

Over the years, the AMA has opposed voluntary health insurance, the social security law, compulsory smallpox vaccination, public immunization against diphtheria, Federal aid to reduce infant and maternal deaths, public venereal disease clinics, school health services, government-financed medical care for dependents of men in the Armed Forces, workmen's compensation for industrial injuries, and the Red Cross blood banks. When the Social Security Act was under consideration in the early 1930's, the AMA denounced it as a "compulsory socialistic tax." It damned group-practice plans as "medical soviets." It assailed extension of social security benefits to the permanently and totally disabled at the age of fifty as "a serious threat to American medicine." It called elimination of the means test in the state-Federal crippled children's program a "socialistic regulation." It decried Federal grants to the states for maternal and child welfare programs as "unsound policy, wasteful and extravagant, unproductive of results and tending to promote communism." When the idea for voluntary health insurance was first advanced some thirty years ago, the AMA dismissed it as "contrary to sound public policy." It once termed Blue Cross a "half-baked scheme" that would result in "mechanization of medical practice." It has fought Federal aid to medical schools as "a back-door route to socialized medicine."

The AMA is absolutely right, however, in one of its strident arguments against the Administration's program for the aged: that it is a key test of power and that its enactment into law would provide the proponents of wider governmental controls on medical care with a formidable foot in the door.

It is true that the Administration's plan would mainly provide only for the payment of hospital and nursing-home bills for those sixty-five years of age and over and does not cover physicians' services. Nevertheless, its implications are sweeping. In the first place, use of Federal tax funds on a large scale for hospital and nursing-home care must eventually mean some Federal intervention in setting the standards of these facilities. This in itself would significantly affect the medical profession. Secondly, expansion of the program beyond its original limited scope, to cover all medical services for older people, would probably be only a matter of years. And once the principle of the financing of medical care for a large segment of the population through compulsory payroll deductions has been established by statute, the way would be opened for its ultimate extension to other categories, if not to everybody. Whatever scheme finally emerges for the handling of the health needs of the aged will inevitably have a profound effect on the pattern of medical services for the rest of us.

Some sort of legislation for health services for the elderly financed through the social security system will undoubtedly be voted into law sooner or later. But some of its most ardent supporters have been either too naïve or too disingenuous, which is probably more likely, to acknowledge its connotations. Nor have they been quite candid in their failure to admit that the proposal does not go far enough and must be regarded as merely a first step in the direction of adequate health care for the aged. Political realism in trying to sell a bill to a recalcitrant Congress is one thing, but it is idle to try to pretend that the coverage of surgery and other services by physicians and possibly also of out-of-hospital drug costs can be excluded for long from any meaningful medical care program.

Under the pending legislation, the aged would be assured of up to sixty days of hospitalization a year, an equal number of days of nursing-home care and up to 240 calls by visiting nurses or physical therapists at home. The offer of more economical out-of-hospital care is commendable but it would require a tremendous expansion of nursing-home facilities and nursing personnel, for which provision is yet to be made.

The medical problems of the rapidly growing army of older Americans, whose number has more than quadrupled in the last fifty years, pose what is perhaps the most serious immediate challenge to voluntary health insurance. But while the potential political leverage for action is greatest in this area, the highly charged debate churned up by the issue of the aged is only a preview of the brewing storm in the whole field of health insurance. The considerations figuring in the health care of the aged cannot be separated from those of the rest of the population. There are special difficulties in providing the medical services older people need. But these difficulties are primarily quantitative. Basically, the underlying problems of the most efficient organization and financing of medical care are the same for young and old alike.

The nub of the situation as far as the aged are concerned is that they have a much heavier burden of illness and a sharply reduced ability to pay for the required care. Half of the about eighteen million persons in the United States who are sixty-five or older have incomes of less than $1,000 a year. But their per capita medical expenditures—paid for by themselves, by their children, or with the aid of some governmental agency—are double those of the population in general.

The aged have a high incidence of chronic diseases and are disabled for longer periods than younger people. They are hospitalized much more often than any other group and stay in the hospital longer. Their use of physicians' services also is considerably higher than that of the population as a whole. Their average expenditures for drugs are more than double those of people under sixty-five. The rate of mental illness among the aged is four times as great as for the rest of the population, and one of every three beds in mental hospitals is occupied by a person over sixty-five. Although their medical needs are so much greater, older people find it difficult to obtain health insurance. Only about 55 per cent of them have some form of prepayment coverage, much of it totally inadequate, and their premiums are more expensive. Untouched even for those with insurance is the cost of drugs, long stays in nursing homes, nursing care for the homebound, physical therapy, eyeglasses, dentures, hearing aids, and other burdensome expenses.

It is by now acknowledged by everybody, including the AMA, that the cost of the care of the aged cannot be met by the existing insurance mechanisms without some sort of governmental subsidy. Older people cannot afford to buy prepayment protection for the required scope of care, and no voluntary organization can overload its premium rates to the degree necessary to provide adequate benefits for the aged at reasonable costs. Only the social security approach provides the means of spreading the costs of health services in old age over the working years. It enables men and women to invest a share of their earnings at a time when their income is highest in the greater health needs of later life and gives them assurance that these will be provided for with dignity—as a matter of right and not as charity. It broadens the base of support by relating compulsory contributions to the level of income and by taxing employers as well as employees during an individual's productive years. Assumption of responsibility for the aged by the social security system would relieve voluntary health insurance of the poorest risks and make its problems considerably less onerous. Premium costs for the lower age groups could be reduced or wider benefits provided at the same rates.

The rising tide of older people has in recent years focused greater attention on their plight than on any other health care issue and is certain to keep it in the forefront of national controversy. The Bureau of the Census estimates that the number of Americans past the landmark of their sixty-fifth birthday will reach a total of about 20,000,000 by 1970. By 1980, it is anticipated, 24,500,000 persons—about 10 per cent of the country's projected population—will be sixty-five or older. The aged already constitute a hefty 15 per cent of the electorate. This is almost double the proportion of the voting-age population represented by the nation's farmers, who have for many years wielded great political influence. In twelve states, men and women who are sixty-five and over now make up between 18 to 20 per cent of those eligible to vote. The medical care needs of the aged are, moreover, of urgent concern to many millions of other people. They concern their children because of the heavy financial strain resulting from the prolonged illness of an aged parent. In a broad sense, they concern just about everybody.

In view of the merits of the controversy and the overpowering political realities of the situation, the AMA's position is of interest more than anything else as a case study in shortsightedness and ineptitude. As is its wont, the AMA started out by refusing to acknowledge the facts of life. It denied that the aged represent any special health insurance problem or that the job could not be fully handled on a voluntary basis. Its first reaction to the initial legislation for social security health coverage for the aged, introduced by former Congressman Aime J. Forand of Rhode Island, was to strengthen its Washington lobby and to raise its public relations budgets by one-third. Letters were sent to prominent doctors throughout the country to inquire about the personal background and habits of every member of Congress and how he could best be influenced. A favorite AMA tactic in the battle against the Forand measure and its later watered-down version, the King-Anderson Bill, has been to try to link the legislation with socialism, compulsion, and poor quality of care. The aid of personal physicians to members of Congress was enlisted. Doctors were even urged to write to their Congressmen on their prescription pads, presumably as a means of lending emphasis to their strong feelings about the issue.

As the controversy waxed and pressure mounted for relief for the aged, the AMA finally conceded that some governmental subsidy might be needed. In 1960, to head off the social security approach, it threw its support behind enactment of the Kerr-Mills Act for joint Federal-state financing health services for older people who are not on relief but who can prove their medical indigence by passing a means test. The AMA's sudden ardor for the Kerr-Mills Act is ironic on several counts. Not only has organized medicine always opposed federally supported state welfare programs, but the provisions of the Kerr-Mills Act are actually broader and costlier—as well as less equitable and more complicated administratively—than the Administration's proposal would be. Under the former, no statutory limits are set on the medical services to be provided for those who can pass the means test, and each state can establish its own rules and benefits. Relatively few of the aged are now being aided under the Kerr-Mills Act, but costs have skyrocketed to such an extent that some of the participating states already have run into trouble raising the funds needed to match Federal grants.

Meanwhile, the AMA continues to plump for the handling of the bulk of the aged problem under voluntary auspices. In cooperation with the National Association of Blue Shield Plans, it has proposed a cut-rate insurance contract for older people within certain income limits that would provide a wide range of surgical and medical benefits at a premium cost of only about $3 a month. The trouble with this plan, however, is that it is contingent upon agreement by participating physicians to accept fees that are lower than their normal charges, a proposition for which most doctors have thus far displayed a conspicuous lack of enthusiasm. The sliding scale of fees does not easily slide downward. Physicians are inclined to put most of the blame for the high costs of medical care on hospital and drug prices. Furthermore, they see no reason why, as one of them has put it, "we should provide the government with a ready-made schedule of ridiculously low fees for the time when the blow falls and some sort of social security scheme is enacted into law."

At two recent annual meetings, the AMA barely stopped short of a threat to call its members out on strike if Congress should adopt the social security plan. At its 1961 session, the House of Delegates unanimously passed a resolution warning that the medical profession "will not be a party to implementing any system which is un-American and detrimental to the public welfare." After an inquiry by newspapermen about whether this implied strike action, the delegates were hastily recalled into session, and the wording was amended to read that the doctors would not be "a willing party" to any scheme of which they disapproved. Strike action was openly advocated in 1962 by a number of local medical societies, but cooler heads prevailed at the AMA meeting, and a resolution was passed leaving it up to the conscience of individual physicians whether or not they should cooperate in any social security health program for the aged.

Reports at the 1962 annual meeting were that up to that time, the AMA had spent nearly $4 million in its campaign to defeat the social security legislation. In October, 1964, the AMA poured more than $1 million into a Community Health Week campaign primarily designed to build a backfire against the Administration's proposed medical care program for the aged. Like King Canute, organized medicine will spare no effort to roll back the tide.

V

The hospitals and the medical profession have been shocked to discover in the last few years that locking the front door against the Federal government's intrusion into their business is not enough. The state governments have been moving in through the back door. Increasingly, state insurance commissioners have taken the position that their legal authority over Blue Cross and Blue Shield premium rates gives them much more power than the mere checking of actuarial tables and extends to the things that pyramid costs. Rejecting the argument that rate increases can be justified solely on the gound that benefit payments exceed premium income, they have begun to ask searching questions about abuses and inefficiencies.

Blue Cross plans have been ordered to take vigorous action to control needless hospital admissions and excessively prolonged stays and prodded to extent their outpatient coverage. They also have been instructed to try to prevail upon their member hospitals to cut costs by improving their operating efficiency and eliminating wasteful duplication of facilities and services. Some of the states have proclaimed their authority over the level of the fees paid by Blue Shield plans to physicians. The insurance commissioners have in some cases backed up their orders by cutting down requested premium increases and by serving notice that no further boosts would be approved until certain economy measures are put into effect.

"I am convinced," Pennsylvania's former insurance commissioner, Francis R. Smith, a pioneer in the direction of more forceful state regulation of health prepayment, said in one of his rate decisions, "that we should not resign ourselves to ever-increasing hospital costs and to unnecessary utilization of hospital services, and consequently to steadily climbing Blue Cross rates. I do not believe that everything has been done to bring about the most efficient and economical management of our hospitals. In fact, I believe very little has been done. I do not believe that everything has been done by hospital administrators, by the Blue Cross organizations and by the medical profession to eliminate unnecessary admissions and to reduce protracted hospital stays. In fact, I believe, with few exceptions, very little has been done."

Among the steps directed by Smith—and since emulated by his counterparts in a number of other states—are wider use of opportunities for outpatient diagnosis and treatment; tighter controls on hospital admissions and length of stay; better scheduling of hospital procedures to avoid needless delays; more effective utilization of nurses and technicians; centralized planning for the sharing of specialized equipment among hospitals and for the coordination of the expansion of hospital facilities; increased standardization of hospital supplies, along with joint purchasing; the establishment of medical review teams to ferret out insurance abuses; and greater consumer representation on the boards of directors of the prepayment organizations.

Smith has taken a dim view of the arrangement under which the hospitals are, in effect, negotiating with themselves regarding the terms of their contracts with Blue Cross by virtue of their domination of the Blue Cross boards of directors. He therefore has proposed that subscriber representatives make up a majority of the Blue Cross boards. "The organized medical profession," he also has said, "has no more moral or legal right to control Blue Shield policies than does the bar association to control judicial and other offices occupied by members of the legal profession. Blue Shield is not the doctors' plan; it is the public's plan."

The former commissioner was the first to move in on one of the doctors' most sacred preserves—their right to decide for themselves what they should charge their patients. In turning down a request for increases in the fee schedules of the Pennsylvania Blue Shield, which has more than 4,200,000 subscribers and about 13,000 participating physicians, Smith expressed the opinion that many of the subscribers already are being charged too much. The doctors, he said, can afford to give their services "at lower than normal charges" to insured patients because they are "sure of receiving their fees."

In the absence of Federal laws governing health insurance, more active exercise of state regulatory authority was to be fully expected in an effort to check the continued upsurge of hospital and prepayment costs. This paves the way for public intervention in the manner in which hospitals are built, operated, and used and in many of the practices of the medical profession that contribute to spiraling costs. Logic dictates that since the premium rates of Blue Cross and Blue Shield are subject to state control, the state must gradually extend its concern to hospital operating procedures and other elements that enter into health insurance costs. It is nevertheless ironic that while voluntary health prepayment was in large part the answer of the medical profession and the hospitals to the agitation for compulsory national insurance, it has become a vehicle for state regulation of medical services.

In many places, hearings on Blue Cross and Blue Shield rates have provided a platform for critics of their operations and of hospital efficiency. Demands have mounted that the insurance plans be less subservient to the interests of the hospitals and the medical profession and take a more active part in watching over the costs of the services they cover instead of simply acting as fiscal agents. A number of state study commissions have put their finger on the doctors as the ones who can do most to keep down costs by hospitalizing fewer patients, sending them home sooner, and eliminating excessive laboratory procedures and medication. In New York, the report of a two-year study made for the state health and insurance departments by the Columbia University School of Public Health and Administrative Medicine called not only for extension of Blue Cross coverage to nursing-home care and ambulatory diagnostic services but also for a state master plan to coordinate all health facilities. It recommended establishment of a central state agency, with a subsidiary chain of regional planning councils, to review and license all new hospital construction in order to ensure a more orderly and efficient pattern of expansion.

As medical services get ever more complex and costly, two fundamental propositions are becoming amply clear. One of these factors is the inadequacy of the prevailing forms of health insurance, which are hedged by many limitations, ignore the preventive aspects of medical care, and exclude, wholly or in part, the costs of physicians' home and office visits, hospital outpatient services, chronic disease, mental illness, dental care, eye care, and out-of-hospital drugs. While there is room for legitimate argument about whether prepayment ought to cover all aspects of health care, there is no question that it can and should be far more inclusive than it now is. The other essential point is that the mechanisms of health insurance are far too crucial to be left wholly in the hands of the purveyors of medical services. There is little ground for expecting those now largely in control of these mechanisms to initiate daring extensions in the scope and major improvements in the design of prepayment protection without outside prompting. In fact, it is primarily their vested interests that stand in the way of such extensions and improvements.

The implementation of the goals of wider insurance coverage will require greater exercise of public initiative and regulation. It also will call for the highest restraint and sagacity on the part of the medical profession, as well as its cooperation in urgently needed controls on costs, utilization, and quality of services. Only through the wholehearted collaboration of all concerned can the objectives of broader and more effective insurance protection at a practical price be achieved principally on a voluntary basis.

Whether these goals can be met within the confines of the present free-enterprise medical economy is yet to be demonstrated. The extension of health prepayment into new segments of care that are inherently more difficult to insure will require far more effective controls than now exist if we are to avert the danger of runaway costs. Massive use of tax funds on behalf of the aged and other disadvantaged groups appears inescapable. But the full extent of the government's role in the health care picture will depend on the degree to which it proves feasible to do the job under voluntary auspices.

Whatever the final outcome is, insurance already has wrought sweeping changes in the economics of medical care and brought new intermediaries into the relationship between doctors and patients. Insurance programs have great potentialities for becoming the defenders of patients' interests. To castigate the introduction of "third parties" is as fatuous as it is futile.

During the health care debate in and out of Congress in the 1940's, the issues seemed quite simple—compulsory government-operated insurance versus voluntary insurance. By now, as we continue to grope for answers, we have come to understand that the problems are infinitely more complicated and cannot be that easily compartmentalized. The voluntary approach has many desirable qualities and guards against the freezing of patterns in an area of constant flux. But it also calls for a sense of responsibility, for a readiness to subordinate narrow guild interests to the public welfare, for a willingness to experiment, for imagination and boldness—all attributes that organized medicine has thus far failed to display in anything like the measure required for the challenge.

CHAPTER SEVEN

Group Practice:
Blueprint for the Future

I

THE ORGANIZATION of medical care and practice in the United States has yet to adjust itself fully to the pivotal fact that what medicine has to offer can no longer be mastered by any one individual and requires the utilization of a wide range of diverse skills and expensive equipment. Out of this central development stem both the enormous benefits and the baffling problems of modern medicine.

The implications of the tremendous expansion of medical knowledge and of the resulting growth of specialization are crystal clear. Medicine, like industry, has reached the stage of development when individual effort in itself is no longer adequate. Just as in industrial production, technological advances in medicine demand a grouping of skills and tools into functional units.

What this means is that up-to-date medicine cannot be practiced effectively without institutional arrangements, that professional teamwork is far superior to isolated individual practice, and that specialization without collaboration is inefficient, costly, often makes for poor medical care. The mounting scarcity of medical personnel, moreover, makes imperative its optimal use through more efficient organization.

While the family doctor was once able to take care of everything, including surgery, the patient is now frequently shunted from one specialist to another, each of whom must be paid separately. What the patient wants, and by and large has yet to get, is some scheme whereby most of the nonhospital health services he may need would be concentrated in one place and he could budget in advance to insure himself adequately against their costs. Many doctors are at the same time looking for a more stimulating and professionally rewarding environment for the practice of their craft. A physician with the best of training may still do an inadequate job if he is obliged to work in isolation, with no opportunity for continued education, and is preoccupied with curing illness rather than preventing it.

The foremost corollary of the revolution in medicine is that doctors must work in groups to complement one another in coping with the vast body of medical science, to realize their potential abilities to the utmost, and to render their services with the greatest possible economy of their patients' time and money. They can do so best through group practice, a systematic association of physicians who share offices, equipment, patients, and income in order to render more complete and balanced services. The truism that group practice is a logical outgrowth of the complexity of medicine has long been recognized in the hospital. But it is still ignored by the great majority of doctors, who continue to adhere to a pattern of solo practice that is becoming an anachronism under the impact of profound scientific and socioeconomic changes.

Group practice, particularly when combined with comprehensive insurance, is regarded by many of the best minds in the health field as the most efficacious answer to the problem of the orderly integration of the various specialties for the benefit of the patient. It is, the late Dr. Alan Gregg once said, "the most nearly satisfactory practical corrective of the defects of specialism," with its splintering of medicine and its tendency to place more emphasis upon the disease than upon the totality of the individual. "I don't see," Dr. Walter Bauer, professor of clinical medicine at Harvard Medical School and chief of medical services at Massachusetts General Hospital in Boston, has said, "how we can provide good medicine without group practice."

Group practice has many variants, ranging all the way from small rural partnerships to such famed private institutions as the Mayo Clinic in Rochester, Minnesota, and the Lahey Clinic in Boston and to large prepayment organizations under consumer or labor union sponsorship with hundreds of thousands of subscribers. Notable in the latter category are the Health Insurance Plan of Greater New York (HIP), the Kaiser Foundation Health Plan on the West Coast and in Hawaii, and the chain of hospitals and clinics operated until recently by the Welfare and Retirement Fund of the United Mine Workers of America, all of which have established enviable records of high quality of care, emphasis on preventive services, and economy.

Immensely significant is the fact that the best in American medicine is now being provided on an organizational basis different from that of the prevailing pattern of solo practice. It is salaried physicians rather than solo practitioners who render the high-quality services in some of our great teaching hospitals and in the outstanding group-practice organizations.

Group practice is cooperative rather than competitive medicine. At its best, it brings doctors together within an economic framework that divorces financial considerations from medical decisions. It reduces wasteful overhead, minimizes costly hospitalization by laying stress on ambulatory diagnosis and treatment, and permits supervision and review of professional performance. By pooling the training, experience, and equipment of a number of physicians under one roof, it eliminates needless duplication, saves time and effort for doctors as well as patients, and results in better care. It makes teamwork among physicians a readily available and not just an occasional procedure, providing that unity and continuity that medical care now so often lacks.

Group-practice insurance encourages the crucially important preventive approach, making doctors responsible not just for treating illness as it occurs but for total health care. It gives physicians an economic stake in health rather than in sickness and removes the economic barriers to timely diagnosis and treatment that are inherent in fee-for-service practice. With its cluster of medical talent and apparatus, group practice is far better equipped than solo practice to detect and treat illness in its early stages, before it becomes serious or chronic. The doctor is in a much stronger position to practice the best medicine he knows how and to advise the patient about the procedures that should be used without worrying about whether he can afford them.

The solo practitioner is subject to some quality controls when he treats his patients in a hospital. But he is completely on his own in his office practice, where no mechanism exists for policing the level of care he provides. Group discipline is the most effective instrument of quality. When doctors work in groups, a systematic organization of standards replaces individual good intentions. They are constantly exposed to stimulating interplay with their peers and are on the alert against slipshod performance.

Prepaid group practice also removes the shopkeeper element from medicine. It eliminates a major source of friction over fees and helps to resolve the doctor's basic conflict between the image he has of himself as an idealistic benefactor and his mundane interests as a breadwinner. The physician does not have to worry about his bill. He is not tempted to do what is beyond his competence when he can refer his patients freely to specialist colleagues in the group. He is relieved of the financial incentives for unnecessary procedures and of the economic pressure to take on more work than he can handle, since his income does not depend on the number of patients sitting in his waiting room. While doctors in private groups usually share the joint income, those in prepayment groups are paid by salary or by capitation, a specified amount for each subscriber for whom the physician is responsible, regardless of the number of services rendered.

From the patient's point of view, there are numerous advantages to group practice. He is spared an exhausting round of specialists' offices and the separate charges for each visit and procedure. He does not have to wait for days, as is now frequently the case, until his own doctor gets the reports of X-ray examinations or other tests. All diagnostic facilities are available in the group-practice medical center, and ready access to consultation minimizes the possibility of medical error. Physicians can go into a huddle on the spot to talk over the problem from the point of view of their respective fields of specialization, so that a decision can promptly be reached on the next treatment step.

The savings of group practice through the sharing of office expenses are obvious and substantial. The equipping of individual doctors' offices with such costly apparatus as X-ray, fluoroscopic, electrocardiographic, and physiotherapy machines, which at best are used only a few hours daily, represents an enormous waste. When, as is often the case, a physician spends much of his time in the hospital, his office equipment and help are virtually idle. The required heavy investment is much more quickly amortized through large-scale use in the group-practice clinic. Much lower also are the shared costs of rent, telephone service, electricity, office furnishings, laboratory technicians, nurses, receptionists, and other personnel and services required for the running of a medical practice.

Association in groups also helps to solve the extremely difficult problem of how doctors can manage to find time to keep up with the torrent of scientific advances. A planned schedule offers members an escape from the average practitioner's working week of at least sixty hours and allows them time off for study and relaxation. They can take turns handling night and weekend calls, attend refresher courses, take extended vacations, and generally lead a more normal life.

Group-practice insurance plans appear to have the most promising potential not only for control of quality and costs but also for providing the comprehensive services that are the crying need of today's medical care. One of the greatest frustrations of modern medicine is that the more specialized doctors become, the less competent they are to take responsibility for the overall care of the patient. Group practice counteracts this by vesting primary responsibility for each patient in a single physician and backing him up with ready access to the knowledge and skills of whatever specialties may be called for. As the isolated, hurried, and fractionized practitioner is gradually replaced by doctors working as team members, more and more physicians will again be able to see the patient as a whole and perhaps even to gain an integrated view of the whole body of medical science.

Much of this, however, lies in the future. With all its merits, group-practice prepayment is still in the throes of experimentation and has many problems to contend with and a long way to go toward the ideal of protecting its subscribers against the bulk of their medical expenses. It cannot solve completely all the economic and professional dilemmas of American medicine, but it is the essential underpinning for the bridge that will firmly link medical practice to advanced medical science.

The problems of the group-practice prepayment plans have been compounded and their development often distorted by the hostility of organized medicine and its insistence on the sanctity of the obsolete concepts of a bygone age. The big group-practice organizations also are continuing to struggle with the basic quandary of how the advantages of a close personal relationship between doctor and patient can be carried over to the large medical center, with its tendency toward bureaucratic red tape and assembly-line treatment.

But despite the shortcomings it has yet to overcome, prepaid group practice is far more conducive to good quality of medical care than the general run of solo practice and comes much closer to a solution of the problems of doctors and patients alike than any other available mechanism. Admittedly, it entails some limitations on the medical profession's traditional prerogatives and also calls for some new adaptations on the part of patients. But the need for these readjustments is more than outweighed by many compensations.

Organized medicine has long tended to regard group-practice prepayment as an opening wedge for full governmental control of medical services. Actually, it can become the most solid bulwark of the voluntary system and the strongest safeguard against compulsory health insurance.

II

Striking evidence that better and more economical medical care can be provided through group practice is furnished by the records of several of the nation's largest comprehensive prepayment plans employing their own staffs of physicians. So impressive are the economies of this type of organization that the Twentieth Century Fund, a leading private research foundation, estimates that their application to all medical practice would cut the costs of health care in the United States by nearly half, saving some $15 billion a year.

The fundamental ingredients of the economies of comprehensive health insurance based on group practice are substantially lower use of hospital services—the most expensive form of medical care—and tight controls on the utilization and costs of non-hospital services, made possible by effective professional restraints, wider use of auxiliary personnel, and other efficiencies of large-scale organization.

The extent to which hospitalization can be reduced by putting greater emphasis on ambulatory services and by eliminating the inducements to abuses inherent in fee-for-service practice is dramatically demonstrated by the experience of HIP in New

York, the Kaiser Foundation Health Plan, the United Mine Workers of America, and the Group Health Association of Washington, D.C. HIP insures its more than six hundred thousand subscribers for a wide range of medical services on a group-practice basis. But since it does not provide any hospital care, its members are required to supplement their coverage by taking out Blue Cross insurance for hospitalization. The most significant feature of this arrangement, as several studies over a period of years have shown, is that HIP subscribers go to the hospital between one-fifth and one-fourth less often than other Blue Cross members in New York. HIP subscribers also have considerably lower surgical rates than do subscribers to Blue Shield, which pays physicians on a fee-for-service basis. The HIP hospital admission rate for tonsillectomies and adenoidectomies, for instance, is about half that of Blue Shield.

Even more instructive is a comparison of the hospitalization and surgical rates of HIP with those of Group Health Insurance (GHI), another New York insurance plan that provides comparable comprehensive benefits but uses solo practitioners, also on a fee-for-service basis. The average annual GHI hospital admission rate of 110 per 1,000 subscribers is almost double HIP's figure of 63 per 1,000. HIP enrollees not only use less hospitalization but go home sooner when they do have hospital care. GHI's average number of days of hospitalization in a year per 1,000 persons is more than double that of HIP, 870 as compared with 410. And while GHI members average 76 operations in the hospital per 1,000 subscribers a year, the HIP in-hospital surgical rate is only 43 for every 1,000.

It has been estimated that the bill for hospital care in New York City alone could be reduced by about $100 million a year, to say nothing of the saving of capital investment in future hospital construction, if the city's entire population could receive its health care from such well-organized and supervised medical groups as those of HIP.

The reasons why HIP subscribers have so much less hospitalization than comparable groups with more conventional insurance coverage are fairly clear. HIP patients receive preventive services that sometimes curb incipient disease before it becomes serious. They are not hospitalized just for diagnostic purposes, as complete diagnostic facilities are available in the prepayment plan's own medical centers. Patients who do require hospitalization have the diagnostic work-up done in these centers before they are admitted to hospitals, so that their length of stay is shorter. Another reason why they can be discharged earlier is that they are insured for unlimited nursing services in the home. And since HIP doctors are paid a fixed annual fee for each subscriber and receive no additional payments for surgery or any other services, there is no possible incentive for unnecessary operations.

Equally revealing are the findings of a study of a year's hospitalization and surgical experience by the 1,250,000 persons covered under the medical care contracts of the United Steel Workers of America. Like the experience of HIP subscribers, that of members of the steelworkers' union and their families lends itself readily to a comparison of how group-practice prepayment stacks up against other forms of insurance. While most of the union members have Blue Cross–Blue Shield coverage, many of those who live in California are insured by the Kaiser Foundation group-practice plan, which operates its own hospitals. The steelworker study showed that those under the care of solo practitioners on a fee-for-service basis through Blue Cross–Blue Shield insurance had 135 hospital admissions and a total of 1,032 days of hospital care for every 1,000 enrollees in the course of a year. But union members and their families served by the salaried physicians of the Kaiser Foundation program had only 90 hospital admissions a year and averaged only 570 days of hospitalization for each 1,000 subscribers.

Fully as significant is the finding of the steelworker study that the frequency of surgery under group-practice prepayment was less than half of what it was for those under fee-for-service coverage. Whereas 69 out of every 1,000 union members insured by Blue Shield were hospitalized for operations in a year's time, only 33 of each 1,000 covered by the Kaiser Foundation plan had in-hospital surgery.

The costs of the union's medical care program could be reduced by many millions of dollars a year if the savings of nearly 45 per cent in hospital care and of more than 50 per cent in the incidence of surgery could be applied to all its members and their families.

The United Mine Workers was able to cut the medical and hospital expenses of its welfare and retirement fund by several million dollars a year after its own group-practice teams of salaried physicians took over the care of some of the fund's beneficiaries and rigid controls were imposed on the services rendered to others by solo practitioners. As a result of these measures, hospital admissions declined by 32.5 per cent, the total of days of hospitalization was reduced by 36.8 per cent, and the amount of surgery went down by 16.5 per cent.

The Group Health Association of Washington, D.C., which also employs salaried physicians and runs its own hospitalization insurance program, has an average annual total of 76 admissions and 499 days of hospital care per 1,000 members as compared with an average of 122 admissions and 762 days of hospitalization a year for every 1,000 subscribers of the local Blue Cross.

The only conclusion to be drawn from these and other professional studies is that hospitalization and surgery are excessive under the predominant pattern of medical care and that very substantial economies can be achieved by more effective utilization of outpatient services rendered by organized groups of physicians in well-equipped clinics.

The large group-practice plans have been able to pass along their operational savings to their subscribers in the form of reasonable premium rates. HIP's monthly premium charges, for instance, run from $9.74 for an individual to $26.02 for a family of three or more for a broad range of services, including Blue Cross hospitalization insurance, physicians' home and office visits, full medical, surgical, maternal, and pediatric care, anesthesia, prescribed drugs, psychiatric diagnosis, physical therapy, X rays, laboratory tests, and visiting-nurse services at home. There is no limit on doctors' office visits and on home calls in the daytime, but an extra $2 charge may be made for such calls between 10 P.M. and 7 A.M. There is an extensive health education program, and subscribers are encouraged to get periodic physical checkups, for which there is no charge, to enable early detection and treatment of disease. The Kaiser Foundation plan provides complete coverage, including hospitalization, for monthly premiums of $7.95 for an individual and $19.45 for a family.

With proper organization, economies can not only be obtained without sacrificing the quality of medical services, but they often actually enhance it. Stress on prevention, provisions for timely diagnosis and treatment, ready accessibility to a wide spectrum of professional skills, and other things that in the long run make for economy also contribute to a better level of medical care and health. So do the rigid standards observed in selecting the members of the salaried teams of physicians, their constant professional supervision, and the stimulating give-and-take of teamwork. The consensus of competent authorities who have examined in detail the HIP, Kaiser, Mine Workers', and Group Health Association medical programs is that the care they provide is of uniformly high quality.

A notable example of HIP's high standards is its record in regard to premature deliveries and perinatal mortality (death between the twentieth week of gestation and the seventh day after birth). A study of the pregnancies and deliveries of HIP enrollees, made with the cooperation of the New York City Health Department, showed a perinatal mortality rate of 21.3 per 1,000 live births as compared with 30.1 per 1,000 among women of similar social and economic background who were under the care of solo practitioners. Here again, the reasons for HIP's better performance, with its substantial saving of human life, are no secret. HIP subscribers come under prenatal care early in pregnancy and are under the supervision of board-certified obstetricians and gynecologists, with no extra charges as a deterrent to seeking their services.

The Kaiser plan, biggest and fastest growing of the group-practice prepayment organizations, has more than nine hundred thousand subscribers, employs eight hundred doctors, and owns and operates twelve hospitals and thirty-eight outpatient medical centers. Although it was started by the Kaiser family's industrial interests during World War II as an employee program, enrollment is now open to anyone who wishes to join. HIP, the largest community-sponsored comprehensive health insurance plan, was developed with municipal backing in 1947 and operates through thirty-two medical groups, each with its own group center, employing more than one thousand physicians.

Both of them lusty innovators, the Kaiser and HIP plans have been invaluable laboratories for the testing of new techniques in the organization of medical services. But while their coverage is the most comprehensive available, it still falls far short of complete protection against medical costs. Excluded are psychiatric treatment, dental care, eyeglasses, and some other important items. It has been estimated that HIP meets about 35 per cent of the total medical care expenditures of its members. While this is considerably better than the ratio of about 25 per cent for health insurance as a whole, it is clearly not nearly enough. The gap between HIP benefits and its subscribers' medical expenses is largely owing, however, to the goods and services still left uninsured. HIP's record on the insured portions of medical costs is unexcelled. It meets 92 per cent of its subscribers' surgical costs, 87 per cent of obstetrical costs, 80 per cent of the costs of physicians' services, and—together with Blue Cross—88 per cent of hospital costs.

Even though their range of coverage is in need of further expansion, the two pilot programs on both coasts already have successfully demonstrated that extensive services for the detection and treatment of disease and for the care of prolonged chronic illness can be furnished economically through group-practice prepayment. There is no question that they are providing their subscribers with greater health security and better medical care at lower cost than these families could obtain through any other method.

In blazing new trails in the field of medical economics, the Kaiser Foundation Health Plan, HIP, and other prepaid group-practice organizations have had to contend not only with the numerous problems inherent in the complexities of health care but also with the bitter antagonism of organized medicine, which has been consistently opposed to innovation and experimentation. The harassing tactics have included state legislation prohibiting or restraining the organization of health insurance groups without the approval of local medical societies, various kinds of pressure against physicians active in group-practice prepayment plans, and boycotts of such groups. Doctors engaged in prepaid group practice have in the past even been expelled from medical societies, with consequent loss of hospital privileges and the right to accreditation by specialty boards.

Some of the group prepayment programs are still fighting

with the organized profession for the right to exist. Sanctions against doctors straying from the path of fee-for-service ortho-doxy have continued, though in somewhat modified form, despite a resounding denunciation by the nation's highest judicial tri-bunal in a famous test case more than twenty years ago. In 1943, the United States Supreme Court unanimously upheld a lower-court conviction of the AMA and the District of Columbia Med-ical Society for violating the antitrust laws by conspiring to pre-vent the successful operation of Washington's Group Health Association, one of the pioneering prepaid group-practice plans. In its decision, the High Court had some cogent things to say about the rights and responsibilities of the medical profession that are still fully pertinent today. "Professions exist," it declared, "because people believe they will be better served by licensing especially prepared experts to minister to their needs. The li-censed monopolies which professions enjoy constitute in them-selves severe restraints upon competition. But they are restraints which depend upon capacity and training, not privilege. Neither do they justify concerted criminal action to prevent the people from developing new methods of serving their needs. The people give the privilege of professional monopoly and the people may take it away."

Another classic battle was fought for years by the AMA and a number of state medical societies against the United Mine Workers, which had been operating a massive medical care pro-gram for its members and their dependents in twenty-six states at a cost of more than $60 million a year. When the union's welfare and retirement fund launched its program in 1949, it found a scandalously low level of medical care and professional vigilance in many of the mining areas. There were not enough doctors, and some of them were obviously incompetent, some of the hospitals were poorly equipped and filthy, fees were often exorbitant, and there was a high rate of unnecessary surgery and hospitalization. Dr. Warren F. Draper, the fund's capable and vigorous medical director, decided to do something about it and was soon em-broiled in a furious controversy with the medical profession.

Dr. Draper, who had previously had a distinguished career in the U.S. Public Health Service and as a major general in the Army Medical Corps during World War II, served notice that the fund would insist on the right to be selective in the choice of physicians for its beneficiaries and on some controls on fees. He ruled that, except in emergencies, no patient could be hospitalized without consultation with a qualified specialist. He also initiated plans for the construction of a chain of ten miners' hospitals, each to be operated with a salaried staff and to have its own outpatient clinic.

The medical societies in the areas involved and the AMA reacted violently to this challenge to the profession's prerogative to render unsupervised services and to charge what it pleases. They protested that the sacred right of every patient to "free choice" of his own doctor had to be protected at all costs and that no outsider was entitled to pass judgment on the level of professional performance. A statement of policy adopted by the AMA House of Delegates asserted that "every physician duly licensed by the state to practice medicine and surgery should be assumed at the outset to be competent in the field in which he claims to be, unless considered otherwise by his peers."

Dr. Draper and his associates have stuck to their guns. They have taken the position that since medical societies rarely, if ever, do anything to enforce standards of competence and ethics, the shibboleth of "free choice" amounts in practice to little more than a license for incompetence and fee gouging. They have maintained that the automatic assumption of the equal competence of every doctor "is conducive neither to the best medical care nor to economy in operation" and have continued to affirm their right "to limit our payments to physicians whose services are necessary and essential in providing the medical benefits authorized by the fund." The quality of medical care in the coalfield areas has been immeasurably improved through the union's hospitals and outpatient clincs and its supervision of services rendered by independent practitioners. An outstanding rehabilitation job has been done in restoring to usefulness thousands of men crippled over the years in mining accidents.

Organized medicine condemns so-called closed-panel practice, which is limited to groups of salaried physicians, on the ground that it restricts the patient's choice of doctor; that this impairs the physician-patient relationship and makes for assembly-line care; and that under such an arrangement, the doctor's primary loyalty is likely to be to his employer rather than to his patient. But while the opposition is expressed in terms of principle and medical ethics, it really stems from economics. What the profession is worried about is that potential customers are being taken out of circulation and offered, in effect, cut-rate prices.

"The solo practitioner who charges a fee for each separate service looks upon the prepaid group-practice medical centers with the same emotions that the corner grocery merchant must have felt when he saw the first supermarket," one observer has said. "Limitation of the choice of doctors to the physicians serving the group means that the subscribers stop buying medical care in the open market. Comprehensive-care plans, moreover, offer a variety of services for one premium payment and thus threaten to undersell the fee-for-service doctor and to lure away his patients. If prepaid group medicine should really become popular, the economic future of the solo practitioners would be gravely endangered."

The doctors also are incensed at the idea that representatives of the consumers should have the impudence to tell them how to run their business, to negotiate about the organization of medical services and the fees charged, and to insist on professional and administrative devices aimed at improving the quality of medical care. The basic clash is between the demands of today's complex medical economy and the rugged individualism of a profession long accustomed to operating completely on its own, without any effective controls on its fees or the level of its performance. What the majority of physicians have yet to perceive and acknowledge is that no enterprise of the magnitude of our medical care services can be run in the public interest without some managerial cost and quality controls.

The medical profession's socioeconomic lag is nowhere more evident than in the hullabaloo about the sacredness of "free choice" of doctor, an emotion-drenched concept equated with personal freedom, free enterprise, and democracy and held to be indispensable to rapport between physician and patient and to high standards of medical care. Actually, the term "free choice" is a specious defense of the *status quo* and a smoke screen for the preservation of the existing laissez-faire anarchy in the medical market. The slogan's principal value to organized medicine is that it provides a superficially plausible and idealistic rationale for the cherished and profitable fee-for-service system.

It is ludicrous to assume that the average patient is competent to judge professional qualifications and is therefore invariably able to make a wise choice and to protect himself against poorly trained and incompetent physicians. Doctors are by no means equally able or equally conscientious. The only means of choosing a doctor that the layman now has is by reputation, which puts a premium on glibness and popularity and is a far from dependable criterion, or by shopping around, which wastes time and money and can turn out to be a dangerous gamble. There is now an appalling amount of medical shopping, with duplication of cost and work and sometimes tragic results, as patients go on their own initiative to specialist after specialist without any one taking responsibility. Another serious impediment to proper choice is the curious rule of medical ethics that forbids doctors to speak ill of their colleagues even when opprobrium is richly deserved. It is, furthermore, preposterous to take it for granted that haphazard selection of a physician without expert guidance and paying him on a piecework basis are somehow in themselves a guarantee of establishing a close personal relationship with him.

The complexity of medicine and the growth of specialization have greatly increased the need for enlightened choice, which can best be attained under an organizational setup where the staff is selected by professionals, where there is a constant check on the quality of the work, and where medical services are not primarily governed by the condition of the patient's pocketbook. If there are some limitations on choice under group-practice prepayment, these must be regarded as an essential adaptation to altered conditions rather than as a denial of freedom.

Many physicians take an extremely patronizing attitude toward the average layman's medical ignorance. And yet they enthusiastically laud the virtues of "free choice." Isn't the patient's right to the best possible quality of medical care of a higher order than his right to indiscriminate choice of his own physician? Moreover, freedom of choice means very little without an assurance that the patient will be able to pay a well-qualified doctor after he has managed to select him. Clearly, it is the doctors, not the patients, who are mostly concerned about possible restraints on freedom of choice of physicians. Patients are worried about the high costs of medical care and its growing impersonality. They want doctors who are competent, who will see them promptly, and who will give them unhurried attention. But there is no reason to think that their ideas of "free choice" is necessarily identical with that of organized medicine. What the medical profession is really insisting upon is obligatory "free choice," by which the patient is not allowed to choose an organized group of physicians but must pick an independent solo practitioner. This violates the right of the doctor, as well as the patient, to be free to choose his own brand of medicine.

Despite the obeisance regularly paid by organized medicine to the crucial role of the doctor-patient relationship as the cornerstone of good medical care, the sober reality is that such a meaningful relationship exists for all too few people and that millions of Americans are groping their way through a jumbled array of health services without the guidance of a personal physician.

In a lengthy report made in 1958 after a four-year study of a large number of group-practice prepayment programs, the AMA's Commission on Medical Care Plans conceded that the absence of the traditional form of "free choice" does not automatically impair the level of health services. "The introduction of a third party in the physician-patient relationship changes it," the report said, "but not necessarily in such a way as to result in an inferior quality of medical care." The commission was high in its praise of many of the closed-panel organizations and reported that "medical care for many persons in the low-income groups now covered by these plans has improved."

In approving the commission's recommendations for greater tolerance toward experimentation in the provision of medical care, the AMA House of Delegates seemed to depart from its inflexible stand on the "free choice" issue by adopting a policy statement which said that an individual should have the freedom to choose his physician or the medical plan he prefers. But at its next meeting, the House of Delegates had some second thoughts about the unwonted liberalism of its new position. "Lest there be any misinterpretation," it declared in an amendment to the policy statement, "we state unequivocally that the American Medical

Association firmly subscribes to freedom of choice of physicians and free competition among physicians as being prerequisites to optimal medical care. The benefits of any system which provides medical care must be judged on the degree to which it allows of, or abridges, such freedom of choice and such competition."

Officially, the AMA and its component societies now maintain an attitude of cool neutrality toward group-practice insurance. But while some of the more flagrant punitive measures of the past against nonconforming physicians have been abandoned, the development of group-practice prepayment plans continues to be hindered. It is extremely doubtful that the medical profession will ever voluntarily surrender its self-arrogated prerogative of being the sole arbiter of the cost and quality of health care.

III

Only about six million persons, or less than 5 per cent of those who have health insurance, are now covered by group-practice prepayment plans. But the independent programs already have had a pervasive influence on the mainstream of health insurance out of all proportion to their share of subscribers and expenditures. They not only have survived in the face of vigorous opposition from organized medicine but have demonstrated what the efficiencies of large-scale organization can do for improved and more economical health care. Although still far from perfect and beset by many problems that are yet to be solved, they point the way to the pattern of the future.

For obvious reasons, the growth of consumer-sponsored group-practice insurance plans has been much slower than that of private group practice that has no prepayment angle. Both forms of organization involve doctoring by teams of physicians who pool their skills and resources to improve patient care, cut costs, and make their own professional lives more leisurely and satisfying. The establishment of private groups may still cause raised eyebrows among some of the diehards in the profession. But such groups avoid most of the obstacles posed by the outright challenging of orthodoxy. They are, essentially, no more than partnerships of varying size. They offer a number of conveniences to patients and sometimes pass along the savings of reduced overhead through lower fees. While this is decidedly a step in the right direction, private group practice represents no basic departure from the prevailing format of charging for each separate service and of concentrating on the episodic care of illness as it occurs rather than on the total care of health.

Group-practice insurance, on the other hand, involves a fundamental reorganization of the manner in which medical services are rendered and paid for. Participating physicians are compensated by salary or a fixed sum for each subscriber and assume full responsibility for a substantial share of the medical needs of the enrollees. In this form of practice, there is emphasis on the preventive approach and on continuity of care, and there is regular professional supervision of the quality of services. In the best of the larger prepaid group-practice organizations there is more than a mere sharing of office space and secretarial help. There are the constant stimulus of teamwork and the genuine sharing of experiences, facilities, and patients by the specialists and general practitioners who are members of the group. The patients benefit from ready access to a wide range of specialties and the varied apparatus of up-to-date medicine.

The salaried doctor operating within the framework of a large group is in a much better position to practice good medicine than his colleague who is an independent entrepreneur. He can offer the best advice of which he is capable without having to worry that the patient may be unable to afford the required treatment, that he may be frightened away by the unvarnished truth, or that he may never come back if he is referred to another physician. As in all other lines of endeavor, salaried employment represents the most sensible way of compensating doctors. It makes it possible to take into account training, experience, competence, and responsibility as no other method can.

A cardinal element of good medical care—and one which is often missing in solo practice—is the kind of continuity that encompasses the patient's overall health needs, preventive as well as curative. This sort of integrated care can best be provided through a prepayment group, where the physician who has primary responsibility for the patient can easily obtain the aid of consultants and of auxiliary personnel. Such a framework eliminates financial barriers to early detection of disease and minimizes recourse to hospitalization. It makes the conservation of health an integral part of the medical program, since the income of the doctors in the group does not depend upon the amount or seriousness of illness among their patients.

About sixteen thousand doctors, or about 9 per cent of all active practicing physicians, are now in some form of group practice. In the past fifteen years, the number of groups of three or more physicians organized to provide services in more than one medical specialty has tripled to about 1,200.

In a class by themselves are the large group-practice clinics, wholly staffed by salaried physicians and usually limited to cases referred by other practitioners. Some of these have developd over the years in conjunction with famous hospitals and have become great centers of clinical teaching and research. Many smaller group-practice clinics also have been established in hospitals, which provide a natural setting for such service with their array of professional talent, auxiliary personnel, and equipment.

Small private groups are beginning to dot the hinterlands as doctors in rural areas increasingly discover that they can best afford the equipment essential to modern medical care by pooling their resources. Such groups usually include an internist, a surgeon, an obstetrician, and a pediatrician and are thus able to provide through their clinics a sort of composite general practice to fill the void left by the gradual disappearance of the broad-gauged general practitioner. Group practice is the best available device for enticing capable young physicians into small communities.

The environment of the medical schools and teaching hospitals, with their emphasis on the integration of various professional and ancillary skills, is guiding students not only into the specialties but also into group practice. In a random sampling of one thousand medical students a few years ago, 61 per cent expressed a preference for group or partnership arrangements when they go into practice. Another study showed that only 26 per cent of recent medical graduates were interested in individual practice. More than one-third of the 1950 medical school graduates now in private practice are in partnerships or broader groups.

With or without formal affiliation in group-practice units, more and more doctors are finding that they can no longer rely exclusively on their own omniscience and must depend on one another for special knowledge and skills. While solo practice is still likely to remain predominant for quite a while, it is slowly but steadily being undermined. The growth of specialization is inevitably leading to the evolution of various types of combination practice. Simple partnerships are becoming increasingly common, and some of them are gradually developing into a systematic association of various specialties. The pressures of the technological advances in medicine and of the corresponding socioeconomic forces in our society toward the coordinated organization of diagnostic and treatment facilities are proving too potent even for the powerful dogmas of the past. The profound changes under way in the organizational context of American medical practice under the impact of health insurance and group practice are indicated by the fact that more than 45 per cent of the nation's physicians already receive all or part of their remuneration on other than a fee-for-service basis.

But when it comes to the next logical step—the massive conjunction of group-practice arrangements with comprehensive health insurance protection—the barriers of professional resistance and other obstacles remain formidable. It is not easy to get highly individualistic physicians to defy the long-standing tradition of solo practice and to risk ostracism by their colleagues and other serious professional handicaps, particularly at a time when the predominant system is so lucrative for most doctors. Nor do members of a profession in which the virtuoso role is held up as an ideal always adjust readily to the subordination of idiosyncrasies and the harmony required by team effort.

About half of the states have restrictive laws—passed at the instigation of medical societies—that give the organized medical profession a veto power over the establishment of group-practice prepayment programs under consumer sponsorship. These statutes virtually limit medical service insurance to the Blue Shield plans, which are controlled by the profession, thus giving the doctors a monopoly in the medical prepayment field. There is no tenable reason why such laws hampering urgently needed new approaches to the economics of medical care should be allowed to stay on the books.

Another major difficulty is the problem of the initial financing of comprehensive health insurance organizations. It takes considerable capital for groups of doctors to buy or build and to equip the necessary medical centers. There is also the hindrance of slow public acceptance. Potential subscribers have to be educated to the proposition that it is cheaper, in the long run, to pay a higher premium for comprehensive insurance and to get a lot more for the money than they do through other forms of prepayment. It is noteworthy that of the two biggest group-practice programs, the Kaiser plan started on an industrial base, while HIP was launched with loans from several foundations and a ready-made patient following provided by the bulk of New York City's municipal employees, with the enthusiastic backing of the late Mayor Fiorello La Guardia. It is certainly in the public interest that group-practice plans should be eligible for the same kind of Federal aid in the construction of their facilities as hospitals are under the Hill-Burton Act.

The obstacles in the path of large-scale group-practice prepayment organization, despite the stanch support of organized labor, are illustrated by the troubles of Detroit's Community Health Association (CHA), the latest newcomer to this category. CHA was set up more than seven years ago by the United Automobile Workers of America, with Walter Reuther as its president. Disillusioned by the spiraling costs of its members' Blue Cross and Blue Shield coverage, the UAW took the lead in a move to establish a chain of prepaid group-practice units. It started the project with a $500,000 loan from its own treasury and grants from a number of other unions in Michigan and from several foundations. Two outstanding experts in medical administration were brought in from outside the state to direct the undertaking. But serious difficulties were soon encountered in trying to recruit doctors for the projected groups and to get the cooperation of any of the hospitals in the city. CHA began operating on a modest scale two years ago, but at the moment it appears to be a long way off from the dimensions originally envisaged by its sponsors.

But while the progress of group-practice prepayment has been arduous, the economics of medical care, the mounting demand for broader health insurance protection, and the growing labor involvement in the situation will continue to operate in favor of its further expansion. Discontent with the prevailing insurance plans, which are laden with restrictions and meet only a small part of overall costs, is certain to increase and to accelerate pressures for new departures. Scare slogans alone are not going to obstruct forever the drive for the fullest possible advance budgeting for medical needs and the evolution of mechanisms that satisfy the twin criteria of effectiveness and economy. It is impossible to forcast the precise form of group organization that will ultimately prove to be the most efficacious, but its advantages are indisputable.

IV

The experience of the large group-practice prepayment plans is providing valuable and reassuring lessons regarding the feasibility of broad insurance coverage for the bulk of medical needs. At the same time, however, it also underscores the still unresolved conflicts between the patient's deep-seated need for a close personal relationship with his doctor and the dictates of technological progress and large-scale organization, which work inexorably in the direction of impersonal treatment. While group practice offers some very promising possibilities for improving rapport between patients and physicians, it also appears to have some built-in drawbacks in this regard.

On the positive side is the refutation of fears that unlimited insurance coverage of physicians' services would unavoidably lead to overutilization. It has long been a common assumption in some medical circles that the removal of all deterrents on the use of doctors would lead to unbridled abuse and malingering. The contention has been that hypochondriacs and those determined to get their money's worth would haunt physicians' offices with mythical complaints and requests for needless tests and drugs and make unreasonable demands for house calls. This premise has been decisively disproved by the experience of the leading prepaid group-practice plans.

Subscribers to HIP in New York have an average of 5.5 doctors' visits per year, exclusive of those for surgery and obstetrics. While this is higher than the average for the country as a whole, it is well below the original estimates when the program was inaugurated. Interestingly enough, enrollees of Group Health Insurance—another New York comprehensive prepayment plan, which uses physicians on the conventional fee-for-service basis— have an average of 6 physicians' visits per year. A recent study showed that fully one-fourth of the HIP membership saw no doctor at all in the course of a year, even though the only financial barrier is a $2 charge for night home calls. While this may be construed as evidence of an unusually high level of good health, HIP is not wholly pleased with such a record of abstention. On the contrary, it tries to encourage its subscribers to come in for periodic physical examinations, with the idea that a timely checkup can often avert much doctoring later on. An annual average of about seven physician services is regarded by HIP officials as desirable from the long-range standpoint of health maintenance and economy through early treatment.

HIP's emphasis on nonhospital care is underlined by the fact that only 10 per cent of the professional services to its subscribers are given in hospitals. The great bulk of services, 78 per cent, is rendered in doctors' offices, and the remaining 12 per cent in homes.

Another significant fact is that more than half of HIP's services are provided by internists, general physicians, and pediatricians. Generalists are key members of the prepayment plan's medical teams. This points up to the value of group practice in restoring the denigrated family physician to his rightful role in meeting a wide range of basic health needs, once he is backed up by a team of specialist colleagues and is otherwise placed in a framework of integrated professional interests and skills. Only in such a setting can general practitioners regain their full usefulness and help to maintain the stability of the essential doctor-patient relationship instead of being relegated to the status of subordinates whose main function is to feed business to the specialists. Group practice rescues the family physician from his professional isolation, the greatest threat to his adequacy, and from the serious inequities in the present remuneration of physicians. It enhances his role as personal counselor by giving him primary responsibility for patient management.

In theory, at any rate, the integrated approach of prepaid group practice and the prominent role it assigns to the general physician should counteract some of the forces now tending to impair the affinity between doctor and patient and should lay the groundwork for a more satisfactory relationship. That this is apparently not always the case is probably owing more than anything else to the pains of transition from an individualistic to a group framework. It will take doctors and patients alike quite a while to reorient themselves fully to such a radically altered pattern.

There are no intrinsic reasons why group practice should be impersonal. In the leading group prepayment plans, every patient picks a personal physician. The patient may be seen by half a dozen doctors on a visit to the group medical center, but it is his own physician who rides herd on the case and whose job it is to coordinate diagnosis and treatment, to interpret medical findings to the patient, to develop continuity of care, and to take overall charge of the patient's health problems. Along with this personal relationship, the patient gradually develops an allegiance toward the whole medical team, which meets his dual and often concurrent needs for the generalist and for specialists. Contributing to the improved relationship are the availability of the whole range of diagnostic and treatment services and the elimination of financial obstacles to their use.

Nevertheless, it still remains to be seen whether these organizational devices will completely satisfy the patient's need for a personal doctor. All too often, the patient's craving for assurance that his doctor takes a personal interest in him is now cruelly rebuffed in solo practice. Prolonged waiting in the anteroom and curt and hasty handling are common occurrences these days in the offices of thousands of solo practitioners. But there is something about the institutional setting, even if it is a splendidly equipped medical center, that accentuates in the patient's mind the mechanistic attitude of "processing" the sick. The mere assembly of a large number of patients in one spot tends to bring back recollections of the dreary and demeaning atmosphere of some hospital dispensaries.

The healthy individual who joins a group health care program can assess its advantages with some detachment and usually does not object very strongly to the idea of being treated by a group of physicians in centralized facilities. But when that person becomes sick, his role changes appreciably. He becomes self-centered, and his yearning for personal attention grows. Any element in his medical care that seems mechanical is interpreted by him as indifference and rejection. In this context, the impersonal aspects of the large group center can become particularly threatening.

Ironically, prepayment for future services through a single premium may rob some patients of the assurance that payment of a separate fee for each service gives them that they are fully entitled to what they are getting and are not receiving charity. Rightly or wrongly, patients sometimes feel that payment in advance leads doctors to take them for granted, whereas in fee-for-service practice the physician's interest is likely to be bolstered by the fact that he has not yet been paid and that he may lose the patient if he does not satisfy him.

Like many doctors, but for wholly different reasons, patients are often resistant to drastic changes in the setting of medical care. Patients come to physicians with diverse expectations rooted in social class, educational background, and past experience. Those who have been able to afford medical services of high quality under the prevailing system are naturally apt to be reluctant to strike out into new territory. For people in the lower-income brackets who in the past have had to depend on hospital charity services, it is a step upward in the social scale to be able to receive care in a private physician's office. They are thus liable to resent the clinic connotations of the group medical center.

A further source of conflict and of patient disaffection in the prepaid medical group is the greater likelihood of a clash between professional judgment and the views of the patients as to what ought to be done for them. Private practitioners are not infrequently inclined to humor their patients or at least to feign indulgence of their outlandish notions of what ails them. But in the group operating under firm professional control, there is less accommodation to the subjective attitudes of the clientele, and thus there is less opportunity for the patients to get their own way. For one thing, economy in the use of the group doctors' time and of facilities is essential if comprehensive services are to be provided at reasonable cost. Secondly, standards of performance are more rigid when there are mechanisms for supervision of the quality of the work. But having already paid for his care, the patient is inclined to feel that he should get whatever he thinks he needs. He concludes that the doctor is not looking after him properly if he is denied sufficiently prompt service or if he does not get the prescription or X rays that he feels he ought to have but that actually are uncalled for.

A basic quandary of modern medicine is that high technical standards and the organized sharing of skills do not necessarily make the treatment setting more attractive for the patient. On the contrary, even though the care he gets may be better than that in the more permissive environment of traditional practice, he begins to feel neglected when he loses some of his leverage in his dealings with doctors. The underlying trouble is that while good medicine requires the wholehearted collaboration of the patient and the assuagement of his anxieties, it also tends to widen in some respects the gulf between him and the physician.

This basic problem confronts medicine generally but is accentuated within group practice. Still to be fully found under any form of practice is the answer to how the patient's deepest needs can be met and yet be reconciled with scientific requirements. Patients are frequently motivated to seek medical care for no other reason than because of emotional problems. But since such problems cannot possibly be detected through the tubular views provided by a battery of diagnostic procedures, the frustration of patients in trying to communicate with their doctors is widespread.

A relatively minor but nevertheless suggestive symptom of the friction between doctors and patients under prepaid group practice is the home-call problem. This is a disconcerting issue under all forms of medical practice but has a distinctive twist in group care. There is general agreement among physicians that they can serve most patients better in the office than at the patient's home. The more time the doctor spends on the road, the less time he has for treating sick people. It is estimated that a physician can care for three patients in his office in the time required to make one home visit. Many doctors complain of unreasonable patient demands for house calls, particularly at night. But what they may overlook is that, aside from strictly medical considerations, there are sometimes important psychological indications for home calls. Patients accused of abuse are often individuals racked by anxieties and urgently in need of compassionate understanding. A timely house call may forestall a later need for lengthy care. A home visit also gives the physician a better insight into the patient's background.

In fee-for-service practice, the patient is more likely to accept the doctor's judgment that a house call is unnecessary. He knows that the physician is giving up the opportunity to collect a fee and may actually be grateful for the free telephone advice. But in HIP, where the only charge for home calls is made between 10 P.M. and 7 A.M. and even this is often waived, the patient is more likely to feel that the only reason for the doctor's reluctance to come to the house is lack of interest.

Another element in the picture is that while resentments against private practitioners remain largely unexpressed and unpublicized, group practice provides both a concentrated target and a channel for the venting of patients' gripes. The patient who has a complaint against a particular doctor in private practice does not necessarily condemn the whole profession. But in group practice he is apt to institutionalize his discontent and to blame the entire program.

Like everybody else, doctors differ, of course, in the degree to which they are endowed with a genuine interest in people. But what complicates matters is that the removal of the direct financial bond with the patient—the fee for each service rendered—unfortunately seems to have an adverse effect on the attitude of some physicians, so that they become less sympathetic and more perfunctory. To what extent the bureaucratic tendency of large organizations figures in this is a moot question. On the other hand, many of the capable and progressive doctors who practice in groups have a sincere interest in the problems of their patients but have to contend with the image of impersonality associated in the public mind with organization.

Whatever the merits of this image are, everything that has happened in modern medicine makes inevitable the trend toward ever-greater institutionalization. While some of the problems of group practice are vexing, its flaws appear to be far more amenable to correction than are those of solo practice, with its grave barriers to economy and frequently also to quality. But the group center will have to come closer in form and content to meeting the consumer's need for understanding and cohesive care before it can gain wider public acceptance. A way will have to be found to combine its efficiencies with more of the amenities and intimacies of private practice at its best.

The benefit structure of group-practice prepayment is another area in need of improvement. While the coverage of the group plans is broader than that of conventional health insurance, it must be materially expanded before they can claim to be truly comprehensive. Most of the group programs still exclude psychiatric and dental care and drugs and appliances. Complete insurance protection for all medical expenses is probably an ideal beyond attainment for the foreseeable future. But many health authorities agree that more inclusive coverage is desirable and feasible. This will obviously require materially higher premium charges. The added premium costs must be weighed, however, in relation to current out-of-pocket expenditures for the items that are now left out. Elimination of unnecessary and wasteful practices and the application of careful administrative controls can achieve sufficient economy to make broader prepayment possible.

Experience with the provision of dental services and prescription drugs by a few prepaid groups is demonstrating the practicality of insurance for these important elements of comprehensive care. Competent opinion is that psychiatric care, at least for short-term conditions, also is insurable. Dental care, which accounts for about 10 per cent of the average family's health expenditures, is clearly an essential component of health protection. But it has long been considered uninsurable because of the heavy backlog of unmet need and the consequent fear of prohibitive costs. A number of pilot programs have shown, however, that through special organizational techniques and economies—including early tooth-conservation methods and the use of multiple dental chairs and of adequate technical assistance—groups can provide their members at a reasonable cost with services that they must otherwise purchase more expensively and less effectively on their own. An example is the St. Louis Labor Health Institute, which for a number of years has found it possible to provide fairly complete dental service at an annual cost of about $10 per subscriber. More than a million persons now have some sort of dental care insurance, and coverage in this field may be expected to continue to expand.

The same principle applies to prescription drugs, which take an even bigger bite of the health dollar than dental care does. The requirements for bringing drugs under the insurance umbrella are again supervision and economy. They call for specially organized pharmacies, the elimination of duplicate stocks of proprietary products, controls over amounts and refills of prescriptions, and self-discipline in the rational use of medicines. The experience of several prepaid group centers has demonstrated that drugs can be provided for ambulatory patients at a cost of about $4 a year per person. This compares with the current annual per capita cost of more than $20, much of it spent for medications of questionable value.

Full coverage of enormously expensive long-term psychiatric therapy is undoubtedly beyond the capability of the modestly priced health plan. But the essentials of diagnosis, consultation, limited group and individual therapy, and even short-term psychiatric hospitalization can be included through a rational organization of professional staff and proper utilization of clinical psychologists and social workers.

An important element in the outlook for further expansion of group practice is its enthusiastic support by the labor movement, an increasingly potent force in the health care field. So thoughtful a publication as the *New England Journal of Medicine* has predicted that "the eventual patterns of administering and financing medical care in this country will be established by the leaders of organized labor." Labor unions, which constitute the largest and most articulate body of consumers, are pressing with mounting success for greater returns for their premium dollars and broader health insurance benefits. A number of unions have developed their own health care programs. Others are using their large health and welfare funds to support already existing group-practice and other comprehensive prepayment plans. As the source of these funds, management, too, is developing a growing stake in the economical provision of medical services.

Typical of the industrial leaders who have not succumbed to the propaganda of organized medicine is Benson Ford, vice-president of the Ford Motor Company. "Inclusive health care," Ford has said, "should provide to every American citizen, at a cost that he can reasonably meet, all of the services necessary to keep him healthy and productive. Ultimately it must involve preventive, diagnostic care as well as curative. I for one am not in the least worried about the so-called threat of socialized medicine. Nor do I worry about the tremendous demand for more and better medical service at lower cost. Certainly I don't regard it as being out of step with American traditions. It is very much in step with them. There must be no hard-and-fast barriers to the expansion of commercial credit for all our medical needs. While progress toward the idea of an inclusive health system must be evolutionary, it must evolve visibly—at something more than a snail's pace."

Continued opposition by the medical profession to the form of insurance that can best meet health needs will leave the consumers no choice but the use of the weight of their political power to get it.

CHAPTER EIGHT

Is American Medical Care
the Best in the World?

I

THE PROUDEST boast in the armory of organized medicine is that the United States has "the best medical care in the world." This is the sort of bombastic generalization that deliberately ducks the question as to how prevalent and accessible the "best" care is. It has just enough truth in it to sound plausible, but it withers under close examination.

"Whenever I hear this sweeping claim," remarked a leading authority on medical administration, "it reminds me of the statement that 'my wife is the best little woman in the world.' It is vague and hard to prove, however real it may seem.

"If I should say that my wife is above average height, there might be some basis for examining the claim, since there are height tables for women that would settle the question. If one were to argue that the United States had the lowest death rate or more psychiatrists than any other nation, we could then have a measure that would allow us to settle the argument. The problem is to define what we mean by good medical care and to decide how to measure it. Various people might define good medical care in terms of efficiency, reasonable price, friendly concern, medical competence, beautiful hospitals, numbers of physicians, or general state of health. Some of these criteria are and others are not subject to fairly precise measurement. Very often the problem becomes one of comparing apples with oranges. But even granting the difficulty of meaningful comparisons between countries in this area, it is not too hard to demonstrate that, at least in some respects, we do not appear to have the best medical care in the world."

The paramount issue, moreover, is not whether medical care in the United States is superior to that in other countries but whether it is as good as it ought to be with our rich resources in medical personnel and facilities, our unparalleled standard of living, and our vaunted dedication to the ideal of equal opportunity. The most valid test of the adequacy of our medical services is not that the health of Americans is better than it was a decade or a generation or a century ago or that it is better than in some other countries. The real test is whether we are using the tools placed at our command by the remarkable advances of medical science as well and as effectively as we know how. By this gauge, there is certainly no ground for braggadocio or complacency.

The allegation that American medical care is unequaled anywhere else on earth runs smack into the fact that a number of countries with poorer economic resources than ours consistently outrank us in some of the most dependable measurements of health status. By these yardsticks, we clearly are neither the healthiest nor the most physically fit country in the world.

Infant mortality has always been considered the most accurate index of a nation's progress in the health field. Ten countries have a lower infant death rate than the United States. The rate for Sweden, the lowest, amounts to less than 60 per cent of ours. Sweden also has a mortality rate among mothers in childbirth that is nearly 15 per cent lower than in this country and an average life expectancy that is three years longer. In ten other nations there is also a higher life expectancy at birth than in the United States. In twelve countries there is a higher life expectancy at the age of sixty. Ten countries have outstripped us in the reduction of general death rates. In the Netherlands, these rates are 20 per cent lower for men and 10 per cent lower for women than ours. The United States has the highest mortality in the world from cardiovascular diseases, diabetes, and accidents. Comparative studies show that the physical fitness of our young people is well below that of European children measured by the same standards. Seven countries, including the Soviet Union, have a higher proportion of doctors to population than the United States.

Disturbing as these disparities between the United States and some other countries are, there is ground for even greater concern in the sharp differentials in health conditions, and particularly in maternal and infant mortality, between our richer and poorer citizens and states. Our disadvantaged Negro citizens have always had much higher rates of illness and death than their white neighbors. Considerable progress in improving health conditions among Negroes has been made in recent years, and the general mortality differential between the races has by now been narrowed to a nonwhite excess of only about 6 per cent. But life expectancy at birth for Negro men is still 6.4 years under that for white males, while in the case of women the difference is 7.7 years.

There is a much lower use of medical and dental services among Negroes, they have fewer hospital births, and immunization and other preventive measures are far less common among nonwhite than among white children. The gaps in the sensitive areas of maternal and child health are even greater. This is reflected in a Negro maternal mortality rate that is nearly four times as high as that for whites and in an infant death rate that is almost twice as high. Although Negroes make up only 10.5 per cent of the population, they account for more than 40 per cent of the annual toll of life among mothers in childbirth.

Mississippi still has 8.3 maternal deaths for each 10,000 live births as compared with only 1.7 for Massachusetts. The same two states have 39 and 22.3 deaths among babies under one year of age, respectively, per 1,000 live births.

We also have a long way to go yet to correct the shockingly high proportion of poor health brought to light by the draft rejections during World War II. Out of 14,297,000 men between the ages of eighteen and thirty-seven called up under the Selective Service System in that conflict, 4,217,000, or 29.7 per cent, were turned down as unfit for medical reasons. Many more were qualified only for limited service because of physical impairments. That illness and poverty go hand in hand is clearly shown by the fact that the proportion of draft rejections in the states with the lowest per capita income was 25 per cent greater than in those with the highest income. The ratio of rejections was higher in rural than in urban areas, demonstrating that any beneficial effects of country living are more than offset by poorer medical facilities.

If nearly one out of every three men in the prime of life is suffering from some physical or mental impairment, it is fair to assume that there is a much higher rate of disability in the rest of the population. This and other indices point to a huge backlog of need for medical care and to a continuing high volume of future need.

One of the paradoxes of the medical revolution is that the striking decline in mortality rates has increased rather than decreased the incidence of disease. "Life remains the one illness that cannot be cured," a medical authority has said. With the preservation of life at all ages has come a vast increase in chronic diseases and enduring disabilities. The control of a number of formerly fatal ailments has created a broad need for continuous lifetime medical supervision. A national health survey conducted by the U.S. Public Health Service shows that about seventy million persons, or more than 35 per cent of the population of the United States, are suffering from one or more chronic conditions.

Not only do we need more medical care than ever before, but the kind of care required is quite different from what it was when the infectious diseases were the leading causes of disability and death. There is relatively less need in today's medical practice for immediate and dramatic lifesaving measures in the treatment of acute illness. The emphasis in dealing with the prevailing disorders of middle and old age must instead be on preventive therapy and early diagnosis, maintenance rather than cure, rehabilitation of the handicapped, and much more attention to the emotional and social aspects of illness. These are precisely the areas that our existing organization of medical services is least equipped to handle adequately, with the result that many urgent needs are either wholly neglected or only partially met.

The quality of the best medical care in the United States is probably unexcelled anywhere else in the world. But there is considerable evidence that the level of much of the care Americans are getting is mediocre and that some of it is atrocious. Since under our notoriously weak system of professional regulation a doctor is, in essence, answerable to nothing but his own conscience and judgment, the character of performance fluctuates widely, ranging all the way from superb craftsmanship and bounteous dedication to gross incompetence and outright venality.

The problem of the quality of health care has been enormously aggravated by the steadily growing complexity of

modern medicine and by the average busy practitioner's difficulties in keeping abreast of medical progress. While the organized profession puts up a front of pious platitudes for the lay
public, physicians are sometimes quite outspoken within the
"family" about the shortcomings of their craft. The professional
journals not infrequently carry documented reports of slapdash
and shoddy performance, of glaring errors in diagnosis and
treatment, of the scandalous degree to which drug company
salesmen and promotional material have taken over the postgraduate education of doctors, and of such evils as kickbacks, fee
splitting, ghost surgery, and unnecessary surgery.

Informed opinion is that there are thousands of physicians
who continue to treat patients suffering from conditions that are
far beyond the realm of their professional competence, that the
benefits of good medical care are not equally available to all,
that the wide variations in health and efficiency from one individual to another and from one group to another constitute a
tremendous challenge, that the nation's overall health record
leaves plenty of room for improvement, and that rosy general
statistics hide numerous deficiencies.

II

"Medical statistics," one authority has said, "are human beings
with the tears wiped off." Nowhere does this observation apply
with greater force than to the statistics of the vicious circle of
poverty and ill health in the richest country in the world. The
needy have a much higher incidence and severity of disease because of squalid living conditions and the lack of adequate medical care. Illness, in turn, is a major cause of further impoverish-
ment. A well-known phenomenon is the distressing and costly
results of neglect reflected in the clustering of diseases among the
chronic recipients of public assistance. Less well known are the
facts about the close relationship between income status and
the frequency and adequacy of medical care and about the extent
to which self-supporting families of limited means continue to be
deprived of the health services they need.

Despite material gains in income levels and our unexcelled
standard of living, the anguish of want is still a searing reality for

millions of families in the United States. About 7,600,000 persons are dependent on public assistance for the bare necessities of life, at a cost of about $4.5 billion a year. It is estimated that almost one-fifth of the families in this country, with nearly one-fourth of the children, have incomes below the taxable limits under the present income tax laws. The aged, the chronically ill, the disabled, and members of some racial minorities frequently live on the very edge of destitution. The soaring costs of medical care, furthermore, pose the threat of pauperization to millions of families of modest income in the case of prolonged illness that is only partially covered by health insurance.

A stock argument of the apologists for the *status quo* is that no one in this country is denied adequate medical care, regardless of ability to pay. A companion and somewhat contradictory cliché is that only the poor and the rich can afford the best in medicine. Neither contention holds up under close examination. While it is true that the very poor who live in the larger cities sometimes get excellent free medical care in the big teaching hospitals, it is sheer nonsense to maintain that the needy generally receive the same amount and quality of services as the wealthy do. Even in the finest medical school hospitals, the poor rarely get the same care as those who are able to pay their way. The patient who is operated on by a resident is not getting the same care as the one who is operated on by a seasoned surgeon. The disparity between need and care is even greater outside the general hospital. By no stretch of the imagination can it be claimed that low-income patients or even some of those in the middle-income brackets get the same level of physicians' services, diagnostic tests, prescribed drugs, and dental care as the well-to-do. Nor can any amount of sophistry explain away the sharp class difference in the treatment of the mentally ill. None but the rich can afford the cost of care in a top-notch private mental hospital. The great majority of the victims of mental disease are doomed instead to the degrading stagnation of the crowded wards of our state institutions.

In some respects the advent of health insurance has actually aggravated the medical care problem of those in the lowest-income group, who usually lack prepayment protection. With the growth of insurance, the time-honored tradition under which doctors treated poor patients free of charge or for a reduced fee is rapidly becoming obsolete. Physicians are more and more inclined nowadays to shun nonpaying patients. All too often those who cannot pay for medical services are forced to go without them.

Much of disease is self-limited in the sense that the human body's remarkable capacity for recovery often manages to correct disorders with little treatment or none at all. This does not mean, however, that it is safe to dismiss out of hand any symptom as trivial. The cough of a common cold and that of cancer of the lung may be identical. The bleeding from cancer of the rectum may be indistinguishable from that of hemorrhoids. Only a careful examination by a competent physician can establish beyond reasonable doubt whether a complaint is potentially serious or trifling. The tragedy is that millions of people meet the problem of medical costs by seeing a doctor as rarely as possible and by neglecting early symptoms of ill health, with the result that diseases that might have been prevented or controlled if they had been detected at the outset are sometimes permitted to develop into irreparable calamities.

On the average, Americans now go to doctors twice as often as they did thirty years ago. But four out of every ten persons still do not see a physician even once in the course of a year. The strong relationship between income and the frequency of visits to a doctor has been documented by many studies. One of the latest, the national health survey conducted by the U.S. Public Health Service, shows, for instance, that children from families with incomes of $4,000 a year or more see physicians at a rate one and one-half times that for youngsters in families with lower incomes.

A truly shocking picture of the state of the nation's dental health care and of its income differentials emerges, among other things, from this large-scale government study. In the five- to fourteen-year age group, children in the higher-income families were found to have a rate of dental visits three times that for those from lower-income families. The discrepancy in the use of dental services on the basis of income continues with age. While only 19 per cent of individuals in families with incomes under $2,000 consult a dentist at least once a year, 54 per cent of those with incomes over $7,000 do so. About two out of every three Americans do not see a dentist at all in a year's time. More than thirty-three million persons, or nearly 18 per cent of the population, have never been to a dentist. Nearly 40 per cent have not seen a dentist for three or more years. Whereas 39 per cent of white persons go to a dentist at least once a year, only 17 per cent of Negroes do so. Reputable estimates are that only 15 to 20 per cent of the population make regular periodic dental visits. Men consult dentists less often than women do, and adults of both sexes receive less dental care than their children.

The role of income and education status in the dental care situation also is underscored in another extensive study of the health habits of Americans. This survey, sponsored by the Health Information Foundation, found that while 63 per cent of those who have attended college reported seeing a dentist at least once a year, only 18 per cent of those with eight years or less schooling did so. More than half of the lower-income families questioned gave inability to pay as the reason for failure to get needed dental attention.

Tooth decay is the most common disease in the United States and is the source of many other ailments. Authoritative estimates are that the average American has four untreated cavities and that by the age of fifty about half of the population have gum ailments that cause even more tooth loss than do cavities.

These appalling statistics emphasize the urgent need for a concerted effort in the field of dental health. Dental care applied only when pain becomes unbearable is both inefficient and expensive. A program of regular dental care begun in early childhood and continued throughout life is a much more effective and, in the long run, less costly procedure. The resigned attitude of the past, which accepted the ultimate loss of teeth as inevitable, is no longer justified by available dental techniques. But before any material progress can be made, Americans will have to be educated to give a higher priority to dental care, we shall need many more dentists than we now have and a more efficient organization of dental practice, and, above all else, some way will have to be found to enable a large proportion of the population to pay for adequate dental services. A special study commission reported in 1960 that per capita expenditures for dental care in the United

States amounted to only twenty-five cents a year and recommended that they be increased twenty-fold by 1972.

Study after study has shown a higher incidence of illness and higher death rates in the lower-income groups. The poor have a higher mortality at all ages, including that from diseases of the young that can be most readily prevented or treated. More prevalent among them are most forms of cancer, arthritis, asthma, respiratory infections, skin diseases, and even heart ailments, which are commonly regarded as the affliction of the prosperous. Their illnesses are often of longer duration.

Although the poor need the most medical care, they usually get the least. While the well-to-do enjoy the benefit of such preventive services as immunizations and regular checkups and are in the habit of consulting physicians even for minor conditions, patients of limited means usually postpone seeing a doctor until the illness becomes serious and they are driven by the goad of discomfort. Investigators have found that there are even different class concepts of what constitutes illness. The lower the income status, the less concern is apt to be shown for every symptom and the greater is the dependence on home remedies. As the educational level rises, so does the amount of accurate information about the etiology, symptoms, and treatment of common diseases that prompts seeking medical aid.

As a rule, there also are marked differences in the quality of care received by upper- and lower-income families. While the patients of the top specialists on the staffs of the best hospitals are largely the affluent, people who live in the poorer neighborhoods get much of their care from general practitioners, some of them of questionable competence. And regardless of the doctor's qualifications, the question of what the patient can afford to pay for often has a great deal to do, consciously or subconsciously, with the kind of treatment given.

There is no doubt that the lack of a rational organization of health care makes for considerable misuse and overuse of costly resources. But neither is there any question that there is a vast amount of underutilization of medical services by the underprivileged. The consensus of medical authorities is that very great improvements could be brought about in the health of millions of Americans if they could obtain the amount and quality of up-to-date care now available to those who can pay the bill. Even the toll of heart disease and cancer, the two major killers yet to be conquered by medical science, could be substantially reduced if present knowledge were fully applied. It is estimated that some 90,000 of the 285,000 persons, on the average, who die each year of cancer could be saved by timely diagnosis and optimal treatment. About 20,000 persons still die annually of rheumatic fever or rheumatic heart disease, even though penicillin can control the streptococcal infections that cause these ailments.

The grim reality is that, even with the aid of health insurance, most American families are unable to afford modern medical care, that many health needs are being neglected, that a substantial time lag remains between new medical discoveries and their widespread application, that we have yet to face up to the challenge of chronic disease and mental illness, and that we have barely begun to utilize the enormous potentialities of preventive medicine.

III

How many of our doctors are less than fully competent or unscrupulous or both? This, obviously, is the sort of question that no one can attempt to answer with any degree of precision. But enough direct and inferential evidence is available to indicate that the problems of competence and ethics within the medical profession are of considerable dimensions. Aggravating their seriousness is the fact that very little is being done about it.

Under our flaccid system of professional regulation, a doctor can be grossly incompetent and yet continue to practice. Only minor punishment, or none at all, is now handed out to mentally sluggish, careless, inept, or dishonest physicians—the practitioners who frequently make the wrong diagnoses, use outmoded or worthless treatments, prescribe the wrong drugs, refuse to visit seriously ill patients, bungle operations for which they are not trained, perform unnecessary surgery, charge exorbitant fees, split fees to get business, and cheat on health and other insurance.

While the number of such miscreants is a matter of controversy, there is the probably even graver problem of the conscientious doctors who are trying to do their best but who lack adequate training and are unaware of their limitations. The enormous intricacy of modern medicine and the great difficulties encountered by the average overworked physician in keeping abreast of its rapid advances completely belie the medical profession's mystique that the mere possession of a license is automatically conclusive proof of competence.

Incompetence and venality are, of course, two different phenomena. But there is good reason to believe that they often go hand in hand. In either case, sick people are particularly vulnerable to exploitation and peculiarly handicapped by their inability to appraise the quality of the doctor's performance. The unscrupulous physician, especially if he is poorly trained, can do infinite harm and drain the patient's pocketbook through ignorance, neglect, questionable procedures, superfluous visits, overcharging, and a variety of other abuses.

The stock contention of organized medicine is that medical corruption is confined to an insignificantly small proportion of unethical practitioners. There appears to be no factual basis for this comforting assertion, even though it cannot be flatly disproved. On the issue of incompetence, the AMA's frequently reiterated position has been that every licensed physician must be presumed to be competent, "unless considered otherwise by his peers." Since doctors rarely, if ever, do anything about an incompetent colleague, this policy completely begs the question.

Although the full extent of questionable practices in the medical profession must of necessity remain the province of guesswork, one authoritative source has placed the proportion of malfeasance among doctors at close to 10 per cent and possibly even more. Dr. Harold E. Jervey, a former president of the Federation of State Medical Boards, the official agencies whose job it is to license and discipline physicians, has told the AMA's annual Congress on Medical Education and Licensure that, in his opinion, fifteen to twenty thousand doctors have been guilty of unethical practices.

AMA spokesmen have estimated that incompetent practitioners probably represent no more than 3 to 5 per cent of the physicians now in practice. Both the source of their estimate and their definition of incompetence remain undisclosed. Their assessment of the situation is considerably more sanguine than the view taken by some authorities that there are many doctors who should be either barred from practice or reeducated. But even if the official estimate is taken at face value, it means that unqualified physicians are being entrusted with the care of more than five million Americans.

Contributing to the not uncommon breakdown of professional ethics, which sometimes takes the form of outright fraud, is the frequent lack of social motivation in what is increasingly coming to be looked upon as a business rather than as a calling of dedication. Another factor is the absence of that positive cultivation of quality of service that is best achieved not when each doctor works alone, as most of them now do, but through teamwork in groups and within the integrated hospital structure.

Vigorous policing of professional conduct and performance, now so sadly lacking, is essential. But it can never be a substitute for the incentives nurtured by rational organization and public-spirited leadership. How physicians behave depends not only on their caliber but also on the organizational mechanisms through which they render their services. High quality of medical care cannot be established by fiat. Rather, it is something that must be inspired. It is a subtly nebulous but very real attribute, the doctor giving freely not only of his knowledge and skills but also of himself when he is properly motivated. Many devoted physicians do so now. But there are quite a few who do not.

Two of the latest exposés of the kind of flagrant transgressions possible within the present framework of medical practice have been made in New York. One of them is a state investigation of large-scale collusion between doctors and ambulance-chasing lawyers to bilk insurance companies through heavily padded or wholly fraudulent bills in accident cases. The other is an exhaustive analysis of more than four hundred cases of hospitalization in New York City that uncovered a shockingly high ratio of substandard care, unnecessary hospital admissions, and poor and needless surgery.

The accident-racket probe, which is still under way, is reported to involve about 1,300 physicians. Out of thirty doctors already disciplined, fourteen have had their licenses revoked and the rest have been suspended or censured. The extent of the medical swindling thus far established has been officially described as "staggering the imagination." One physician rigged what should normally have been a $10 charge into $184. Another saw a patient only once but submitted bills for forty-five visits.

"We have evidence," the head of the New York State division investigating professional conduct reported, "of doctors conspiring with lawyers to submit false claims, exaggerating medical reports, submitting bills for treatment not administered, and listing X rays that were never taken. In many instances, the exaggerated bills and reports led to larger settlements by the insurance companies or larger awards when the cases went to court."

This is not the first time that doctors have been involved in a big insurance scandal in New York. Nor, according to reliable reports in insurance circles, in such rascality on the part of physicians by any means confined to that state.

Nearly twenty years ago, a special state commission investigating the plunder of insurance funds in workmen's compensation cases reported to Governor Dewey that "kickbacks ranging from 15 to 50 per cent were paid to more than 3,000 physicians in New York, Kings, Bronx and Queens counties alone. The medical societies of those counties have seemingly closed their eyes to this widespread system. Indeed, it was proved that these kickbacks were common in private as well as in compensation cases. They constitute a secret and illegal tax." Testimony at hearings before the commission revealed numerous cases where fees were charged for mythical services and where referring physicians in industrial accidents received kickbacks from surgeons, X-ray laboratories, surgical-appliance companies, opticians, and specimen-analysis laboratories. One X-ray specialist, who admitted kicking back 50 per cent of his fees to more than two hundred doctors, said the physicians had told him that "if there were nothing in it for them, they couldn't afford to send me their work." Proprietors of firms supplying braces, trusses, and other appliances for injured workers testified that they had slipped doctors one-third of the prices charged.

Equally reprehensible are the conditions brought to light in a study of medical records covering the hospitalization of a group of Teamsters' Union members and their families in New York City over a period of more than four years. The panel of prominent medical specialists who made the study for Columbia University's School of Public Health and Administrative Medicine reported that one-fifth of the patients had received "poor care" and another fifth only "fair care." One-fifth of the hospital admissions were held to have been completely unnecessary. The quality of surgery was labeled "poor" in 20 per cent of the cases and only "fair" in another 26 per cent.

The report of the specialists was particularly critical of the hysterectomies (removal of the womb) performed during the period studied. It held that at least twenty of sixty such operations were unnecessary and that the advisability of six others was questionable. In one instance, the report said, "absolutely nothing was found" in laboratory tests to indicate the need for the operation, "but the surgeon had the gall to go ahead and perform a total hysterectomy anyway." Before a hysterectomy is performed, competent gynecologists usually attempt to bring the symptoms under control with a much simpler—and less expensive —operation called a dilatation and curettage. This procedure was done in only two of the twenty hysterectomies deemed needless.

Out of thirteen Caesarean sections performed, the report said, there was a "serious question" about the need for seven. Regarding one case in which an outmoded type of Caesarean operation was performed, one of the surveying specialists declared that "this is the worse case I ever saw. The two doctors [who performed the operation] should be castigated."

In another instance, a surgeon was accused of making "a mountain" out of a routine removal of a small vaginal cyst by an unnecessary incision through the flank. In the process, he also removed the woman's perfectly normal appendix. And to top it off, he refused to permit her discharge from the hospital until his $450 bill had been paid. The report described the duration of the hospital stay in this case as "scandalous" and said that the woman should have been discharged twelve days earlier.

"Essentially, there were two causes for care that was judged to be inferior," the report stated. "One was related to surgery performed on essentially normal organs, where the grave suspicion of patient exploitation could be raised. The other factor, equally discouraging in a city that has such a large number of fine hospitals and a high proportion of well-trained physicians, was inferior care resulting from poor clinical judgment on the part of a certain number of physicians without either adequate training or supervision."

Dr. Ray E. Trussell, director of Columbia's School of Public Health and Administrative Medicine, now on leave as New York City's hospital commissioner, declared that the findings of the study "pose serious questions as to the wisdom, self-discipline, and ethical conduct of certain physicians and hospitals" and indicate that "much money is being spent on unnecessary or incompetent medical care."

If such a high proportion of poor medicine is found in New York City, with its concentration of excellent teaching hospitals associated with some of the nation's best medical schools, one cannot but wonder how prevalent the situation is in hundreds of smaller communities with insufficient medical facilities and many isolated and inadequately trained physicians. There is general agreement among competent authorities that in many small towns, much of medical practice is of a deplorably low level, with a great deal of superficial and symptomatic treatment.

A vivid illustration of the difference between therapy based on accurate diagnosis and treatment on the basis of symptomatology has been given by Dr. Caldwell B. Esselstyn, director of the Rip Van Winkle Clinic of Hudson, New York, an outstanding group-practice organization. "Let us take the example of a man who comes to a doctor complaining of a cough," Dr. Esselstyn said. "The doctor listens to his story, hands him a prescription for cough medicine or the medicine itself, more likely than not gives him some kind of antibiotic, and sends him on his way. The visit is short, and the patient has an 85 to 90 per cent chance of getting well. The odds are good, but the quality of medicine is bad because no one knows the diagnosis. This is symptomatic medicine—quick and highly productive on a fee-for-service piecework production line. Take the same man who is seen by a careful doctor. A history is taken, the patient is asked to undress—which takes time—and an examination is made of the nose and throat; the chest is percussed and listened to through a stethoscope; perhaps even an X ray of the chest is taken, together with laboratory tests. At the end of this examination, both patient and doctor know what the diagnosis is, and proper therapy can be prescribed to treat the specific cause of the trouble. This is diagnostic medicine. There is no comparison between the quality of care of these two visits. Yet, under our present most common method of remuneration, the first doctor has seen thrity-five to forty patients in the afternoon and drives off in his Cadillac. The latter may have seen ten to twelve patients and takes off for home in the family Chevrolet."

IV

"In medical care, more so than in any other vocation, the love of money is the root of all evil. Perhaps because the financial rewards are greater, the temptation is stronger." Statements like this one have not been calculated to endear Dr. Paul R. Hawley, for many years director of the American College of Surgeons, to the medical profession. But his courageous and often lonely battle for higher standards of competence and probity in medicine has shed a pitiless light on some of the more unsavory byways of medical practice in the United States.

In no field of medicine are the rewards greater than in surgery. It is hardly surprising, therefore, that more doctors yield to temptation in this area than in any other. Competent opinion is that there is a great deal of surgery that is either wholly unwarranted or poorly done by physicians who undertake procedures that they are unqualified to perform.

Dr. I. S. Ravdin of the University of Pennsylvania's School of Medicine, one of the nation's most prominent surgeons and another leading figure in the campaign for surgical reforms, has estimated that more than half of the surgery in this country is now being done by doctors lacking the requisite training. "Many patients are being subjected to needless operations," Dr. Ravdin also has said, "and preoperative and postoperative care is not always the best. . . . The so-called successful surgeon is not always the best individual to do a particular operation or to give the patient the full benefits that surgical science now has to offer."

Under existing legal provisions, any licensed physician can do any kind of surgery he likes, provided he can find the patient who is willing to let him operate and the hospital to do it in if the procedure is too complicated to be performed in the office. In a number of states, this latitude to perform the most complex surgery extends even to osteopaths. In the larger hospitals, most of the surgery is usually done by board-certified surgeons. But in many hospitals, the qualifications for surgical-staff privileges have not kept pace with the advances in surgery. In smaller hospitals, especially in unaccredited institutions, a large number of operations, including tonsillectomies, appendectomies, and many gynecological procedures, are performed by general practitioners who lack the necessary surgical training. It is true that much of the surgical work done by general practitioners involves the more common operations, those that are sometimes characterized as "minor." But as Dr. Robert S. Myers, executive assistant director of the College of Surgeons, has commented, "There is no such thing as minor surgery; there are only minor surgeons."

The results of surgery done by poorly trained practitioners are sometimes gruesome. There is a story, possibly apocryphal, of a general practitioner who, after opening up a patient, spent two hours vainly trying to locate the appendix and finally had to send out an emergency call for a surgeon to do the job. In another and fully authenticated case, four-fifths of the appendixes removed by a Michigan doctor were found to have been normal. He had mistaken menstrual pains in young girls for appendicitis.

Dr. Paul R. Hawley reported being told by "one of the most distinguished surgeons in the world" that at least half of his practice consists in attempts to correct the poor results of operations performed by inadequately trained physicians. "I shall never cease to be amazed," he said, "at the millions of people who would not invest a penny in any enterprise without full assurance of its safety . . . yet who will hop on an operating table and permit anyone holding a medical license to commit mayhem upon their internal organs."

In the days when surgery was a hazardous and terrifying business, no patient could be prevailed upon to submit to an operation, nor would a physician attempt one, unless it was really imperative. But the picture has radically changed as surgery has become progressively safer and vastly more effective with the constant improvements in anesthesia, antisepsis, and other techniques. Instead of being urgently required to save life and limb, many operations are now elective, being designed to relieve discomfort or to correct some abnormality of function. Much of surgery has thus become a matter of judgment rather than clear indication. This leaves the way wide open for needless procedures undertaken because of poor judgment or for mercenary reasons. Many surgeons have itchy fingers and sometimes prematurely rush the patient into the operating room, not because of greed but because they believe in active surgical intervention and tend to be impatient of lengthy conservative medical therapy. The patient himself not infrequently insists on an operation, even though the need for it may be questionable, and shops around until he finds a doctor willing to perform one.

There has been a steady increase in the sales appeal of surgery. Aside from whatever real benefits accrue from it, people have learned that going to a hospital for an operation need not be too unpleasant an experience and that the period of lazy convalescence may even by enjoyable. For a good many frustrated individuals, and this appears to be particularly true in the case of some neurotic women, an operation can be a form of exorcism for imaginary ills and a welcome means of getting the attention they crave. This is one of the reasons why gynecological surgery offers such a fertile field for abuse. Even when there are the best of motivations, it is highly questionable whether a surgeon who agrees to operate for no other reason than to improve his patient's morale has any business trying to practice psychiatry in this manner.

The growing popularity of surgery has understandably led to a rise in the status of the impressively masked and gowned surgeon flanked by hushed and obsequious assistants and nurses and performing miracles with his gleaming instruments. He has been placed on a financial pedestal that the less glamorous general practitioner and even the specialist in internal medicine have failed to share. A patient who will shell out several hundred dollars for an operation sometimes balks at paying the family physician more than $5 or $10 for the initial diagnosis that led to the decision for the surgery.

Out of this disparity in the remuneration of doctors has grown a string of abuses. Rather than turn over the lucrative business to someone else, general practitioners sometimes undertake surgical procedures that they are incompetent to handle.

Another outcome is the evil of fee splitting, or kickbacks. Considering himself unfairly treated, the referring doctor may insist on a rebate from the surgeon to whom he sends the patient. This practice is reported to be quite widespread in many communities. Where it exists, the patient's bill is usually padded and, what is even more serious, physicians are likely to be guided by the commission arrangements they can make with certain surgeons rather than by their competence. The racket, which often leads to unnecessary surgery, is difficult to stamp out because the patient does not know about the fee-splitting deal and because the two other parties directly involved are both guilty. Young surgeons starting in practice sometimes have no choice but to split fees with the established practitioners who control the patients or move elsewhere.

Rebates are an old abomination in medical practice. Unprincipled doctors have from time to time been known to accept them from a variety of sources, including consultants, X-ray specialists, opticians, druggists, commercial clinical laboratories, and even undertakers. Some years ago opticians' kickbacks to doctors, forcing up the retail price of eyeglasses by at least 25 per cent, reached such scandalous proportions in a number of cities that the U.S. Department of Justice had to step in and put an end to the corrupt arrangement.

The most flagrantly deceptive variety of fee splitting is ghost surgery, a scheme in which a general practitioner hires a surgeon to come in and do the cutting after the patient has been anesthetized. The patient is led to believe that the surgery was done by his trusted family doctor, who splits the fee with the surgeon. The phantom operator lurking in the shadows has no opportunity to examine the patient beforehand, to determine whether the operation is necessary in the first place, and he has no hand in the vitally important postoperative care. And after watching the ghost surgeon operate a few times, the general practitioner may himself begin to do surgery, not because he is competent but because the patients believe he is and a hospital permits him to operate.

For surgeons and general practitioners alike, the lure of fat fees sometimes strains professional judgment and ethics to the breaking point. Dr. Edward H. Daseler, a California physician who has served as a hospital surveyor for the American College of Surgeons, has had this to say on the basis of his observation of surgical practices in various parts of the country: "It is obvious to me that huge numbers of perfectly normal, undiseased organs —for example, appendixes, uteruses, fallopian tubes, ovaries, and even gallbladders—are being removed for one reason only: extirpation of the customary fee from the unwary patient or his relatives. . . . I feel that this problem is not confined to a few small isolated communities but exists in the majority of hospitals in the United States today."

Substantial support of this sweeping indictment is lent by the findings of a series of investigations conducted by the College of Surgeons. Its on-the-spot study of conditions in a number of hospitals found that most surgeons are upright and competent and that the bulk of unjustified operations and of fee splitting and fee gouging is usually confined to a small minority of slippery operators. But the trouble is that the reputable practitioners frequently condone the misdeeds of their unscrupulous colleagues by shutting their eyes to what is going on. In expressing in one of his reports his frustration over this lamentable state of affairs, Dr. Daseler quoted Edmund Burke's observation that "all that is necessary for the triumph of evil is that good men do nothing."

A case in point is the disgraceful situation uncovered by the College of Surgeons in a small Southeastern hospital. Out of a total of 879 surgical procedures performed over a fourteen-month period by twelve members of the staff of this hospital, two doctors accounted for 113 unnecessary operations as against only 27 such operations by the ten other physicians. The needless operations represented 24 per cent of the surgery done by the two miscreant practitioners in the period studied. One of these surgeons had performed eighteen appendectomies on children under the age of four. Thirteen of these were held to have been unjustified. Seven of the children operated on were between the ages of ten months and two years, when acute appendicitis is a rarity. One woman who had undergone an unwarranted hysterectomy died four days later of a blood clot. One of the shameful aspects of the situation was that the hospital's pathologists obligingly slanted the tissue diagnosis to justify retrospectively each of the unnecessary operations. Microscopic review of the tissue slides by the College of Surgeons surveyors who visited the hospital and their subsequent examination by pathologists in Chicago established that the tissues were perfectly normal.

"It is common knowledge," the College of Surgeons has stated, "that final tissue diagnoses which are not true, and which are actually camouflage, are applied by some pathologists to those tissues which lend themselves to surgery and therefore are frequently removed. . . . These euphemisms are used by the pathologist when he finds the tissue to be essentially normal, and the camouflage is accepted and said to be justified because everyone on the medical staff understands that the tissue is actually normal. The truth is that these subterfuges are used to avoid conflict with one or more surgeons on the hospital staff."

Seventy-one per cent of the appendixes removed by a surgeon in a New Jersey hospital were later found to have been normal, according to another report of the College of Surgeons. In still another case, twenty-nine of fifty-four appendectomies were held to have been unjustified. So widespread is the abuse of appendectomies that it is a standard quip among physicians that a diagnosis of chronic appendicitis frequently coincides with "chronic remunerative appendicitis."

"What are all the operations for chronic appendicitis, noncalculous cholecystitis [gallbladder surgery not involving gallstones], and abdominal adhesions being done for?" Dr. I. S. Ravdin has asked. "Are the organs which are being removed causing any of the symptoms which have brought the patient to the surgeon? Are not the adhesions at times due to a previous operation which in reality was not justified? The removal of an appendix for burning pain in the right lower quadrant will too often be followed by an operation for adhesions in six months or a year and then by a cholecystectomy [removal of the gallbladder] and another operation for adhesions. Most of these operations are unnecessary, for the symptoms which these patients present are psychosomatic in origin; operation does not cure them."

Dr. Ravdin also has often spoken out against "the rape of the pelvis" through the "wholesale removal" of wombs, ovaries, and fallopian tubes "without consideration of the harm which is being done the women involved." Next to the appendix, these female organs are the favorite targets for unconscionable or overzealous surgeons and are frequently excised on such flimsy clinical grounds as vaginal discharge, backache, headache, dizziness, palpitation, fatigue, and nervousness. The fear of cancer has led to many hysterectomies that reputable gynecologists regard as totally unjustified. Between 40 and 50 per cent of all women develop small fibroid tumors in the womb as they grow older. These growths rarely become malignant, and yet they are used as an excuse for removal of the womb and the ovaries in thousands of cases. In a large-scale study of gynecologic operations in the Los Angeles area, it was found that nearly half of the ovaries removed in hysterectomies were wholly normal. Out of a total of 6,248 hysterectomies covered in this survey, only 3,790, or about 60 per cent, were considered justifiable. Competent estimates are that at least one-third of all hysterectomies are unwarranted.

Another commonly abused procedure is the operation for uterine suspension to relieve backache. This is major surgery and involves the tucking in of the ligaments of a tipped or displaced womb. But since the ligaments are elastic, they eventually stretch again, and the womb finally has to be removed altogether. Some gynecologists feel that about 90 per cent of the hundreds of uterine suspensions performed annually are unnecessary.

While conscientious surgeons insist on good medical reasons for any operation, others are only too glad to cater to the whims of their patients. In the category of fads are tubal ligations to avoid any future worry about pregnancy and Caesarean sections that are undergone merely to escape labor pains. Unfortunately, the scar tissues left by such operations and their other aftereffects can cause many difficulties later on. "You can't put a scar in the wall of the uterus," Dr. Hawley has said, "and have it as strong as before the Caesarean. There is a possibility of rupture there in case of a later pregnancy."

The best clue to the amount of needless surgery is the dramatic drop in the number of operations, in hospital after hospital, after the formation of vigorous staff tissue committees. One hospital's surgery rates, with the same patient load, dropped from 769 operations in one year to 298, from 305 appendectomies to 66, and from 30 Caesarean sections in 556 births to 1 such procedure in 652 births. In another hospital, the annual number of hysterectomies fell from 492 to 149.

V

The errors of medical men are not as well publicized as those of surgeons. While the mistakes and misdeeds of surgeons are made in hospitals, where the entire staff is in a position to know about them, what a physician does in his own office and his oversights, omissions, and blunders are not generally subject to scrutiny. But there is good reason to believe that, on the whole, the standards of office practice are well below those prevailing in hospitals.

Although the mistakes of private practitioners are sometimes apt to be buried without anyone being the wiser, reports of laxity and of failures due to incompetence or haste not infrequently find their way into the professional literature. The element of uncertainty is still great in medicine, and honest errors in diagnosis and treatment are unavoidable. What is far less excusable is the all too frequent dodging of the laborious and time-consuming pick-and-shovel work of medicine, the widespread tendency toward overmedication, the neglect of the emotional components of disease, and the variety of other evils stemming from excessive specialization and assembly-line treatment.

It is certainly no accident that iatrogenic disease—illness unwittingly induced or aggravated by what the doctor does or says or by his failure to act when he should have done certain things—has increasingly come to the fore in recent years. The rise in iatrogenic illness, which one authority has described as "one of the commonest conditions" encountered nowadays, is partly the inevitable outcome of the complexity of medicine and of the bewildering variety and potency of the available drugs.

Even with the best intentions, the chances of harming the patient have enormously increased with the vastly greater effectiveness of medicine's tools and procedures. With increased therapeutic potential have come much greater therapeutic hazards. None of the frequently indispensable diagnostic tests can be undertaken without risk. The virus of hepatitis and other serious infections may be introduced by insufficiently sterilized hypodermic needles. Transfusions may cause bloodstream disorders. The intravenous administration of even some relatively inert substance may cause sudden death. No agent that can modify the internal environment or organic integrity of the body can be used without hazard, particularly since no drug has been found with a single effect and since there are wide individual variations of reaction. Because of the inherent toxicity of potent medications, only a narrow margin separates therapeutic and toxic dosage. Many drugs are known to cause allergic reactions and have other risky side effects that can become severe upon long-term administration. As new drugs continue to flood the market, there is often inadequate knowledge of sensitivity reactions, toxic manifestations, the modification and masking of symptoms, the problems associated with resistant strains of organisms, and the possibility of permanent physiologic alterations. But hasty prescribing without a careful weighing of individual needs has become widely prevalent.

Significantly, in 1949, the National Office of Vital Statistics instituted the listing of a new category of "deaths ascribed to therapeutic misadventure as primary cause." A total of 6,201 such deaths are listed for the 1949–1958 period. Of these, 2,965 were attributed to surgical mistakes or accidents, 1,035 to the administration of drugs, 824 to transfusions, 665 to anesthesia, and 712 to "local applications and other or unspecified therapeutic misadventure."

For a number of reasons, these figures are believed to understate to a considerable extent the total of fatalities due to iatrogenic causes. In the first place, the label "therapeutic misadventure" is not used "for primary death classification if the condition for which the treatment was given is known." In other words, it is not used if the attending physician lists the original condition as the cause of death on the death certificate instead of admitting that "misadventure" was at fault. Secondly, the "therapeutic misadventure" category specifically excludes fatalities resulting from an accidental overdose, from a wrong drug given in error, and from an allergic reaction to drugs. Nor does it cover deaths due to blood-cell diseases and a number of other conditions that may directly result from drug therapy. The iatrogenic classification applies only to deaths caused by the administration of drugs in accordance with recommended dosage.

There are so many ways in which the activities of doctors may produce undesirable effects upon their patients and in which they can create disease almost as readily as they can cure it that the ratio of good results to poor ones is remarkably high. But aside from the multiplicity of frequently uncontrollable hazards, incalculable damage is being done by physicians who are over-worked and whose skills have become rusty, who are impatient of or disinterested in the infinite entanglements of human emo-tions, who are in a hurry to go golfing or hostile because the symptoms are "ridiculous and unreasonable," forgetting that there is nothing unreasonable in medicine.

The extent and variety of dangers intrinsic in the modern management of disease make all the more vital the discriminating selection of therapy and careful listening to what the patient has to say. Under these circumstances, knowing when not to treat is fully as important as knowing when to treat. The tragedy is that time for reflective thoroughness is often lacking in today's medi-cal practice, so that the use of potentially dangerous drugs and excessive reliance on the laboratory become a substitute for a careful diagnosis that can be based only on the orderly sorting out of the details of the clinical history.

The effects of the torrent of new medications, and particularly of the antibotics, have not been "all for the good," one authority has commented. "The care which used to be exercised in making a diagnosis has largely given way to hit-and-miss trial of anti-biotics."

Along with the failure to perceive the emotional and envi-ronmental factors in illness, there is sometimes a lack of aware-ness of the role that the physician's feelings and attitudes can play in the cause and cure of sickness. Since the doctor himself func-tions as an important therapeutic agent, many ailments improve with nothing more than his intelligent and sympathetic concern. But like other therapeutic agents, his behavior may also evoke adverse reactions. "We are still not sufficiently aware," the late Dr. Frances Dunbar once said, "that the physician himself is often pathogenic. He is so when he concentrates on symptoms without adequate attempt to ascertain or remove their causes."

When emotional disorders are ignored and the physician is preoccupied with the pursuit of organic pathology, which may not exist at all or may be trivial, a new source of anxiety is created for the patient. On top of whatever difficulty was originally present, he is now enjoying the dubious pleasure of iatrogenic apprehension. The doctor has supplied him with an organic red herring which may temporarily provide him with a certified rationalization for his anxiety but which in the long run may only aggravate the underlying concern.

Considerable attention has been devoted in the professional literature to the phenomenon of iatrogenic heart disease. This is a condition in which the patient's cardiac incapacity is made worse by the doctor's words or he develops such symptoms as palpitation, chest pain, shortness of breath, and faintness because he has been led to believe by something the physician had said that he has heart disease when he actually does not. "Almost 60 per cent of patients who consult a cardiac specialist," a prominent physician has said, "are suffering either from an exaggerated or wholly unnecessary anxiety about their hearts, arising from suggestion and not based on reason. Most of the suggestions arise from the careless or inconsidered remarks of doctors." A study of 631 New Yorkers who had employment difficulties attributed to cardiac conditions showed that 28 per cent of them did not have any heart disease at all. Ill-considered remarks by physicians after a routine examination were a major factor in a substantial portion of these cases.

There is no malady, except perhaps cancer, that is so fraught with emotional implications as is heart disease. Many people are highly conscious of the frequency of cardiovascular disease, underscored by the numerous accounts of heart attacks and sudden deaths in the press, and are becoming more and more familiar with its symptoms. But such symptoms as fatiguability, breathlessness, or chest pain also are commonly produced by anxiety. The doctor can easily precipitate or enhance the difficulty by thoughtlessly calling the patient's attention to an innocent heart murmur, a slight blood-pressure elevation, or some other relatively insignificant cardiovascular abnormality. Some symptoms may be misinterpreted as cardiac in origin, not only by the patient but also by the physician without a sufficiently thorough examination. Even the most innocuous statement by the doctor can set off a hazardous chain of anxiety reactions in the apprehensive patient.

Many cardiologists feel that much needless disability has resulted from ill-advised restrictions placed upon the activities of patients who really have heart disease. The effects can be calamitous when patients without any cardiac disorders or with only trifling defects are carelessly labeled heart cases and advised to limit their activities.

Another form of iatrogenically aggravated cardiac disease is that resulting from the administration of medications that have a deleterious effect on the heart muscle. The incidence and severity of digitalis poisoning have increased materially as a result of the widespread use of diuretics, cortisone, and other durgs that affect the electrolyte balance and change the reaction of the heart muscle to digitalis.

The chances for jumping at conclusions and for misconstruing the doctor's imprudent offhand statements are immeasurably increased under the conditions prevailing in today's hurried medical practice. Contributing to the situation is the common neglect of such fundamentals of the physicial examination as thumping the chest and using the stethoscope to listen to it. The information supplied by an X-ray plate or an electrocardiogram can be of immense complementary value, but it is sadly incomplete without the enlightenment afforded by the clinical history, the appearance of the patient, and the results of a physical examination. The physician who percusses the chest and palpates the abdomen also has an opportunity to observe the patient, which is something no X-ray machine or electrocardiograph can do.

Thirty years ago, as the tide of advances in medical technology was just beginning to roll in, the late great Dr. Harvey Cushing warned: "We have instruments of precision in increasing numbers with which we and our hospital assistants at untold expense make tests and take observations, the vast majority of which are but supplementary to and as nothing compared with the careful study of the patient by a keen observer using his eyes and ears and fingers and a few simple aids." No matter how many additional new techniques are invented, there will never be a time when an accurate history of the patient's illness and a complete physical examination will cease to be the most valuable means of arriving at a correct diagnosis. If these basic procedures are rushed, they become not only worthless but confusing.

The worship of the laboratory cannot replace the careful clinical evaluation of the patient and his disease. Many laboratory procedures not only unnecessarily inflate the bill but can lead to an erroneous diagnosis, particularly when a trifling organic deviation from the normal serves only to obscure the functional nature of the disorder. Excessive dependence on tests lulls doctors into apathy and leads them to turn over their own responsibilities to the laboratory. Mechanical tests will not supply answers to diagnostic problems about disease states in which abnormal function cannot be measured biochemically or radiologically. It merely enhances the tendency to stress the abnormal function of the organ rather than that of the individual. Moreover, the uncritical use of X rays, both for diagnostic examinations and for treatment, raises the issue of unnecessary exposure to radiation. While the threshold for safe radiation is still a matter of dispute, many authorities are concerned over the indiscriminate use of thousands of X-ray machines in the offices of doctors and dentists.

Doctors have a higher coronary rate than any other professional group. But despite the heavy patient loads with which many practitioners are overburdened these days, overtreatment is not uncommon. A flagrant area of abuse is the excessive use of gadgets in certain orthopedic conditions. Since the physician has the privilege of defining illness and since he alone can determine when the patient is well, the line between the necessary and unnecessary visit is extremely difficult to draw. Some doctors have a distaste for terminating a source of income and keep patients coming back for procedures that either are worthless or could just as well be taken care of at home.

The other side of the coin of overdoing by way of needless treatments and indiscriminate rushing of patients into surgery is the neglect of fundamental diagnostic methods, which sometimes leads to irreparable tragedies. Here are a few examples of delays and errors culled from the professional literature:

A study of the records of a random sample of one hundred cases of verified brain tumors showed that only in four of them was the correct diagnosis of malignancy made by the physicians who first examined the patients. Twenty of the patients had been told by general practitioners that there was "nothing wrong" with them. In about half of the cases, the definite diagnosis was delayed for more than a year; in nearly one-fourth of them, the delay exceeded two years. While many of the delays were owing to ignorance and inertia on the part of the patients' families, some of them were the direct result of medical incompetence. The striking failure of the examining physicians to detect symptoms of brain malignancy was ascribed in the study report to "pressure of time" and to the omission of even cursory neurologic and ophthalmoscopic examinations. In most of the cases, no attention was paid to such obvious clues as headaches, visual impairment, muscular weaknesses, and reflex changes.

A similar high ratio of diagnostic mistakes and unjustified delays was found in a review of ninety-three cases of primary malignant bone tumor. Only eight of the patients survived, even though such bone malignancies usually manifest themselves early through pain and swelling, methods for definitive diagnosis are easily available, and the tumor site is generally accessible for surgery. In nearly two-thirds of the cases, delays in making the correct diagnosis ran from three to six months, by which time metastasis had already set in. Some of the costly delays were due to initial erroneous diagnoses of sprain, arthritis, rheumatism, sciatica, neuritis, and bursitis. Among the treatment measures used, some of which were actually harmful, were the application of local heat, liniments, massage, osteopathic manipulation, and the use of aspirin and antibiotics. "Misguided treatment prior to the correct diagnosis has, in some cases at least, very likely prejudiced a favorable outcome," the specialists who made the survey concluded.

A shocking account of a review of the records of two hundred cases of stomach cancer in a New Orleans hospital, published in the *Journal of the American Medical Association*, reported that there was a tendency to treat the patient's symptoms without any effort being made to diagnose the true cause of the symptoms. Dr. Frederick Fitzherbert Boyce, the author of the report, indicated that the study shows quite clearly that, due to errors of omission and commission on the part of the doctors involved, certain patients with curable carcinoma are not permitted a proper chance of cure.

Out of the 101 patients in this group who consulted physicians without undue delay, only 16 were promptly sent to the hospital, most of them with the correct diagnosis. The rest were treated medically for periods of up to two years before being hospitalized for surgery. Some patients were treated for ulcers, Dr. Boyce reported, and others underwent treatment for an assortment of other conditions many of which they did not possess. One patient was operated on for gallbladder disease, another for chronic appendicitis, a third for prostatic disease, and two for umbilical hernia. Among the drugs used "for reasons that are not clear" were penicillin, sulfas, belladonna, and paregoric. A majority of the patients were apparently treated in this fashion, according to the report. Stomach carcinoma was either not suspected or, if it was, diagnostic procedures were superficial and negative findings quite readily accepted.

A report covering a survey of 561 cases of pelvic cancer treated in a North Carolina hospital over a five-year period noted "grave errors of omission and commission" by doctors and "an unfortunately large incidence of delay" in making the right diagnosis and instituting treatment.

Another North Carolina study found that although 79 per cent of the 23,628 patients seen in cancer-detection clinics in that state had visited their physicians in the previous twelve months, "only 17.4 per cent had received a complete physical examination, 27.3 per cent had not had an examination of the breast, 37 per cent had not had a pelvic examination, and 25 per cent had not had a rectal examination." A total of 3,460 of these patients reported that they had specifically asked their doctors for a complete physical examination. But less than half of them actually got one.

The late Dr. Evarts A. Graham of Washington University's School of Medicine, a distinguished pioneer in the field of lung-cancer surgery, bemoaned the fact that only 25 to 30 per cent of the patients with this disease are referred to a competent surgeon "at a time when there is a good chance of eradicating the cancer by a suitable resection." One of the reasons is the patient's delay in seeking medical advice, Dr. Graham said, "but much too often the fatal delay can be charged to the physician who first sees him. Nearly 50 per cent of our patients have been diagnosed as having virus pneumonia before they reach us."

It is hardly accidental that the considerable frequency of

bungling diagnosis, hasty and sloppy treatment, and questionable surgery has been accompanied by a phenomenal increase in malpractice suits in recent years. Estimates are that the number of damage suits has increased twenty-five-fold since the end of World War II and that physicians now are paying some $50 million a year in court awards and out-of-court settlements arising from malpractice claims. One out of every seven physicians now in practice has been sued by a disgruntled patient at one time or another. The cost of the liability insurance carried by doctors has risen steeply in many communities as a result of the increased number of court actions.

Malpractice suits cover a variety of real or imagined grievances, running all the way from claims by patients for injuries sustained in falls from a hospital bed or in a doctor's office to cases of glaring medical laxity. Among the latter are the incidents involving one surgeon who amputated a limb from the wrong patient and another who operated on the right patient but cut off the wrong leg. In a third case, a surgeon killed a patient by removing a diseased kidney without realizing that it was the only one the man had left. In a fourth incident, uncommon but actual, a Michigan woman was taken to a hospital for treatment of an infected finger but wound up in the operating room and had her gallbladder removed. Some of the actions are nuisance suits brought on flimsy grounds or none at all in the hope of quick settlements. But there is little question that many of them arise legitimately from serious cases of medical negligence or carelessness. There is a great deal of difference between the type of accident that cannot be prevented and indefensible medical practice.

The growing estrangement of doctors and patients has undoubtedly been an important factor in the situation. The physician who is admired by his patients is never sued. The idea of malpractice litigation would hardly occur to the patient who is satisfied with the care he is getting and enjoys a warm and mature relationship with his doctor. As the family doctor who was beloved friend and confidant has given way to the busy specialist who treats the patient impersonally, the bond that once made a lawsuit against a physician unthinkable has been steadily weakened.

The act of suing a doctor is often the culmination of prolonged friction and anger, sometimes directed not only against the physician involved but also against the medical profession in general. Regardless of whether the patient's complaint is justified or stems from expecting altogether too much not only from his doctor but from medical science, his malpractice suit is a protest against being denied the help that he feels he was entitled to. Interestingly enough, the frequency of malpractice litigation has been found to be highest in areas where surgeons, who are the most common targets of such suits, charge the biggest fees.

A study made several years ago in California, which has the highest incidence of malpractice actions in the nation, found that two out of every three plaintiffs brought suit only because they felt that their doctors had failed to show ordinary sympathy and concern over the results of their incompetence or negligence. A number of those interviewed said that they would not have sued if the physicians had taken the time to explain what had gone wrong and had offered to help pay the extra medical expense incurred or if they had at least refrained from promptly sending a bill. These plaintiffs clearly interpreted the bill as an expression of the doctor's greed, callousness, and lack of any feeling of guilt. The study concluded that malpractice suits "are drastic symptoms of a breakdown in the relationship between the doctor and his patient" and that most of them arise "from the interaction of the suit-prone doctor and the suit-prone patient. . . . The patient expects powers that medical science cannot offer. The doctor, in his efforts to bolster his self-esteem, tends to promise more than medicine can deliver. The feelings of inadequacy that both patient and doctor feel erupt into disputes, despair and mutual recriminations."

The growing concern over the threat of damage suits already has had considerable effects on medical practice, not all of them necessarily favorable from the patient's point of view. By way of protecting themselves against possible litigation, many physicians are now resorting to a greater number of diagnostic tests than they would ordinarily use and are insisting more frequently on medical consultation, even when there are no positive grounds for seeking additional advice. The fear of lawsuits sometimes restrains doctors from undertaking any new and experimental procedures or any surgery that has a high element of risk. Urging physicians to be on their guard, a medical journal has warned that "every new patient should be regarded as a potential litigant."

Although some malpractice suits are baseless, there are at least as many, and probably more, cases in which patients are not recompensed for the harm done them by incompetent or careless practitioners because of the traditional conspiracy of silence when doctors are asked to testify against their colleagues. Far from uncommon are the cases in which physicians privately concur that certain doctors are criminally incompetent but flatly refuse to take the stand against them. Regardless of how flagrant the case may be, it is almost impossible to get one doctor to testify against another. Covering up one another's mistakes, either by refusing to appear in court against a negligent colleague or by actual lying on the witness stand, seems to be the unwritten rule, even though all physicians are pledged in their code of ethics to expose the misdeeds of their colleagues. Doctors who have dared to flaunt the tradition by testifying on behalf of patients in damage suits have been snubbed at medical society meetings, have suffered a marked decline in referrals from other physicians, and have sometimes even been dropped from hospital staffs.

Malpractice suits are occasionally little more than attempts to blackmail honest and fully qualified practitioners. But the primary causes of malpractice litigation are medical incompetence and carelessness. The basic trouble, as one attorney who has handled a large number of malpractice cases has said, is that "many doctors today run their patients through like a sausage factory."

VI

Doctors have always been in the enviable position of selling services whose quality the customers are unable to judge, and the doctors would like to keep it that way. Much of their resistance to new departures in the organization of medical care arises out of their determination to preserve this immunity from outside scrutiny of their professional performance.

"Although medical societies talk much of preserving competition and free enterprise," Dr. William A. Dorsey, area administrator of the United Mine Workers' medical care program in

Colorado, has said, "they want this competition to remain at a level where the incompetent compete with the competent on equal terms. There can be no other reason for their declaration that organized medicine does not grant any third party the prerogative of passing on the quality of care."

But the doctor's right to be accountable to no one is certainly far less important than the patient's right to get good medical care. That he does not always get it under the existing system, in which standards of competence and professional behavior are largely left to individual good intentions, is amply clear from the available evidence and has been fully acknowledged in the extraordinarily frank and challenging reports of two AMA study committees. The fact that the reform recommendations of both groups have been shelved strengthens the doubts about whether the medical profession can be depended upon to institute anything like a vigorous housecleaning on its own.

In 1955, after a nationwide study of complaints against unethical and incompetent physicians, the AMA's Special Committee on Medical Practices concluded that "the present supervision of organized medicine over the ethical standards of doctors is not adequate to protect the public or the good name of the profession." The committee reported the widespread existence of improper practices, "a lack of vigorous activity" on the part of medical societies in disciplining erring members, and "confusion in everybody's mind about altruism and self-interest." It called for a "more precise differentiation between ethics and professional etiquette" and for more effective liaison between medical societies and state licensing bodies to enforce higher standards of competence and conduct and to protect patients against exploitation.

The AMA's reaction to this candid appraisal of the situation was typical. After receiving the report, the AMA board of trustees announced that it "is determined that the public and the good name of the profession shall be protected from the small minority of physicians who engage in unethical practices." It thereupon promptly ordered that the report be locked in the files and withheld from publication. It was not until a few copies of the fifteen thousand-word report were leaked to the press, apparently by some committee members who resented the secrecy edict, that the AMA *Journal* published a one-page summary. This represented the sum total of the action ever taken on the report of the Special Committee on Medical Practices.

But sweeping the unsavory facts under the rug would not still criticism of medical abuses. Stung by continuing adverse publicity, the AMA set up a new study group in 1959 to take another look at the situation. After an exhaustive two-and-one-half-year survey, the new Medical Disciplinary Committee arrived at substantially the same conclusions as its predecessor. It found that "disciplinary action by both medical societies and boards of medical examiners [state licensing bodies] is inadequate," that there is a "lack of forceful leadership" in the policing of standards of quality and ethics, that medical society grievance committees are generally toothless watchdogs, and that, as a rule, the only offenders ever penalized are those who consistently violate the narcotics or abortion laws. The committee recommended a number of corrective steps, but except for a couple of piddling proposals voted by the AMA House of Delegates, these too have so far been ignored.

Even more outspoken than the earlier study group, the Medical Disciplinary Committee deplored what it described as "apathy, substantial ignorance and a lack of sense of individual responsibility by physicians as a whole . . . demonstrated by the 'hear no evil, see no evil' attitude of many doctors and through the complaints which are received concerning physicians when the complaining physician later refuses to testify or give a deposition."

The committee reported that in addition to drug addicts, alcoholics, and outright incompetents in the professional ranks, "there are those who overcharge and who charge one fee when the patient has no insurance and a much higher fee if the patient is insured. There are those who perform unnecessary surgery. There are those who consort with quacks and faddists. There are fee splitters and rebaters." Other offenses, it said, include the bilking of insurance programs, charging for services never performed, and the promiscuous prescribing of sedatives or stimulants.

The committee cited the puny record of punishments for these transgressions. It noted that medical societies throughout the United States disciplined only thirty-two doctors in 1960. Of these, seven were expelled, nine were suspended, and "other actions" were taken against the rest. State licensing boards were somewhat more active, revoking the licenses of sixty-eight physicians. This is less than three-hundredths of 1 per cent of those now licensed to practice medicine.

Warning that "the public is looking with an increasingly critical eye at failings and delinquencies of the physician," the committee called for a review of policing mechanisms "critically and at once." It urged that "American medicine at the national, state and local level maintain an active, aggressive and continuing interest in medical disciplinary matters so that, by a demonstration of good faith, medicine will be permitted to continue to discipline its own members when necessary." Whether this pious hope will ever be implemented is highly problematic. While the AMA and its component societies are clarion-voiced in their pronouncements against sin, they have displayed a consistent reluctance to crack down on unscrupulous or incompetent practitioners.

The Medical Disciplinary Committee put its finger on one of the basic flaws in the existing method of professional regulation by pointing out that the functions of state boards of medical examiners are almost entirely confined to the granting of licenses. "All too seldom," it declared, "are licensed physicians called to task by the boards. Greater emphasis should be given in ensuring competence and observance of law and ethics after licensure."

The present system, under which neither the state licensing agencies nor the profession itself exercises any effective controls on the conduct of medical practice, is based on two dangerous fallacies. One of them is the assumption that because a doctor is adequately equipped at the time he passes his examinations and receives a license, he will remain equally qualified for the rest of his life. The other is the premise that all physicians are equally devoted to the high ideals of their calling. Neither assumption holds water. Both are based on the unwarranted suppositions that all doctors will keep themselves well abreast of the rapidly accumulating body of medical knowledge and that all of them will invariably put the interests of their patients ahead of their own. A license granted twenty or thirty years ago is little proof that the holder is now competent. And the result of the lack of teeth in the medical practice statutes is that, short of seeking re-dress for glaring mistakes through malpractice litigation, patients now have virtually no protection against disreputable or incom-petent doctors.

Another perilous assumption behind the existing setup is that a medical degree qualifies a physician to practice any branch of medicine he wants to. Most of the state medical practice and licensing laws date back to the days when there was generally little difference in the qualifications of doctors. But the drastic changes in the dimensions of medical science have destroyed the myth of total competence. It now takes from five to seven years of postgraduate training to turn out a competent, well-rounded general surgeon. It takes several years of postgraduate study to produce a competent internist. What justification is there for granting a physician a license to practice surgery and to under-take the management of all kinds of complex problems in diag-nosis and treatment after a one-year internship?

Not only is a realistic overhauling of the medical licensing laws long overdue, but the state boards of medical examiners should be freed of the domination now exercised over them by medical societies. In many states, medical societies are authorized by law to appoint or recommend members of regulatory bodies. In most places, there are close personal and professional ties be-tween the medical society leadership and those charged with en-forcement of the regulatory laws. Since the curious ethics of the medical profession puts up an almost impenetrable protective wall around its members, regardless of their conduct, organized medicine's hold over the public regulatory authority all too often means that everybody's business becomes nobody's business.

There is a crying need for far more vigorous supervision of private medical practice and for bringing licensure requirements into line with the advances in medicine. But while the need is acknowledged by all objective observers, the precise mechanisms for meeting it remain a matter of controversy. Proposed reforms range all the way from making medical society membership, with all the privileges accruing from it, contingent upon participation in continuing medical education programs to making medical licensure valid only for a limited period, with renewal by exami-nation. One former AMA president has advocated a minimum of two years of hospital training instead of the present one-year internship as a requirement for licensure, compulsory postgraduate study, and the periodic reexamination, perhaps every five years, of physicians to establish their continued competence. Another suggestion has been that doctors be required to take regular sabbaticals for renewed study. All these proposals are certain to encounter strong opposition from the medical profession, and there are serious practical problems standing in the way of their implementation.

But whatever the difficulties, there can be no question that the present system of professional regulation is woefully inadequate and that the assurance of more satisfactory standards of medical services is an urgent necessity. While the medical profession insists that it alone should have the authority to judge and discipline its members, it has been unable or unwilling to establish and enforce effective standards. Doctors regard what is essentially a public utility as their own private preserve, resenting the slightest implication of outside intrusion into their affairs. At the same time, however, they not only are reluctant to pass judgment on their fellows but have been known to join hands with crooked practitioners against lay interference with what they consider their exclusive prerogatives. All too frequently, the individual physician's conscience somehow becomes benumbed when he acts collectively. The challenging question is how much longer a vested interest can be allowed to block the establishment of quality controls in an enterprise in which the welfare and lives of all of us are so deeply involved.

CHAPTER NINE

The United States
Faces a Mounting Shortage
of Medical Manpower

I

FEW OF the multifold medical care problems can be decisively tackled unless something is done about the inadequate supply of doctors and auxiliary personnel to meet the challenge of an explosively changing pattern of population, disease, and health services.

The growing shortage of physicians, dentists, medical therapists and technicians, nurses, and other health workers is not something which has burst upon us overnight. It has been building up for years as the output of our medical and other professional schools has failed to keep pace with the rapid growth of the population of the United States, now proceeding at the rate of three million a year, and the steady expansion of demand for medical services and for research personnel. The health manpower picture is already alarming. It will become more and more critical unless we step up our training of doctors within the next decade or two on a scale involving an outlay of effort and money so massive as to make its effective accomplishment quite unlikely.

The problem is far from academic. Available medical manpower is stretched tight, with serious scarcities in many key areas. The effects of the mounting shortage of physicians are felt in many hospitals that are desperate for house staffs. It plagues parents who are trying to find a doctor for a sick child at night, residents of many rural areas left with only one or two doctors or none at all, and, potentially, anybody in a time of emergency. It threatens the whole fabric of medical care, and it also exerts a terrible strain on the medical profession itself. But in the years ahead, the supply of physicians is likely to lag still further behind our needs. Immediate and vigorous action to expand the nation's medical education facilities is therefore a matter of the utmost concern to every American. The quality of tomorrow's medical care—and of the level of our health—will be determined by what is done today.

Several governmental study commissions have in the past few years come to the same challenging conclusion: it would require 11,000 medical school graduates annually, or about 3,500 more than we now get, merely to keep up with the anticipated growth of the country's population and to maintain by 1975 even the present inadequate ratio of doctors. Such an expansion would involve the establishment of some twenty new medical schools, with a capital investment of up to a billion dollars and the outlay of additional millions every year to meet their large operating deficits. The opposition of organized medicine constitutes a formidable barrier to the only possible source of the required large-scale financial aid, the Federal government. Money, moreover, is not the only problem. There has been an alarming decline in recent years in the number as well as the caliber of medical school applicants. Neither the reservoir of qualified students who are willing to become doctors nor the trained faculty personnel is available for the needed new medical schools.

The gravity of the situation is graphically told by these statistics: in 1900, there was one practicing private physician for every 500 persons in the United States; today, the ratio is approximately one for every 1,100; by 1975, it may be one for every 1,500. Many authorities feel that the existing proportion of physicians to population is far too low for the optimal requirements of health protection. An additional decline in the ratio will mean that already overworked doctors will have to put in still longer and more tiring days, with a further reduction in the amount of personal attention they are able to give their patients and an increasing trend toward assembly-line medicine. It will put ever greater pressures on the price of medical care. It will make all the more imperative greater efficiency in the organization of medical services for maximum use of the available personnel.

The lagging supply of doctors will force them to turn over more and more of the things they have been doing to nurses and other paramedical workers. While these auxiliary workers also are in short supply, they can be trained much more rapidly and cheaply than doctors. Wider use of ancillary personnel would be all to the good, as high-priced physicians and dentists are now performing many services that could be done just as well and much more economically by people with less strenuous and costly training. Ophthalmologists are doing refractive work—the correction of visual defects through eyeglasses—that optometrists are fully qualified to do. Giving injections, changing dressings, taking blood-pressure readings, testing urine, and many other simple tasks can be done fully as well by nurses and technicians. Many of the less complicated dental services can likewise be competently performed by technicians.

But improvements in medical productivity and the more effective utilization of paramedical personnel are contingent upon new and more logical institutional arrangements, which the organized medical profession has been bitterly resisting. To no small degree, the present scarcity of physicians is the result not only of insufficient educational facilities but also of the inefficient utilization of the trained manpower we have. Personnel requirements would be far easier to satisfy under a system that coordinates doctors into rational teams, supports them with suitable cadres of auxiliary workers, organizes health centers and hospitals into functionally related echelons, and removes financial barriers to the redistribution of physicians into the areas of greatest need. These also happen to be the very elements essential to high quality of medical care.

Two things are amply clear in any examination of the medical manpower picture. The first is that the need for more doctors and related skilled help is at the heart of every medical care problem. None of the needed reforms can realize its full potential without them. Without more physicians, there will not be time enough for the patients now crowding waiting rooms, to say nothing of the hordes of new patients joining the parade every year. Without them, we cannot assure medical services at reasonable cost for all those who need them. The second distressing fact is that the shortage is worsening at a time when the average American is demanding more and more medical care, when the number of chronically ill is constantly increasing as the life-span is extended, when the proportion of children also requiring the greatest amount of medical services is steadily rising, and when we must build for the increasing complexity of tomorrow's medical practice.

There is little evidence that even the most conservative of the medical manpower requirements of the immediate future will be met. But the problem is infinitely more complicated than the mere need for a bigger pool of physicians. A simple increase in the number of doctors will not wholly solve it. Equally important is the need for a far-reaching reorganization of medical practice and for a thorough reassessment of the existing system of medical education. The grave shortage of interns and residents, the excessive surge into the specialties, the decline in the ratio of general practitioners, and the diminishing reservoir of candidates for medical schools are closely interrelated phenomena. They are likely to grow worse unless corrective measures are instituted. The quality of medical care will inevitably suffer if ways are not found to counteract these trends.

There are multiple questions in the crisis of both the quantity and the quality of medical care that the United States is facing. Where will tomorrow's doctors come from? Where and how will they be trained? How good will they be? What sort of medicine will they practice? Will they be coldly scientific artisans or have an insight into the social, economic, and emotional context within which their patients live and work? How will their services be organized and paid for? Will most of them continue to be solo practitioners, or will they take advantage of the potentialities for greater economy and effectiveness made possible by group practice?

None of these questions can be dealt with in a vacuum. They are all part of the same picture. This issue of the adequacy of the supply of physicians, for instance, cannot be discussed intelligently without some prior agreement on adequacy for what and for what kind of practice. Are we talking about a setup under which, as is now largely the case, the amount of medical care given is substantially determined by the ability to pay for it? Or do we have in mind a system that would make it possible to provide to a greater extent the health needs now often left unmet? Are we talking primarily in terms of individual practice, with its waste and duplication, or do we envisage wider resort to the pooling of skills, equipment, and ancillary personnel?

The average layman has little, if any, awareness of the enormous complexity and costliness of medical education and of the painful process of reappraisal and experimentation that it is now undergoing as it seeks to reorient itself to continuing scientific, social, and economic change. He has little idea of the precarious financial position of the nation's medical schools, at a time when they must expand. He is hardly aware of the fact that the medical schools have a responsibility not only for training the doctors of tomorrow but also for much of the research in the health field and for helping the physicians already in practice to maintain their competence by keeping fully abreast of scientific progress.

How will the medical schools, confronted with a predicament of financing as well as function, meet the challenge of developing physicians for the practice of the 1970's and 1980's and beyond? How will they attempt to raise the quality, vary the roles, and alter the training of their students as new knowledge keeps on piling up and as the social setting constantly changes? How can the cluttered curriculum be simplified and improved so that doctors well grounded in the basic sciences and with some understanding of the socioeconomics of medicine can be trained in the shortest possible time?

We all have a stake in these and many related questions. Our chances of being helped when we or members of our family are ill will depend directly on the number and quality of doctors that the medical schools turn out. We are all endangered when the medical schools, the wellsprings whence will flow the better health of tomorrow, are in trouble.

A sobering fact to bear in mind in considering the financial plight of the medical schools is that less than 1 per cent of the total annual cost of health services in the United States is now invested in their operation. What the drug companies are spending every year for promotion of their products is about four times the combined budgets of all of the nation's medical schools. And yet these schools are the basic ingredient of the entire endeavor. Without them, there would be no health services. Just as today's research lays the groundwork for tomorrow's medicine, so today's medical education is in no small way shaping the character of tomorrow's medical practice. The medical schools deserve much better support if they are not only to turn out enough doctors but also to equip them for the needs of the space age.

II

Even the AMA now concedes, after stubbornly denying the obvious for years, that we must substantially step up our production of doctors. But there is still a great deal of confusion about the proper yardsticks for measuring the adequacy of the supply of physicians, the difference between active demand and actual need, and the crucial bearing that the type of practice has upon the requirements for medical and paramedical personnel.

The United States now has about 275,000 physicians, which is a ratio of one doctor for every 690 persons. But this figure does not nearly tell the whole story. Not only has the overall supply of physicians fallen far behind the sharp rise in population and demand, but more and more doctors are going into hospital practice and administration, teaching, research, public health work and other governmental employment, and industrial medicine. The ratio of physicians on call when people are sick is thus much smaller than the gross pool of medical manpower would indicate.

The proportion of doctors engaged in private practice has dropped from 86 per cent to 67 per cent in the last thirty years. Whereas the country's population has risen in that period by almost 50 per cent, there has been an increase of only about 25 per cent in the number of private practitioners. The result is that there is now only one active private practitioner for approximately every 1,100 Americans. But well over half of these practitioners are specialists, who are not always available for the initial treatment of disease. The ratio of specialists has jumped nearly four times in the past forty years. On the other hand, the proportion of general practitioners—the first line of defense against illness—has declined by more than 40 per cent since 1930, so that there is at present only one family doctor for every 3,000 persons.

Of the some 170,000 physicians currently in private practice, 99,000 are full-time specialists, 10,000 are part-time specialists, and 61,000 are general practitioners. More than 30,000 MD's, including nearly 10,000 graduates of foreign medical schools, are undergoing their training in hospital internships and residencies. More than 18,000 physicians are in full-time employment in hospitals, on medical school faculties, and in research, administration, and industry. About 17,000 are in government employment in the Armed Forces, the U.S. Public Health Service, and the Veterans Administration. More than 14,000 are either retired or not practicing for other reasons.

In June, 1963, the nation's eighty-seven four-year medical schools graduated 7,324 new MD's. This was one graduate for every 26,000 Americans as compared with one new doctor produced for every 20,000 persons fifty years ago.

It must be borne in mind that the annual output of the medical schools by no means represents a net gain. About four thousand physicians die every year, and a number of others retire from practice. Since we now have an annual net population increase of about three million, there is thus a net increment of only about one new American-trained doctor for every additional 1,000 persons. At this rate, the doctor-population ratio, already at a dangerous point of imbalance, will keep on declining. Just to maintain the present ratio of physicians, our medical education facilities would have to be expanded by about 50 per cent within the next decade or so.

We had many more physicians in private practice in proportion to population thirty years ago than we do today, despite the fact that one out of every six new doctors now being licensed in the United States was educated abroad. The same thing holds true for dentists. There were fifty-nine dentists for every 100,000 Americans in 1930. Today the figure is fifty-five, and it will be down to fifty by 1975 unless there is a broad expansion of dental school capacity. To maintain the existing ratio will require an increase from the present 3,200 to more than 6,000 dental graduates a year by 1975.

The U.S. Public Health Service has predicted that if there is no material enlargement of professional training capacity, there will be only one doctor for every 800 persons by 1975 as against the present figure of one for every 730—and this includes the one out of every three physicians who is not in private practice. We have been able to maintain the present proportion of doctors to population only by importing a large number of foreign-trained physicians, some of them of questionable competence, who now make up close to 10 per cent of the nation's medical practitioners. There is general agreement among authorities that the present and predicted output of our medical schools, plus the graduates of foreign schools licensed to practice in this country, will not meet the surging demands of our rapidly growing population.

Aside from the overall lag in the production of doctors, there are acute scarcities in a number of fields and a gross maldistribution of medical manpower. The geographical distribution of physicians is extremely uneven, ranging all the way from 95.9 for every 100,000 persons in the South to 154.4 per 100,000 in the Northeast. The West is in second place with 144.1 doctors per 100,000 population, and the North Central region has a ratio of 111.2 per 100,000 population. To bring the supply in the country as a whole up to the level of the New England and Central Atlantic regions would require 50,000 additional doctors.

While the great metropolitan centers have an average of 158.4 physicians per 100,000, the ratio in isolated rural areas is only 47.4 per 100,000. Doctors, particularly full-time specialists, tend to concentrate in densely populated areas with a high-income level. New York has an average of one physician for every 510 persons as against an average of one for every 1,555 in South Dakota. In Massachusetts, there is one doctor for each 550 persons; in Mississippi, the average is one for every 1,310.

Similar sharp disparities between the states and between urban and rural areas prevail for all other health-profession groups, including dentists, psychologists, medical and psychiatric social workers, medical therapists, technicians, and nurses. There are 72 dentists and 321 graduate nurses per 100,000 population in the Northeast as against only 35 dentists and 174 nurses for every 100,000 persons in the South. In the District of Columbia, there is one dentist for every 1,100 persons; in Arkansas, the average is one for every 3,700. In Connecticut, there is one gradutate nurse for every 270 persons; in Kentucky, the figure is one for every 860.

Not only are specialists concentrated in the larger cities, but there is a serious maldistribution of physicians within the various branches of medicine in relation to need. While there are more than enough surgeons, for instance, there is a desperate shortage of psychiatrists. There are far too few competent psychiatrists even for the minority who can afford to pay anywhere from $10 *to $40 per treatment, and most of them are bunched in the big cities. One-fifth of the psychiatrists in the United States practice in the New York–New Jersey metropolitan area. As against one psychiatrist for every 6,400 persons in New York, there is only one for every 65,000 in Alabama. The dearth of psychiatrists is most evident in the state mental hospitals, where hundreds of positions remain permanently vacant. To meet the minimum standards of care set by the American Psychiatric Association, these hospitals alone would need about six thousand more psychiatrists. The U.S. Public Health Service estimates that no more than 10 per cent of those suffering from psychoneuroses and other emotional disorders are now getting competent professional attention. The main reason for the scarcity is the inordinate length and costliness of psychiatric training. Not many medical school graduates can afford to become psychiatrists, and still fewer can raise the some $20,000 for the analytic training required to qualify for the practice of psychoanalysis.

There are equally critical shortages in the fields of rehabilitation, public health, and research. We also need many more pediatricians, obstetricians, internists, and general physicians. While the number of internists and pediatricians is slowly increasing, the net result of the rapid decline in the ratio of general practitioners has been a material drop in the total of the three groups available for general medical care. If general practitioners continue to disappear at the same rate that they have over the past three decades, we shall need at least six times as many internists as are now in practice to regain by 1975 the general physician–patient ratio of the early thirties.

The U.S. Office of Vocational Rehabilitation estimates that 1,500,000 of the more than 5,000,000 Americans over the age of forty-five who have been disabled for more than three months by chronic disease or some other impairment could substantially benefit from rehabilitation services. If they were provided such services, many could once again learn to live their lives in independence and with greater dignity. Some could return to work. Others could be brought to conditions of self-care. In either case, the benefits would extend not only to the disabled persons but to their families and to society. But the trained professional personnel for the job is pitifully meager. There are now only about 350 board-certified specialists in physical medicine and rehabilitation in the United States. There are 8,500 physical therapists, and at least 30,000 more are needed. There are 5,800 occupational therapists, and 15,000 more are required. There are 5,500 speech and hearing therapists, and we need four times that number.

About 20 per cent of the budgeted positions for doctors in city and state health departments are reported to be vacant, and this has discouraged the execution of many plans to expand essential public health services. Medical schools have many unfilled faculty positions. Many more skilled investigators are needed in various fields of medical research. The policy of producing a high proportion of medical scientists and specialists has been responsible for the flowering of American medicine. Further scientific progress will be impeded unless enough physicians can be spared from the load of daily practice for the training and effort required for delving into numerous research problems. But the dilemma is that the greater the number of physicians diverted into the specialties and research, the thinner become the ranks of those responsible for general medical care.

Unless at least twenty new dental schools are established within the next decade, we shall have about fifteen thousand fewer dentists by 1975 than the number needed to assure even the present totally inadequate dentist-population ratio. This will mean an average of only one dentist for every 2,000 persons. In 1930, we had one dentist for every 1,700 persons. Any increase in the proportion of persons per dentist will mean that the average amount of professional time available for each patient will be reduced and that the ability of our dental force to protect the nation's oral health will be threatened.

The number of both graduate and practical nurses has increased tremendously in the last few decades. There are now more than 500,000 active graduate nurses and about 225,000 practical nurses. But the demand has risen even more sharply and continues to outrun the supply. Few hospitals have a full complement of trained nurses, and the potentialities for home nursing have barely been scratched. To reach the "conservative" goal set by the National League for Nursing will require graduation of 48,000 nurses a year by 1970, which is about 18,000 more than we now produce. Even to maintain the present average of one nurse for every 350 persons, 100,000 more nurses than we currently have will be needed by the end of the sixties.

The trend of technological evolution in the health field has been toward ever-greater subdivision of labor. The services of physicians are increasingly being augmented by those of members of other health professions, whose numbers have increased at a far greater rate. In 1900, three out of every five professional health workers were doctors. Now only one in ten is a physician. While the supply of doctors has risen 60 per cent since the turn of the century, the number of nurses has jumped by 4,000 per cent. The striking growth of the allied health professions has eased the adjustment to the declining ratio of physicians and has had a profound influence on the patterns and availability of medical care. But shortages of trained people in virtually every one of the professional and technical careers in the health field continue to constitute a serious bottleneck in the provision of medical services. Many more auxiliary workers will have to be trained and greater responsibilities will have to be delegated to them if the health needs of the American people are to be met through higher medical productivity.

The resolution of the need for a sharp increase in the production of doctors presents even more formidable difficulties. Here we are caught in a treadmill of related problems and deficiencies —the length and costliness of medical education, the recruitment of adequate numbers of capable students, the provision of faculties, essential curricular adjustments, and many others. Woven through all of them is the question of financing. Where is the money going to come from to expand the existing medical schools and to build and operate the twenty new ones that we shall need by 1975 merely to maintain the present physician-population ratio? The inescapable answer is that either Federal funds will be provided on a large scale or the job will not get done.

The one thing amply clear, from a practical as well as from a moral standpoint, is that the United States cannot continue to fill the void in its medical manpower by allowing itself to become a dumping ground for foreign doctors, most of whom come from countries with urgent unmet health needs and many of whom are poorly trained. The extent of our growing dependence on imported physicians may be readily seen from the fact that there are now many more of them on the staffs of our hospitals than there are graduates each year from all the medical schools in this country. About a decade ago, American hospitals employed fewer than two thousand graduates of foreign medical schools. Now the figure is almost five times as high. One of every three doctors presently serving as interns or residents in our hospitals was educated abroad. In five states, well over 50 per cent of the hospital internships and residencies were recently filled by foreign MD's.

Why are so many foreign-trained doctors coming here? There are conflicting motivations at play in the situation. The obvious reason is that the young physicians want to further their knowledge in our superior facilities for advanced medical training. Theoretically, the objective of such training is to enable them to do a better job when they go back to their native lands. In practice, however, this end is only partially achieved. About half of the more than twenty thousand alien doctors admitted to this country on temporary visas have stayed on to go into private practice after completing their hospital service. In 1950, the 308 graduates of foreign medical schools who were licensed to practice in this country represented 5.1 per cent of that year's new medical licensees. By 1960, the total of physicians trained abroad who were granted licenses had jumped to 1,419, and they accounted for 17.7 per cent of the new crop of medical practitioners.

Much the same ambivalence has been evident on our side, too. The thinking behind the program approved by Congress some years ago for admitting large numbers of foreign doctors was to make our training facilities available to help lift the standards of medical practice in poorer countries. But as our own shortage has progressively worsened, the original aim, for the most part, has been lost sight of. Hospitals desperately in need of interns and residents have often come to look upon foreign physicians primarily as a source of cheap medical labor. Significantly, state and local hospital associations have strongly resisted attempts to weed out the less competent foreign members of house staffs by requiring them to pass examinations. Of the 8,700 foreign-educated MD's who took the first tests, only 3,700 passed.

There are unquestionably many fine foreign medical schools. But authoritative opinion is that there are also many poor ones, some of them little more than diploma mills. Graduates of schools in the latter category unfortunately predominate among those who have flocked to the United States. Relatively few of the doctors coming here are from Western Europe or England, where standards of medical education are not far behind our own. Most of the physicians admitted to this country have come from the Philippine Islands, Turkey, India, Iran, Korea, Japan, Greece, Spain, Mexico, Brazil, Argentina, Cuba, Peru, Colombia, and the Dominican Republic. Measured by American standards, the training received in most of these countries is perfunctory. The entire teaching program in their medical schools usually consists in formal lectures, a type of education discarded in our schools more than fifty years ago. Emphasis on clinical and laboratory training necessarily limits the size of classes in American medical schools, usually to fewer than a hundred students. But some foreign schools have classes ten times as large as ours, far too large for good training. Some of them admit as many as 1,600 freshmen. Being part of an entering class of this size, one medical educator has remarked, "is like attending school in a $2 seat in Yankee Stadium."

In some cases, American hospitals have been shocked to discover that their interns recruited through advertisements in foreign medical journals or through travel agents abroad were, in reality, graduates of native herb schools in India or Korea. The inadequacy of the training of some of the foreign physicians, here as well as abroad, was dramatically pinpointed a few years ago when Martyn Green, prominent British star of Gilbert and Sullivan operettas, crushed one of his legs in an elevator accident in New York City. The actor's leg was amputated on the spot by an Indian intern who used a pocketknife borrowed from a policeman. In the storm of controversy that subsequently erupted over whether the drastic surgery might have been averted, the hospital involved conceded that there had been a delay of twenty-three minutes in responding to the emergency call and that the intern had failed to take along his kit of medical instruments or an anesthetic.

The language barrier alone can become a danger to human life. It can be extremely hazardous to turn over the care of patients to apprentice physicians whose knowledge of English is sometimes so fragmentary that they can neither understand the instructions of their mentors nor communicate with their patients. There are also cultural barriers, particularly in the case of doctors from such areas as the Far East and Southeast Asia. Coming from social environments radically different from ours, these physicians can hardly be expected to display the understanding of their patients' problems so important in medical treatment.

There are, furthermore, basic differences in health problems in this country and in other parts of the world. "Medical schools in many countries," Dr. Walter S. Wiggins, secretary of the AMA's Council on Medical Education and Hospitals, has said, "dwell heavily on public health measures to eradicate contagious diseases such as typhoid and dysentery. These are no longer major problems here, and we emphasize degenerative diseases of the elderly, such as cancer, heart and arterial ailments. We have to measure these foreign doctors against our peculiar problems, not theirs."

Because of their less adequate training and for other reasons, many of the foreign doctors licensed here go into general practice. What is happening, in effect, is that American students are usually discouraged from entering general practice and graduates of low-grade foreign medical schools are encouraged to fill the gap.

But this is only part of a broader issue. Aside from the threat to our own standards of medical care, there is the question as to whether the wealthiest nation in the world has the right to drain the thin professional resources of poorer countries. In no other field does the United States draw to the same extent on personnel trained abroad as it does in medicine. At a time when we should be in a position to export doctors to help the underdeveloped countries, as the Russians are already doing, we find ourselves unable to staff our hospitals without foreign help and are increasingly coming to depend on imported MD's for a significant proportion of our general physicians. At the same time, some two thousand Americans are forced to study medicine abroad because there is no room for them in our own medical schools.

It will come as a shock to many Americans to learn that the Soviet Union has been outdistancing us not only in space propulsion but also in the training of doctors. It is reported that there are now 180 Soviet physicians per 100,000 population as compared with a ratio of 137 per 100,000 in this country and that the Russians are working toward a goal of 220 doctors for every 100,000 persons within the next few years.

III

A crucial point to bear in mind is that a decision as to the number of doctors we require is a broad problem of national welfare rather than a technical matter. The decision should be made by an informed public with some understanding of its implications for the level of tomorrow's medical care and the nation's future health. While this may seem like laboring the obvious, it is a principle yet to be fully conceded by the organized medical profession, with its record of opposition to Federal aid for the expansion and operation of medical schools and its tendency to limit its ranks.

No other group dominates its professional education and presumes to set limits to the number of recruits to its calling to the extent that the medical profession does. Like other professions, medicine is entitled to have its say about its own educational standards. But in a matter so sensitive as health, a free society can hardly afford to relinquish its discretion to the judgments of a vested interest. National policy and planning must extend not only to the overall supply of physicians we need but also to their quality and subdivision. What kinds of doctors should be trained, and in what proportion? Do we need such a high ratio of specialists, when the ranks of general physicians are becoming ever thinner? A decision on these and related issues will affect the character of medical care as well as the numerical needs for medical manpower. It cannot be left by the consumers wholly to the producers.

Through a variety of interlocking controls, the training of doctors, no less so than the practice of medicine, is a monopoly tightly ruled by the medical profession. Control of entry into medicine is now vested in three groups, all of them wholly or in part in the profession's hands. These groups are the AMA's Council on Medical Education and Hospitals, the medical schools and their national association, and the state boards of medical licensure and their national federation. All medical schools in the United States are subject to inspection and approval by the AMA council and the Association of American Medical Colleges. Under state laws or licensure board regulations, only graduates of schools accredited by the two organizations are permitted to take examinations for admission to practice. As a rule, the licensure boards are made up exclusively of doctors appointed with the explicit or implicit consent of the state medical societies.

In theory, the public has some representation under this setup through the Association of American Medical Colleges. Theoretically, the medical schools are the creatures of the universities with which they are affiliated and which pay their bills. But, in practice, many of the medical schools have over the years acquired an unusual degree of autonomy. All but a handful of the medical school deans are doctors, and so are most members of their faculties. The AMA and the Association of American Medical Colleges have been disagreeing in recent years with increasing frequency and have formally split on the issue of Federal subsidies for medical education. But the AMA has long exercised a powerful influence over the medical school association, particularly with regard to educational and enrollment standards that determine the size of classes. The AMA's authority extends to graduate training, as internships and residencies can be served only in hospitals that have its approval.

There is no question that the AMA Council on Medical Education and Hospitals has over the years made great and positive contributions to the cause of medical education and has exerted its influence to secure higher standards. Many years ago, it spearheaded the fight to rid the nation of diploma mills, to improve medical training, and to systematize state medical licensure. But there is also evidence that the council has at times used its power to discourage expansion of medical training facilities. In one instance, it openly advocated that medical school enrollment be cut down on the ground that the profession was overcrowded.

Organized medicine for years fought a last-ditch battle against legislation for Federal grants to help the medical schools meet part of their large operating deficits and to provide for the construction of new schools. The official line has been that massive Federal aid for medical education would lead to undue governmental interference and an impairment of standards. Having long denied the necessity for large-scale expansion of medical education facilities, the AMA has argued that the medical schools should get the funds they need from private philanthropy or, at most, from the state governments.

The puerility of this ostrichlike position is fully demonstrated by the mediocre response to the money-raising efforts of the National Fund for Medical Education and the American Medical Education Foundation. The former is sponsored by prominent educators and businessmen and solicits gifts from individuals, corporations, and foundations, while the latter is operated under AMA auspices and hits doctors for contributions. The work of the two organizations has been praiseworthy and helpful. But, between them, they have over a period of ten years raised about $30 million, which is only about one-eighth what the nation's medical schools spend on basic operations in a single year. As for the state governments, the budgets of most of them already are strained to the breaking point, and they are hardly in a position to assume the heavy burden of financing medical education. Only the Federal government has resources big enough for the job.

The deans of the medical schools are, of course, no more anxious to sell their institutions into bureaucratic bondage than is the AMA. But they believe that the schools can be bailed out by Federal funds without any threat of their academic independence. The medical schools have been receiving for a number of years multimillion-dollar research grants from the U.S. Public Health Service, but there have been no complaints of undue governmental interference. The grants are made upon recommendation of study panels composed largely of nongovernment scientists from universities and medical schools. The schools see no reason to believe that an expanded aid-to-education program would not be administered in a somewhat similar manner and without impairment of their freedom.

The need for heavy public subsidy of the education of physicians has become increasingly evident as the medical schools have outrun their traditional sources of financing and as the proportion of money derived from both endowments and tuition has dropped alarmingly. Merely to keep going at their present level, without materially increasing their enrollment, the medical schools need about $40 million a year in additional operating income. This is exclusive of the much larger sums required for plant replacement and expansion.

In 1920, it cost an average of about $500 a year to educate a medical student. Now the figure is more than $5,000. Although tuition fees have steadily climbed and the expenses of going to medical school are prohibitively high, the tuition paid by students currently covers less that one-fifth of the cost of educating them. Parent universities have been forced to dig deeply into their endowment funds and other sources of income to make up the deficits. While medical students represent less than 10 per cent of the enrollment of these universities, the medical schools eat up about 40 per cent of their budgets. Even though every doctor's education is now to a large degree subsidized, a further increase in tuition fees would bear heavily on the already overburdened students without doing much to reduce the budget deficiencies. It would eliminate many students of moderate means, cutting still further the shrinking pool of qualified applicants.

The Federal treasury also is the only place we can turn to for the vast investment required to build, equip, and operate the at least twenty additional medical schools needed in the immediate future. A new medical school requires a capital investment of from $35 million to $50 million. The cost of new medical school construction required just to sustain the present physician-population ratio would thus range from $700 million to $1 billion. A medical school's operating costs come, on the average, to more than $2 million a year. The universities with which the new schools would be affiliated would also need help in meeting their operating deficits.

If the proportion of doctors is to be kept from slipping dangerously in the next ten to twenty years, the expansion of training facilities must start without much delay. It takes from three to five years to plan, build, and staff a medical school, and there is a lag of five more years, and often considerably longer, before its graduates are ready to hang out their shingles. But legislation for Federal aid to medical education has so far had little luck in Congress, and there is no evidence that anything like the essential scale of expansion can be attained.

The AMA has gradually, and most reluctantly, come around

to the idea that some limited form of Federal assistance will be needed to finance the education of more physicians. It continues, however, to drag its heels in a situation of the utmost urgency. Still lurking behind organized medicine's attitude are its long-standing hostility to any concerted planning for the improvement of health services and its fear that a Federal aid program of wide scope would constitute a further acknowledgment of government responsibility for medical care and would thus serve as an entering wedge for the scourge of "socialized medicine."

Carefully camouflaged by the rationalization of the AMA's resistance to Federal aid is the apprehension that it may lose some of its present power to influence the level of medical school enrollment and thereby to control the size of the profession's ranks. While this is indignantly denied by AMA spokesmen, there is good reason to believe that, consciously or unconsciously, this is a consideration of no little importance in their motivation.

Direct evidence of a deliberate policy to hold down the number of doctors is naturally hard to come by. Organized medicine has become much more circumspect in its official pronouncements since the early thirties, when it openly launched a drive to restrict the influx of newcomers. While there has been no further equally outspoken move for protection of the profitable medical sellers' market through an artificial shortage, there is little question that the profession is predisposed to limiting its ranks. The issue of the sufficiency of the number of doctors clearly has a direct bearing on the profession's income. And whatever its motivations may be there is certainly no question that the AMA has been a major obstacle to an increase in the supply of physicians.

In 1932, when the Depression was at its peak and the sledding got tough, the AMA *Journal* called editorially for "professional birth control" to mitigate competition. In 1933, moving to carry out this suggestion, the AMA Council on Medical Education and Hospitals publicly invited the cooperation of the Association of American Medical Colleges "in bringing about a substantial reduction of their enrollment." In a speech at the association's annual meeting that year, Dr. William D. Cutler, the AMA council's secretary, deplored the practice of making up medical school classes "without any regard to the needs of the profession or of the country as a whole." A year later, the council reported that "seven schools have definitely stated that their enrollment will be decreased and others have indicated adherence to the council's principles." Between 1935 and 1938, the number of freshmen admitted by the medical schools was slashed by 841, or 13 per cent. There was a drop of 1,617 in total enrollment between 1935 and 1940. It is true that general college enrollment also went down during the Depression years. But the decline was neither as drastic nor as prolonged. "It was appallingly shortsighted," one medical educator has commented, "to take the bottom of the Depression as a guide for the country's future health needs."

Numerous restrictions hedge entry into a group so fervently dedicated to the ideal of competitive free enterprise as the medical profession is. Not only have the medical schools been highly selective in accepting applicants, but the expansion of training facilities has always been approached most conservatively and frequently with a remarkable lack of vigor. Regardless of whether or not this has been by premeditated design, the result has long been a failure to achieve one of the fundamental requirements of a free economy: that the recruited supply be equated with the manifested demand.

The profession is undoubtedly afraid that pressure for increased medical school enrollment may impair the quality of training. But an insistence on preserving quality, in which the consumer of medical care has an equally important stake, can also be used as a cover for other motives. There has been a growing cult of exclusiveness in the medical profession, as well as the almost pathological fear of the possible leveling effect of greater numbers. An increase in the flow of new recruits poses not only the threat of greater competition but also the risk of bringing in people who differ substantially from those already there. In an elite such as the medical profession, there is an almost mystical feeling that something is lost when its esoteric knowledge is spread too thin.

Experienced physicians are in a better position than most of us to judge what the standards of medical education should be. But the wisdom of lodging authority over the medical schools in the organized profession is highly questionable. When the power to determine supply, which is inherent in the power to set standards, is left in the hands of a private group, there is the inevitable temptation to try to keep prices high through limited production. A monopoly is all too likely to confuse its own interests with the public interest.

IV

The standard gauge for measuring the adequacy of the supply of doctors in comparison with the past is the physician-population ratio. But this yardstick is a gross oversimplification because it leaves out such significant factors as the changing patterns of medical services and the greater demand on the part of a society that is steadily becoming better educated and more prosperous. The fact that the average doctor now puts in at least 50 per cent more time working than does the man who has the usual forty-hour week is in itself ample proof that we have fallen behind in the provision of medical manpower. On the other hand, the criteria of personnel requirements are meaningless without reference to methods of practice and of payment. There is good reason to believe that such requirements are lower when medical care is handled through group practice and when hospitals are staffed by full-time physicians than they are under the prevailing system of solo practice.

Another important consideration is that medical services do not lend themselves to the same balance between need and demand that generally prevails in other segments of the economy. Need is the quantity of medical services, preventive and curative, necessary for optimal health for everybody, regardless of ability to pay. But when we talk of demand in the health field we are referring to the amount of medical services that people ask for without prodding and can afford to pay for. At present, we are clearly coming much closer to meeting demand, which is quite a different thing from meeting need. And even this is achieved at the cost of crowded doctors' offices, hasty treatment, and a general reluctance to make home and night calls. There is not the slightest question that a great many people would use more and better medical care if they could afford to pay for it and if the necessary personnel and facilities were available and properly distributed.

Should supply be tailored to effective demand or to medical needs? Those who approach the problem with an interest in extending the benefits of medical science to all segments of the population will obviously make a different evaluation from those who consider it solely from the point of view of the medical profession's income under present conditions. There is a similar gap between those who think primarily in terms of waiting for people to get sick and those who believe that much of the future of medicine lies in the preventive field.

Do the great scientific advances of the past few decades mean that we need a higher or lower ratio of physicians than we once did? It has been claimed that we can get along with a lower ratio because today's medical practitioner is much more efficient and has at his command far more potent tools than his predecessor did. The argument is that the doctor now gets around more easily, that more patients come to see him in his office instead of asking him to come to the home, that he can use much more powerful drugs and more effective equipment to shorten the duration of illness, that he works with more nurses and technicians, and that he can thus accomplish more in less time.

The average physician's productivity has undoubtedly been raised by the progress of medical science and by the automobile, the telephone, the greater concentration of people in cities, and the greatly increased use of hospitals. At the same time, the demand for his services has been lessened to some extent by such things as improved diet and sanitation and by immunization for many of the infectious diseases. But the trouble is that these very gains have simultaneously served to swell both need and demand.

On the other side of the coin are the steadily growing intricacy of medicine and the much wider use of medical services brought about by greater health consciousness, the sharp rise in the standard of living, and the rapid development of health insurance. Some twelve thousand new Americans are born each day. On the other end of the age range is the rising tide of older people, with their much greater incidence of chronic conditions and medical needs. Medical progress has made it possible to treat effectively many diseases that we could formerly do nothing about, and the average American is making twice as many visits to physicians in the course of a year than he did in the 1930's.

Moreover, a new dimension has been added to the doctor-population ratio by the fact that a patient who consults his family physician is now frequently referred to one or more specialists. The mere numerical relationship of doctors to population therefore no longer reflects the true picture. There also are increasing requirements for physicians in public health, teaching, and research positions. All these trends can be expected to continue at an accelerated pace.

A doctor can now care for twice or three times as many patients as his predecessor did a quarter of a century ago. But increasing efficiency can be carried to the point where medicine loses its effectiveness. This point, unfortunately, already is being approached all too often these days. Attention to the psychological and social aspects of illness and the practice of prevention take time. Growing medical sophistication, a greater awareness of diseases, stimulated by the campaigns of the big voluntary health funds, and many sweeping changes in our way of life make patients more demanding of the doctor's time and attention. They want more explanations, need more reassurance, and require more understanding. Frustration is unavoidable when, as is now the case, 36 per cent of doctors see more than thirty patients a day and 17 per cent of them handle more than forty patients daily. "If the individual physician-patient relationship is to be the meaningful personal relationship which both the medical profession and the public believe it should be," the Surgeon General's Consultant Group on Medical Education said in its report several years ago, "it would seem that the individual physician should spend more time, rather than less, with the individual patient. Such a goal can hardly be achieved if we are to have further increases in the patient load of the average doctor."

The spectacular successes in the conquest of epidemic disease, achieved with such weapons as inoculations and the antibiotics, have been relatively cheap in terms of medical manpower. The growing emphasis on the chronic ailments requires more intensive care and more of the doctor's time. The use of a great variety of skills in the management of the degenerative diseases, the advent of intracardiac and intrathoracic surgery, new approaches to the treatment of mental and emotional disorders, and a host of other refined techniques are constantly augmenting the requirements for medical and paramedical manpower. With an increasing proportion of young and old people, with most doctors overworked, and without enough medical graduates to fill internships and residencies even in hospitals with excellent graduate education programs, we obviously cannot afford a further reduction in the physician-population ratio. In fact, many authorities feel that the ratio must be greatly raised to remedy existing shortages and to meet newly emerging needs.

A combination of factors makes it quite certain, however, that the pinch will grow still tighter. For one thing, we are spending more for chewing gum and for permanent waves than for the training of the men and women who are required to keep us well. But it is not just a question of the huge sums of money needed for the expansion of medical education facilities. Other formidable obstacles are the acute scarcity of the necessary teachers and the declining quantity and quality of medical school applicants. Experiments aimed at reducing the extraordinary length of the training period are under way in several medical schools. But it is not easy to cut down substantially the time required to produce a doctor when scientific knowledge keeps on expanding.

The education of a good doctor is not an assembly-line operation, and there are no shortcuts to adequate training. The average medical school enrolls only about ninety new students each year. Expansion of its capacity is difficult, for it must be carried out without impairment of the individualized, apprentice process of teaching, which requires an average of nearly two instructors for each student. "Medicine," as one authority has put it, "does not lend itself to the type of expansion that can be accomplished by putting additional chairs in the back of the classroom and asking the instructor to speak a little louder."

Medical school enrollment has more than doubled since 1920 and is now the highest in our history. But over the years, a steadily decreasing proportion of college students have entered the field of medicine. In 1920, the ratio of medical school students to college students was 1 out of 42. Now the figure is 1 out of 120. The U.S. Public Health Service predicts that by 1970 it will be only 1 out of 160. In 1948, there were 24,242 medical school applicants, and they represented nearly 7 per cent of all college graduates. By 1960, the number of applicants had declined to

14,397, and they accounted for only 3.7 per cent of the swelling college graduating classes.

Not only has the proportion of young people seeking a career in medicine dropped sharply, but fewer of the brighter students are doing so. As the pool of applicants has receded, many of the medical schools have had no choice but to lower their standards. Whereas in 1948 there were 3.5 applicants for every accepted student, the ratio has now slipped to 1.7 applications per acceptance. The number of A students among medical school applicants has declined by nearly two-thirds during the past decade, while the proportion of failures has doubled. "A number of schools have reported privately that they have had to scrape the barrel to fill their classes," Dr. Donald G. Anderson, dean of the University of Rochester Medical School and president of the Association of American Medical Colleges, told a Congressional committee in 1960. Several other leading medical educators have expressed concern as to whether enough qualified applicants could be found if a number of new schools were established.

While all medical schools in the United States are now classified as "Class A" schools, some are better than others because of superior staff, facilities, and programs. The Surgeon General's Consultant Group on Medical Education reported that about a dozen schools are so seriously underfinanced and underequipped that their standards are "only minimal." The wide range in quality among medical schools is shown by the fact that in a recent year, the number of first-year A students ran from none to 57 per cent and the number of C students from none to 59 per cent. The top schools still have many more applicants than they can accommodate. But some of the state-supported schools, which have residence restrictions on admission, are increasingly running into difficulties with regard to both the quantity and the quality of applicants.

When a talented young man wished to enter a profession a century ago, he had three major choices—medicine, law, or the ministry. At that time, 28 per cent of all college graduates entered the practice of medicine. Since then, the number of professional choices has increased more than a hundredfold, and some of them are proving far more attractive than medicine to enterprising young people. The physical sciences, in particular, offer not only ample financial rewards but also plenty of glory and outer space to move around in.

Major factors militating against a medical career are the length and cost of medical education and the strenuous competition for top students in other fields. Not only have opportunities for challenging careers in the physical sciences rapidly multiplied, but graduate study in these fields has been made readily available through many fellowships. About 80 per cent of the current PhD candidates in the physical sciences are on Federal grants. Upon completion of about four years of graduate study, the young physicist, chemist, or biologist can immediately step into a well-paid position. The young physician, on the other hand, must largely pay his own way and often enters the lengthy period of hospital internship and residency deeply in debt. This situation has become especially difficult at a time when early marriage is in vogue—about two out of every three medical students are now married by the time they graduate—since support of a family on the meager salary of a resident or intern is impossible. Able students with a natural bent toward medicine are increasingly tempted into the allied field of biology, in which the period of training is shorter, so that the prospects are brighter for establishing a normal family life at an earlier age.

The education of a physician is probably the most expensive of all types of professional training. It has been estimated that by the time a doctor is ready to practice—after four years of medical school, a year of internship, and as long as seven years as a resident to qualify for some specialties—the sum he has spent on his education, plus the income he might have earned but did not, may add up to as much as $60,000.

While some scholarship aid is available to medical students, grants are generally much lower than those offered for graduate work in other professional fields. The medical curriculum is, furthermore, so demanding that, unlike most other graduate students, medical students can rarely take part-time jobs to help support themselves. The cost of going to medical school now comes to an average of $2,400 a year for unmarried students and $3,300 for those who are married. This means that even the 43 per cent of students who come from families with annual incomes of more than $10,000 frequently have to be supported by working wives. It also means that more than half of the medical school graduates wind up in debt. Forty per cent of the married students have debts of more than $5,000, and one out of every six of them owes more than $10,000 by the time he graduates.

The growing tendency toward early marriage obviously raises a multitude of problems. Foremost is the necessity for support of a family, since half of the married students have at least one child, and out of this develop various pressures. A recent study has shown that at Harvard Medical School the wives contributed more to the support of students than did their parents. When the wife alone is working, the traditional roles of the sexes become materially reversed, since the husband washes dishes and frequently also does the cooking and housework. The wife's financial support tends to load him with a sense of guilt and drives him toward an attitude of expediency in planning for the time when he can start earning a living. This is believed to be one of the main reasons for the shrinkage of altruistic values noted among medical students as their education progresses.

On top of the financial considerations that keep many qualified candidates out of medicine is the medical profession's slipping prestige. With the decline in the profession's glamor and the deterioration of its public image, young people are less likely to make the required sacrifices of the present for the rewards of the far-distant future. Many physicians once urged their sons to go into medicine. But with the specter of the socialization of medical services hanging over their heads, they are at present just as likely to dissuade them from doing so.

The slump in the number and caliber of young people who want to become doctors is alarming not only in view of the projected growing needs for the future but also because the deepening complexity of medical knowledge requires greater rather than lesser intellectual capacity than in the past. If students are not equal to their heavier burden, there can be only compromise with the high level of education necessary to prepare them for the profession and, consequently, a lowering of the future quality of medical care. There is also grave danger in allowing economic status to become an even more paramount element in the selection of future physicians. This can serve only to aggravate the estrangement between doctors and patients.

The medical schools can no longer afford the luxury of waiting for better students to knock on their doors for admission. Clearly called for are intensive efforts to attract capable young people into medicine and to help them financially through adequate scholarships and loans. There also is a need to reexamine the requirements for entry into medical school and to step up the exploration of possibilities for accelerating the educational process. One way of shortening it may be through some integration of premedical courses between high school and college and between college and medical school. Other opportunities for acceleration are believed by some educators to exist in a thorough reorganization of the standard medical curriculum, which over the years has become top-heavy with the constant accretion of factual material.

Because young people are discouraged, under our educational system, from entering college before the age of eighteen, the average student is twenty-two or twenty-three when he begins his medical course and is usually in his thirties by the time he completes his training for a specialty. An average of about eleven years elapses between admission to college and the start of private practice, and this is without allowance for the two years of military service required of many medical graduates. The prospect is bound to discourage all but the most dedicated young men and women.

"There is no really good reason," Dr. Willard C. Rappleye, former dean of the Columbia College of Physicians and Surgeons, has said, "why youngsters interested in medicine could not be permitted to complete their preparation for medical school earlier, either by letting them enter college sooner or by letting them take some of the needed work in high school. If they are not bright enough to do the work sooner, they do not belong in medicine. In Europe, medical training begins at twenty. It should here, too."

There is no getting away from the fact that doctors will always be the product of long and costly training requiring a large investment by themselves and by society. But the time is long overdue for a searching examination of both the educational and the financial underpinning of medical training.

V

Not since the sweeping reforms sparked by the classic Flexner report of the early 1900's has American medical education been caught up in such a turmoil of reappraisal and soul-searching as it has been going through in recent years. Its string of predicaments has received little notice in the lay press. But all of us are vitally affected by it, for the outcome will in large measure determine both the quantity and the quality of the medical care in the years to come.

The medical schools are the fountainhead of our sprawling institutional complex of health care and by all odds its most important asset. The preparation of those who will take up their role as physicians is only one of their functions. Equally crucial is their responsibility as centers of the research upon which much of medicine is based, of advances in the ways of its practice, and of the continuing education of doctors and other health professionals. The medical schools are the tools with which the United States has wrested world leadership in medicine from the great European universities. Many of the spectacular strides in medical science have been made in their laboratories and affiliated teaching hospitals. It is futile even to talk about various proposals for improving the level and distribution of medical care unless there is assurance that the medical colleges can continue to turn out competent doctors and can train them in adequate numbers.

The present patterns of medical education evolved during the past half-century out of the revolution wrought by the historic exposé made by the late Abraham Flexner in 1910. Working under the auspices of the Carnegie Foundation for the Advancement of Teaching, Flexner spent a year and a half investigating all 155 so-called medical schools in this country and Canada—most of them proprietary institutions and many little more than quick, quack diploma mills—and turned the floodlight of publicity on their flagrant inadequacies. In the ensuing crusade undertaken with the aid of the AMA, more than half of the schools were forced out of business and the survivors were completely transformed. Out of Flexner's recommendations, implemented thereafter by grants totaling $80 million from the Rockefeller Foundation and the General Education Board, have emerged the models of today's medical schools. Their underlying principles are that medical education should be under university control and pursued for a full four years and that many of their faculty members should be full-time employees who have given up their private practice and divide their time between teaching, research, and treating patients in university hospitals.

The curricular reforms spurred by the Flexner report brought hospitals and laboratories into the medical schools, integrating clinical medicine with the basic physical sciences and turning it into an expanding, ever-changing discipline based on observation and experiment. Out of the close link forged between the clinician and the research scientist have come the triumphs that have added decades to average life expectancy. But out of it, too, for all its undeniable virtues, has been fashioned the straitjacket of excessive concentration on the science of medicine, at the expense of its art and its social components, from which our most enlightened medical educators are now struggling to free themselves.

At the heart of the whole medical care system and themselves potent vehicles of change, the medical schools are subject to society's shifting demands and expectations and must constantly adjust their educational fare to new needs. The schools are the creative setting in which the character and content of medical practice are continually reshaped under the impact of the latest research findings as well as of the winds of change blowing outside their walls. The finest teaching hospitals affiliated with the medical schools not only provide the best that medicine has to offer but seek to set a standard and style of care that students and house staff can advantageously strive to emulate in the years beyond their training. The ideal toward which they are aiming, as Dr. Walter Bauer has described it, is "patient care in medicine's grand tradition, embodying humanity, wisdom, dignity, and compassion. But it is something more; it is razor-edged scientific analysis, probing, observing, recording, alert to every aberration— from the patient's demeanor to the enzymes in his serum."

The new ideas conceived and tested in the medical schools exert a powerful influence on the profession and, in turn, on everyone's health and happiness. Inexorably, they also are bringing the teaching institutions into mounting conflict with organized medicine's bent for clinging to the molds of the past. Anxious though they usually are not to ruffle the profession's sensibilities, the medical schools are in such a key position of leadership and are so enmeshed in the complexities of hospital operation required to teach their students through firsthand experience that frequent clashes are inevitable. In fact, there is hardly an area in which the schools do not sooner or later find themselves at loggerheads with the organized profession. This holds true for the critical issues of how medical education can be adequately financed and how the required expanded supply of physicians can be provided. It even extends to the continuous reassessment of the curriculum in order to adopt the best from what is new without relinquishing the best of the tried traditional values.

The same forces that have revolutionized the science and practice of medicine have inescapably embroiled the medical schools in a twofold crisis of financing and function. As the horizons of medical science have continued to widen, the problems of what to pick from the superabundance of knowledge and how the student can best be equipped for tomorrow's practice have become no less acute than those of how the inordinately protracted and arduous training can be paid for. Medicine cannot be taught in a vacuum, and its science cannot be divorced from its economics. Its teaching cannot be dissociated from the challenging issues raised by the need for a more equitable and effective organization and distribution of health care. If the medical schools are to meet their responsibilities, they must join with others in providing the leadership for a frontal attack on some of these unsolved problems. In order to instill within their students a keener awareness of the social and economic elements in the practice of medicine, they must provide an expanding range of community medical services through the hospitals and clinics that they use for teaching. They must likewise try to teach their students to maintain a balance between the science and art of medicine, so that they will understand the patient as well as the symptoms.

In performing these and other functions and in seeking to serve as a stimulus and corrective for the medical profession, the medical schools have inevitably also become an irritant. Both theory and practice are involved in the deepening rift between many of the men who are training the new generation of doctors and the leadership of organized medicine. The theory pertains to the role of the medical profession and its responsibility to co-operate with the community in providing the American people with more adequate medical services. The practical disagreements stem from the fact that medical training—which to a striking extent is learning by doing and thus constitutes actual medical service—sometimes impinges on the economic interests of private practitioners.

Medical education itself cannot escape part of the blame for the profession's failure to exhibit the vision and aggressive leadership needed to meet the problems of medical care. The profession's social lag is to no small degree the result of past over-emphasis on the technological know-how of medicine in the training of physicians and the tendency to overlook environmental factors. As the schools are increasingly becoming conscious of their broader obligations, there is a swelling cleavage between them and some of their alumni. The trouble, basically, is that what the medical schools are now teaching is in many respects radically different from what most of today's practitioners were taught. The difference is not only in methods of the diagnosis and treatment of disease. Even more so, it is in the concept of medicine's relationship to society.

The friction between those who are challenging the *status quo* and those who have an economic stake in its preservation is aggravated by the professional compulsions under which doctors often live. Leadership of the AMA, which speaks for the profession but frequently does not reflect the views of many of its members, is in the hands of a tight little group of older and conservative men. The average physician is too busy for the politicking required for advancement in the hierarchy of organized medicine. Nor, being the product of a uniquely technical education, is he easily amenable to new social and political ideas. But even if he is, he may endanger his career by speaking out. So he pays his dues, which are used to finance partisan propaganda campaigns, and keeps quiet. Medical education, on the other hand, is under the guidance of men who have largely surmounted these barriers. First of all, many of the physicians on the medical school faculties are on full-time salary and are thus no longer dependent on private practice and the restraints that go with it. Secondly, the faculties represent, as a rule, the cream of the profession. The opportunities for research and for setting new standards of practice in the teaching hospitals, which furnish some of the best medical services now available, attract physicians of high caliber. Their prestige enables them to wield considerable influence, and they provide most of medicine's gadflies.

The average doctor, busy with the day-to-day problems of his practice, is inclined to regard the medical schools as ivory towers. The riposte of medical educators is that they are just enough removed from private practice to get a wider perspective of the overall picture of medical care. "We're in a position," as one of them put it, "to distinguish between public interest and vested interest, which is something the practitioner can't always do from his own little corner."

Some of the most significant battles in the civil war in the health field have occurred, usually well hidden from public view, over what the AMA has described as "attempts by certain hospitals to inject themselves into the practice of medicine" by caring for patients as a group and billing them in this manner. The leading "offenders" in this regard have been the teaching hospitals connected with medical schools. This is so because the medical colleges not only are teaching the advantages of teamwork through group practice but, to an increasing extent, are actually practicing in this manner. Many of them have developed their affiliated hospitals and clinics into large medical centers staffed to a considerable degree by salaried doctors. Some of these centers are beginning to offer comprehensive medical services to paying patients under insurance arrangements.

The issue of "the corporate practice of medicine" is a very touchy one indeed with the medical profession. For while it is usually cloaked in the windy abstractions of ethics, it directly affects the profession's income. It is bad enough, from organized medicine's point of view, for hospitals to employ radiologists, anesthesiologists, and pathologists on salary instead of letting private practitioners operate what amounts to concessions. But it is even worse for salaried members of medical school faculties to engage in the private practice of medicine in the teaching hospitals and then to turn over the fees from paying patients to the schools. The AMA House of Delegates denounced this practice in a formal resolution a few years ago as "contrary to medical ethics" and amounting, in effect, to "state socialism." The Association of American Medical Colleges retorted that the schools intend to teach and to pay their faculty members as they see fit. But the AMA has refused to budge from its position. The House of Delegates recently rejected a report by its own Council on Medical Education and Hospitals approving the care of paying patients in medical school hospitals by full-time clinical faculty members.

The medical schools also are running counter to the official party line by telling their students about divergent points of view on medical care issues. Organized medicine is likewise perturbed over the steady increase in the proportion of salaried physicians whom it is unable to control. While most private practitioners consider it politic to maintain medical society membership and to pay dues, about 65 per cent of the doctors who are not in private practice do not bother to belong. The AMA is naturally disturbed to have so many physicians outside the fold and is perhaps even more concerned over what is being done to the minds of its future members.

It is hardly surprising that the medical schools have been undergoing an unprecedented period of self-scrutiny and redefinition of objectives. Situated as they are in the very center of a climate of dynamic change, they have had to contend with the impact of such developments as the alterations in the patterns of disease and in the types of patients available for treatment in teaching hospitals, the constant piling up of new scientific knowledge, the continued growth of specialization, the effects of the sharp increase in research activities financed by the Federal government, the increasing emphasis placed on the preventive approach and on the contribution that the social and behavioral sciences can make in gaining a better understanding of the genesis and course of illness, and the changes in the number and quality of medical school applicants at a time when expansion of health personnel has become an urgent necessity.

Foremost in the ferment of experimentation now permeating medical education are an intensive reassessment of the curriculum and a search for possible ways of shortening the period of training. The problem of integrating newly accumulating knowledge into the curriculum is in itself enough to baffle medical school faculties. New information and techniques not only must be made available to students but also must be passed along to the physicians already in practice. The task is all the more difficult when the objective is to develop within the student a competent grasp of what is really essential, to sharpen rather than to satiate his appetite for further learning, and to stimulate rather than to quench whatever imagination he has. All this, furthermore, has to be done in the midst of constantly changing values; and at the same time, shortcuts in the educational process have to be sought.

Many of the health care issues pressing for a solution wind up right on the doorstep of medical education. The training of good clinicians does not completely discharge the medical school's responsibility. It must turn out physicians who also have some grounding in medical economics and are equipped to adjust themselves to the continuing changes in the organization of medical services. To be prepared for the medicine of tomorrow, students must be inculcated with the strongest possible commitment to preventive care and must learn to work more effectively with auxiliary personnel in meeting the needs for the maintenance of health and for rehabilitation, which are no less important than the treatment of episodic illness. Demands are certain to mount for better health insurance, for increased medical productivity, and for a more rational organization of medical practice and hospital services. Medical education cannot escape its obligation to prepare its students to deal with these proliferating problems.

The time is clearly ripe for a general reorganization of medical education, all the way from the premedical courses in high school and college through graduate training for the specialties. But the dilemma is that although the education of doctors already is inordinately long, there is general agreement that there has been excessive concentration on technical subjects and that medical students need more rather than less schooling in the humanities and social sciences to sharpen their insights into the infinite complexities of human relationships. While the curriculum has attempted to keep pace with advances in the natural sciences, it has yet to give full recognition to the social and economic problems confronting medical practice. Only through an understanding of the background of these problems can students learn to look at them with some diagnostic objectivity and to reexamine the clichés.

Progress in psychiatry, including the growing awareness of psychosomatic conditions, justifies far more emphasis on this subject than is now generally given in medical education. No other pathological condition that is so widespread gets so little attention in the training of physicians. If tension and anxiety reactions were more promptly recognized and if doctors were better prepared to deal with them, many of the patients suffering from such disturbances could be successfully treated in general practice. Better grounding in the psychiatric approach would also help the student to understand the types of relationships that may spring up between him and his patients and would enhance his capability to use this awareness positively. While psychiatry is a specialty, it can no longer be relegated to a single department in medical school or to the mental hospitals. It belongs in all of medicine.

Somewhere along the line of the educational process, the embryo doctors must be brought more closely into contact with the economic facts of life. Since most medical students come from a financially select group, they know little or nothing about the economically underprivileged. "Even in their dispensary work," as Dr. E. Richard Weinerman has said, "they are seeing their patients in a frame far more flattering than normal. They have never seen or smelled bad housing; they know nothing of the reality of bad diets, of broken homes, of unemployment, of what it means when the breadwinner is sent to the hospital for a long stay, of the thousand and one things never seen at the hospital bedside or in the dispensary."

When the student sees the patient lying in a clean bed in the hushed atmosphere of the hospital, he has difficulty realizing that the patient may come from a crowded and dirty home, that the patient's wife may also be ill and unable to work, and that school-age youngsters are being denied education and a carefree childhood because the illness of the parents requires them to shoulder domestic responsibilities prematurely. More and more medical schools are beginning to bring their students face to face with reality by sending them into the homes of low-income patients and making them responsible, under supervision, for the health care of families assigned to them. It is important to expose the future doctor to illness within its normal setting as early as possible. Otherwise, his point of view may be permanently constricted by absorption with organic disease entities.

Preoccupation with the natural sciences and the continuing trend toward the specialties have deprived the medical student of the view of the patient as a whole within his familial environment. To do the utmost for his patient, the physician must learn to perceive him within the totality of his situation and as a social as well as a biological organism. Just as the localized pathologic event must be viewed in relation to the functioning of the entire body, so that bodily function must, in turn, be understood in relation to the patient's personality and his role as a member of a family and of a community in a ceaseless state of flux. The medical curriculum, moreover, is still to be fully reoriented to the shift in emphasis from the acute to the long-term diseases.

Many medical educators are fully conscious of the shortcomings in current teaching, and efforts to correct them are under way in curricular revisions instituted in recent years in a number of schools. Attempts are being made to integrate some facets of the medical and social sciences and of medical school and hospital training. The ambitious aim of some of these experiments is not only to turn out better-rounded physicians but also to abbreviate the time it takes to do so.

The rigid division of medical education into the preclinical and clinical years is breaking up in some of the schools. The modulation of this artifical division is designed to give students a more comprehensive view of medicine and to impress upon them, from the start, that all their learning must be related to the needs of sick people and to the task of keeping well people from getting sick. The aim of this and other reforms is to soften the effect of the abrupt divorcement between general and medical education and to eliminate some of the minutiae cluttering the curriculum and concentrate instead on better teaching of the essentials. A physician whose brain has been less strained by the terrific burden of detail is much more apt to use the methods of integration and induction when it comes to diagnosis rather than just try to fit symptoms to memorized facts.

More than sixty years ago William Osler said that "to cover the vast field of medicine in four years is an impossible task." In view of the stupendous growth of knowledge since that time, the task becomes fantastic. "All we can hope to teach students," one medical educator has declared, "are certain basic attitudes toward learning and toward patients, some basic principles, a few techniques which every doctor does or should use, and a reasonable familiarity with the more important diseases. Facts are soon forgotten, and, in any case, the so-called facts of today often are the discarded myths of tomorrow."

Another distinguished authority who feels that the present process of medical education not only is too long but "does not permit today's student to become tomorrow's physician as we envision him" is Dr. George Packer Berry, dean of Harvard Medical School. Dr. Berry believes that the whole medical curriculum must be fundamentally restructured and the system of splintered, departmentalized teaching drastically modified, so that the student does not lose sight of the forest for the trees. This is easier said than done, however. As the better medical schools grope for new approaches, they are finding that a curriculum built up over the years by agglutination is not readily amenable to change. The fundamental difficulty is that medical education has developed the defects of the very virtues for which Flexner argued when he spoke out for the academic decencies. Flexner had urged that the laboratory and the teaching clinic be tied more firmly into the structure of training. But in the effort to make medicine more "scientific," it has been wrenched from its broader context and split into disconnected fragments. Putting these fragments together again is an arduous undertaking, for the parts have a tendency to run away with the whole.

Scientific medicine has given us superb microscopy, masterful biochemistry, incredible precision in diagnosis, and, very often, brilliant therapy. The irony is that, by tying itself to the physical sciences and the laboratory, it has become less than fully scientific through its failure to incorporate some of the new tools of social manipulation.

Among the outstanding examples of curricular reorganization initiated in recent years are those at the medical schools of Johns Hopkins, Northwestern, and Boston Universities. All three combine all or part of undergraduate education with medical education and, by prolonging the school year, offer students the opportunity to complete medical school in six or seven years after graduation from high school instead of the standard eight years. The curriculum is broader and includes some of the standard subjects now thought of as premedical as well as some of the humanities and social sciences. A common feature of these programs is a move to unify, from the very beginning, the student's view of man's structure, function, behavior, and relation to his surroundings. The objective is to teach students to approach patients as people and not as specimens, to observe how they differ from one another, to learn something about the reasons why people act as they do, and to realize that they cannot be treated—in good medicine—by rote or routine.

Boston University has for some time had a home-care program under which students in the last two years of medical school provide medical services, under the supervision of their instructors, to families in the heart of Boston's teeming South End slums. Students thereby gain an understanding of the social setting and its impact on illness that they could never obtain from textbooks, lectures, and demonstrations in the hospital clinic. They begin to learn that sympathetic insight is fully as important as technical proficiency. They get a chance to see disease at the onset rather than in its later stages, as is usually the case in the hospital. The opportunity to observe patients over a sufficiently long period of time gives them a sense of continuity so often lacking in episodic treatment.

Another notable reform of the teaching program has been under way for more than a decade at Western Reserve University, where considerable progress has been made in breaking down departmental barriers in order to integrate subject matter and lay greater emphasis on the environmental aspects of medical care. To provide sustained contact with patients and their families at home as well as in the clinic or hospital ward, each freshman at Western Reserve is assigned to an expectant mother. He visits the family regularly at home and is present at each of the woman's prenatal visits to the hospital clinic. If problems arise, he is the first to hear about them from the patient and reports them to the staff physician responsible for the actual medical care. He is on hand when the baby is born and gives the infant its first physical examination under the direction of the supervising physician. As his training progresses and his competence grows, he is given increasing responsibility in the handling of patients.

These and other ventures in the long-overdue overhaul of the medical curriculum have been described by one medical educator as an attempt "to put the heart back into medicine."

CHAPTER TEN

The Uses and Abuses of Drugs

I

IT TOOK a narrow escape from tragedy in the summer of 1962 to turn the spotlight on one aspect of a situation fraught with peril for many millions of Americans and to shame the politicians into doing something about it. What was finally done to provide greater assurance of the efficacy and safety of some of the drugs we are getting from our doctors was not nearly enough. But even this minimal and long-overdue tightening of the drug control laws would not have been possible if the story of thalidomide, the tranquilizer responsible for the deformities of thousands of European babies, had not hit the nation's front pages.

The furor over thalidomide had all the elements of drama so dear to the hearts of newspaper editors—several thousand armless, legless, earless, and otherwise malformed infants born to women in Germany and Great Britain who had taken the drug in early pregnancy; hundreds of anxious pregnant women in the United States, including an expectant mother who had to go all the way from Arizona to Sweden in her quest for a legal abortion; and a vigilant government official who was singled out for high honors because her stubborn suspicions had kept the preparation off the market in this country. But the episode also had more than its share of ironic and devastatingly revealing sidelights. It cast a pitiless light on the lethargy, if not outright lack of concern for the public interest, often prevalent among the men charged with making our laws. It once again demonstrated the immense power of publicity and the short attention span and memory of the press as well as the public. It showed that sensationalism can be far more potent than a calm appeal to reason.

Despite all the columns of publicity lavished on the thalidomide affair, it was difficult for the casual reader to discover that it was by no means an isolated incident but merely the latest installment of a much bigger story that constitutes a severe indictment not only of the drug industry but also of the medical profession and has the gravest implications for our health and welfare.

The stark reality is that the phenomenal growth of the pharmaceutical industry and the explosive proliferation of medications have led to an excessive and often indiscriminate use of drugs, that doctors are confused and misled by the flood of new preparations, that there is widespread prescribing of fancy new drugs without sufficient knowledge of their side effects and long-range properties, that the prices of drugs are generally much higher than they should be, that legal controls on the manufacture and distribution of medications were grossly inadequate prior to the enactment of the new legislation in 1962 and are still far from sufficient, that premature promotion of pharmaceuticals on the basis of skimpy investigation is common, that there is an unnecessary and confusing duplication of products, that drugs are now frequently marketed in the same atmosphere that produces a rapid turnover in automobile models and women's styles, and that beguiling drug advertising has to a substantial degree replaced formal postgraduate medical education in this country.

These and many other distressing facts about the drug industry's competitive practices, pricing methods, profits, and research and promotional activities were amply documented at the 1959–1961 hearings conducted by a United States Senate subcommittee headed by the late Senator Estes Kefauver of Tennessee and reported in considerable detail in the newspapers. The thalidomide incident nevertheless appeared to come as a bolt out of the blue. It took the press some time even to wake up to the fact that only a few days previously, the Senate Judiciary Committee, acting largely under the influence of the pharmaceutical industry's powerful lobby, had truncated legislation for essential reforms in the drug laws proposed by Senator Kefauver and that a somewhat similar bill sponsored by the Kennedy Administration had been languishing for months in a House committee.

It took the hue and cry generated by the thalidomide contingency to accomplish at least partly what volumes of testimony by some of the nation's most eminent pharmacologists and clinicians at the Kefauver group's hearings had been unable to achieve.

It was only after the story of the baby-deforming drug broke that the Administration, which up to then had shown little vigor in pushing its own legislation, bestirred itself. Under the impact of the drumfire of publicity and of a personal appeal by President Kennedy to strengthen the drug laws so as to avert "even more serious disasters," the Senate Judiciary Committee reversed itself, restoring some of the key provisions it had knocked out from the Kefauver bill, and the measure was then quickly passed by a lopsided 78 to o vote. A similar display of unwonted activity on the House side led to rapid concurrent adoption, by a vote of 374 to o, of legislation requiring substantial proof that drugs are effective as well as safe before they are offered for sale, authorizing the Food and Drug Administration to order withdrawal of medications from the market if they pose an "imminent hazard" to health, giving the FDA greater power in the inspection of drug manufacturing facilities, and otherwise tightening the regulations on the testing, labeling, and advertising of prescription drugs. Rarely has there been such a striking reversal of Congressional apathy and hostility into complete unanimity. And never before had the drug lobby been so strangely quiescent.

But while the thalidomide incident thus turned out to be a sort of blessing in disguise as far as Americans are concerned, it will take a good deal more than a stampeding of Congressional opinion to solve some of the profoundly perplexing professional and economic problems that the age of therapeutic plenty has brought in its train. The enormous increase in the number and variety of drugs has immeasurably contributed to better health and the saving of lives. But it has also had a sweeping and far from beneficial impact upon medical practice and the economics of health care.

The profusion of new and allegedly new drugs and the rapid rate of their turnover have made it extremely difficult for physicians to keep track of these products and to evaluate critically the claims made for them. Whatever knowledge of pharmacology they have acquired in medical school is often obsolete. Doctors have therefore increasingly come to depend on information supplied by pharmaceutical salesmen and by the huge volume of drug advertising. The confusion generated by flamboyant drug promotion has become so great, Dr. Harry F. Dowling of the

University of Illinois Department of Medicine has said, that "the bewildered physician prescribes by suggestion and not from information."

Since the average doctor has neither the time nor the competence to check on the veracity of loose advertising claims in the highly competitive field of drug promotion, this has inevitably led, at best, to what the *New England Journal of Medicine* has described editorially as "the widespread use of nearly worthless medications." But much worse things than waste of patients' money have happened. Not infrequently the toxic or allergic effects of new drugs or the harmful results of improper dosages have not been discovered until the preparations have been widely used and have caused such serious conditions as blood-cell and electrolyte abnormalities, hormone imbalances, and outright addiction and have even caused deaths. Thus, an antidepressant pill called Marsilid is believed to have caused 53 deaths and 246 cases of hepatitis before it was finally withdrawn by the manufacturer in 1961, three years after the first reports of severe adverse effects started coming in.

Significantly, the thalidomide affair brought out into the open the fact that a number of drugs already approved by the FDA for prescription had been withdrawn from the market in the previous few months upon the discovery of dangerous side effects. At the same time, it also became known that the FDA was conducting an investigation into the possibility of rigged drug research. Congress was not the only body, by the way, to be jogged into action by the thalidomide disclosures. The Department of Health, Education, and Welfare, of which the FDA is a part, also exhibited new resolution and, using the administrative authority it has had all along, issued stricter rules for the testing of new drugs on human beings.

The same company that had sent out test samples of the German-developed thalidomide to hundreds of physicians was disclosed to have withdrawn one of its best sellers, MER-29, a drug designed to retard formation of cholesterol in the blood. More than three hundred thousand patients had used this drug before reports began pouring in that some of those who had taken it had developed eye cataracts that could lead to loss of vision and others had suffered hair loss, skin changes, and leukopenia, a dangerous blood disease. Shortly thereafter, the Department of Justice announced that it was seeking to determine whether material facts had been withheld and false statements made in connection with the application for approval of MER-29, which during its first year on the market had netted its manufacturer a profit of more than $1 million.

Dr. Walter Modell, director of clinical pharmacology at Cornell University Medical College and editor of the magazine *Clinical Pharmacology and Therapeutics*, put his finger on one of the principal flaws in the drug situation by commenting that MER-29, along with most other new and potent medications, had been marketed far too quickly. "A drug company," he said, "has to get into the market with a bang in order to establish a new drug before a competitor produces a similar one. The result is that a new drug is promoted as if it were an established therapy."

A total of forty-seven drugs had to be pulled off the market in 1961, and warnings were issued on the need for increased caution in prescribing a number of other preparations. This tends to support the charges of leading pharmacologists that drugs are far too often rushed into distribution without sufficient trials and that doctors are frequently prescribing medications without adequate evidence of either their effectiveness or their safety. The trouble is that because of fierce competitive pressures and the rapid obsolescence of products, manufacturers are trying to cash in on new preparations through "blitz" promotion campaigns rather than relying on careful and gradual introduction that would turn up any adverse side effects before large numbers of patients were involved. Dr. William Bennett Bean of Iowa State University School of Medicine has described this technique as "the quick kill with the quick pill."

The FDA's probe of questionable testing practices was reported to be centered on suspicions that some of the physicians who receive experimental drugs from manufacturers for testing are, as a top official of the agency put it, tailoring their studies "to fit a predetermined result." According to some prominent university drug researchers, these suspicions are well founded. "I personally know three cases of doctors whose services are for sale," one of these researchers has said. "They are told what a drug is supposed to do, and they promptly prove it." There are reliable reports that some drug firms design down to the last detail the experimental procedures to be undertaken by outside clinical investigators, to whom they often give research grants far in excess of the expenses involved, and that they sometimes even ghostwrite the reports of these investigators. Small wonder, then, that some of the reports on new drugs published in medical journals read more like promotional brochures than meticulous scientific studies.

Competent opinion is that, along with the beneficial drugs that it has provided, the pharmaceutical industry also has stimulated the premature use of numerous products and a wasteful and bewildering multiplication of preparations, many of which are almost identical in their effects. There is little question, according to many authorities, that some widely prescribed drugs are worthless and that others have hidden dangers about which doctors are not told enough; that some medications are inadequately tested on animals before being marketed, so that human beings serve as guinea pigs to find out whether they are safe or not; that drugs may be so costly, especially if they are patented, that a patient's drug bill for a single illness can run into thousands of dollars; and that almost any preparation costs far more if it is prescribed by trade name instead of the generic chemical name.

The situation clearly calls for tighter statutory and administrative controls than are now exercised and for a much greater sense of responsibility on the part of the medical profession, individually and collectively. But here we run not only into a many-faceted tie-up between organized medicine and the drug industry but also into the conditions prevailing in today's medical practice that account for the tendency on the part of many doctors toward promiscuous overmedication.

In the whole long record of discreditable actions by the AMA, there has perhaps been no more disgraceful performance than its solid opposition to the legislative proposals for more stringent Federal policing of the manufacture and sale of drugs. Among the provisions to which the AMA had entered particularly strong objections at the hearings on the Kefauver bill were those authorizing the FDA to pass not only on the safety but also on the efficacy of drugs and those aimed at simplifying the nomenclature of medications in an attempt to eliminate needless duplication of products and to bring down their costs. Flying in the face of overwhelming evidence to the contrary, the AMA maintained that the organized profession itself can best do the job of telling its members which of the new drugs are truly effective. It opposed enactment of a requirement that doctors prescribe by chemical rather than trade name on the ground that this would deprive the individual physician of the right to use his own best judgment. It argued that bureaucratic controls would stand in the way of progress if the government were authorized to require proof that drugs can actually do the things that their manufacturers claim they can do. A resolution adopted by the AMA House of Delegates declared grandiloquently that "the marketing of a relatively useless drug is infinitely less serious than would be the arbitrary exclusion from the market of a drug that might have been life saving for many persons."

Curiously enough, two members of the AMA's Council on Drugs later testified that this group, which is the organized profession's top advisory body on the uses of medications, was never even consulted on the matter. They asserted that the stand taken by the AMA did not reflect the opinion of the majority of the council.

"Hectic promotion of unwarranted products subjects patients to illogical and excessive use of drugs," Dr. Charles D. May of Columbia University's College of Physicians and Surgeons, a member of the AMA's Council on Drugs and editor of the official journal of the American Academy of Pediatrics, told the Kefauver subcommittee. "Individual doctors cannot evaluate each drug's usefulness. If they could, they would not have gone on prescribing leeches for so many years." Another distinguished authority who spoke out fervently in favor of more effective Federal controls was Dr. Maxwell Finland of Harvard Medical School. "The argument that the practicing physician is the only one who can determine efficacy," Dr. Finland said, "is an invitation to all manufacturers to dump into the hands of busy practitioners any and all types of good and bad drugs and devices, and let them learn, at the expense and peril of their patients, whether they are any help."

Behind the façade of the tortured rationalizations of the AMA bureaucracy are the close alliance between organized medicine and the profit-swollen pharmaceutical industry, often in brazen disregard of the interests of the consumers, and the fact that in 1963 about $9.5 million of the AMA's operating budget of $20.1 million a year came from drug advertising and other promotional activities.

It is important to bear in mind in considering the economics of the drug industry that the consumers of its products have no choice and no influence over their price and quality. While the patients foot the bill, the sole targets of the strident promotion of the so-called ethical drugs are the doctors, since these medications can be sold only on a physician's prescription. Drug advertising carefully avoids any mention of price. The average doctor is often unaware of the price of the preparation that he prescribes and, in any event, is unlikely to worry about the cost if he has been led to believe that the drug is indicated.

Aside from the millions of dollars spent annually on the advertising of ethical drugs in medical journals, doctors are exposed to a steady barrage of gaudy promotional literature, a lavish distribution of free samples, and the blandishments of an army of some fifteen thousand traveling salesmen whose job is to high-pressure physicians into accepting new medications and specifying proprietary names in their prescriptions. The average doctor now gets in the course of a year about five thousand pieces of drug mail advertising, much of it trash disguised as science. While a lot of this propaganda winds up unread in the wastebasket, its effects nevertheless are reported to be considerable on many doctors who lack the time to follow carefully the scientific literature on new drugs. In a survey made not long ago by the AMA, about two-thirds of the physicians questioned admitted that they depend on detail men as their chief source of information on new drugs. The big pharmaceutical companies themselves have boasted that their promotional efforts constitute a valuable form of "postgraduate education" for busy doctors. But is it really in the public interest to entrust the postgraduate education of the medical profession to salesmen?

With the continuing rise in drug company sales and advertising budgets, the publications of the national, state, and some of the bigger county medical societies have steadily grown heftier and increasingly come to depend on this source of revenue. In a recent year, nearly 53 per cent of the AMA's income came from advertising in its publications, and an additional 2.7 per cent came from exhibits at its meetings, also largely paid for by drug companies. It is reported to be not uncommon for drug firms to subsidize medical society meetings through elaborate exhibits and by other means. Cocktail parties and dinners given by pharmaceutical houses for their friends and clients are a usual feature at many medical conventions.

The AMA *Journal*, which not infrequently runs almost as many pages of advertising as of editorial text, has become organized medicine's most reliable breadwinner. The same thing holds true for the journals published by the component state and county medical societies, which are reported to have an average advertising income of about $500,000 a year. These periodicals not only pay their own way but contribute substantially to the financing of other medical society activities.

It is well worth noting that between 1950 and 1960, the period during which the ties between organized medicine and the pharmaceutical industry became increasingly marked, the AMA's annual drug advertising revenue jumped from $2.6 million to more than $7.9 million. Such revenue nearly doubled between 1955, when the AMA relaxed its acceptability standards for drug advertisements and relieved its Council on Drugs of direct responsibility for advertising control, and 1960. The number of pages of drug advertising in the AMA *Journal* rose from a quarterly volume of 500 pages in 1953 to one of about 1,200 pages in 1961. Latest reports are that the AMA *Journal* is publishing 6,000 pages of advertising a year, at $1,100 a page. Since 1957, advertising revenue has been the chief source of the AMA's income, materially outweighing proceeds from membership dues and subscriptions. It is ironic, to say the least, that while the code of medical ethics sternly forbids doctors to advertise, medical societies now generally find themselves in the advertising business up to their necks.

Senator Kefauver was not the only one who charged that organized medicine was dangerously close to becoming the captive of the drug makers. A number of thoughtful physicians also have raised the question as to whether the organized profession can be expected to maintain a truly objective attitude toward the business from which it derives its principal support. One of those who have publicly accused the AMA leadership of "cuddling up to the Pharmaceutical Manufacturers Association" is Dr. M. Harold Book of the University of Pennsylvania's Graduate School of Medicine. "One senses," Dr. Book has said, "a close, if unofficial, collaboration between these two powerful organizations which has been financially profitable to both but has not been in the best interests of the American people." It is of interest, incidentally, that Dr. Austin Smith, president of the Pharmaceutical Manufacturers Association, the drug industry's principal lobbying arm, is a former editor of the AMA *Journal*.

It is difficult to say, of course, to what extent advertising revenue and drug company largess are directly responsible for the eagerness of organized medicine to rush to the defense of the pharmaceutical industry. Probably another important reason is the feeling that criticism of the drug makers carries the connotation that not all doctors are well trained enough to be impervious to sales ballyhoo. The fact that physicians, ostensibly endowed with scientific skepticism, appear to be as gullible about and susceptible to the huckster's art as is the general public and that drug advertising often creates a demand where no real need exists is certainly a severe reflection on the competence of the medical profession. Then there is the factor of a common interest on the part of organized medicine and the drug manufacturers in the preservation of the *status quo*. Many hospitals and clinics already insist on dispensing drugs on the much more economical generic-name basis. The further expansion of medical services in hospital outpatient departments and group-practice clinics would impinge not only upon what the medical profession regards as some of its most cherished prerogatives but also upon the present system of drug manufacturing and distribution.

Whatever the motivations are for the medical profession's excessive friendliness toward the drug industry, pecuniary pressures sometimes plainly figure in the picture. According to as orthodox an authority as the AMA *Archives of Internal Medicine*, there have been occasions on which medical journals have refused to publish articles criticizing particular drugs for fear of offending advertisers and on which some medical societies have turned down papers scheduled for delivery at their meetings because they were critical of products of exhibitors. Even periodicals of unquestioned editorial integrity have been known to continue running for months advertisements for drugs that have been reported in their own columns to be worthless or to have serious side effects.

The system under which the drug business has been acting as the patron of medical journals obviously raises some very disturbing questions. Does the medical profession have the right to expect such heavy subsidy of its educational literature from an industry so closely tied up with its own practice? A material reduction in drug advertising, with consequent savings to the consumers, undoubtedly would force some medical publications out of business. How much of a loss this would represent is problematical. Although these periodicals help to keep doctors abreast of new scientific developments, they also are an important vehicle for propagating the official party line. Competent opinion is that overworked physicians already are deluged with reading matter, that they could certainly do with less indoctrination by their mossback leadership, and that pharmaceutical advertising is often confusing and misleading. There can hardly be any room for argument that the pressures of a private business must not be allowed to affect so vital a matter as the professional judgment upon which our health and very lives depend.

The individual practitioner's responsibility to resist the veritable torrent of promotional literature and free samples that crosses his desk daily and to maintain a tough-minded scientific attitude is clearer than his ability to discharge it. It would seem basic that no physician should prescribe potent medications if he is in ignorance of their effects. He should never use a drug without careful judgment based on the study of objective reports about its chemical nature, its pharmacological action, and the results of its clinical trials on patients. Except in the rare instances in which a new preparation holds out definite promise of a dramatic beneficial effect on a serious illness, there is every reason why a doctor should wait for reliable information before prescribing a medication that has just come on the market.

Although no one could possibly dispute the physician's duty to be guided by dependable professional sources in arriving at intelligent decisions, the practical difficulties in the way of his doing so are tremendous. The average practitioner not only lacks adequate training in clinical pharmacology to be able to judge the reports of investigators on their merits but also is already overwhelmed by an avalanche of scientific literature that he cannot possibly find the time to tackle. It is much simpler and far less time-consuming to surrender to the lure of commercial advertisements and promotional circulars and to pressures from patients for new drugs for no other reason than that they are new.

At the crux of the problem of the promiscuous overuse of both old and new drugs, and particularly of the antibiotics and tranquilizers, is the fact that their prescription is often an easy substitute for painstaking diagnosis. The watchword of modern medicine, one authority has said, has become, "When in doubt, prescribe." One of the saddest commentaries on the state of today's medical practice is that, all too frequently, powerful medications are used without first establishing a reasonable diagnosis. When he succumbs to the siren song of the purveyors of shotgun preparations instead of using careful clinical judgment and the insights of understanding, the hurried and harried physician is treating his own anxieties rather than the patient.

Drugs have considerably more than a purely physiological effect. They also have a significant psychological meaning, sometimes far beyond their inherent pharmacological properties, by serving as a sort of emotional bridge between the doctor who prescribes the medication and the patient who takes it. All the physician's relations with the patient are invested with a good deal of symbolism, and the act of faith implicit in the doctor-patient association can enhance the potency of a drug to provide a measure of immunity to stress. By the simple ritual of writing a prescription, the doctor is, in effect, saying to the patient that he will use his trained judgment to take care of him. But although there is the placebo ingredient of suggestion in virtually every drug, hastily and thoughtlessly prescribed medication can, by the same token, have not only harmful organic consequences but also deleterious psychological effects on the patient.

Drugs can become, and very often are these days, an act of rejection, wherein the patient feels that he is being palmed off with a prescription instead of getting the warmth and attention that he craves for. Much of our prevailing system of medical care and the clashing loyalties of its practitioners can be viewed in terms of such an antithesis, of a conflict between forbearance and denial, compassion and rejection.

II

The United States "is the most overmedicated, most over-operated, and most overinoculated country in the world," Dr. Herbert Ratner of the Stritch School of Medicine at Loyola University has said. "We are becoming a pill-swallowing civilization." But despite our enthusiastic and frequently unwarranted resort to drugs, Dr. Ratner declared in a widely noted radio interview sponsored by the Fund for the Republic's Center for the Study of Democratic Institutions, we are "one of the unhealthiest countries in the world. . . . We are flabby, overweight, and have a lot of dental caries, fluoridation notwithstanding. Our gastrointestinal system operates like a sputtering gas engine. We can't sleep; we can't get going when we are awake. We have neuroses; we have high blood pressure. Neither our hearts nor our heads last as long as they should. Coronary disease at the peak of life has hit epidemic proportions. Suicide is one of the leading causes of death. We suffer from a plethora of the diseases of civilization."

Dr. Ratner also took note of what he described as a growing national tendency toward hypochondria. "Our preoccupation with health," he stated, "is shown by the medical columns in newspapers, the health articles in popular periodicals, the popularity of television programs and books on medicine. We talk about health all the time. For the most part, all that has been accomplished is an increase in imaginary illnesses. The healthy man should not be wasting his time talking about health; he should be using health for the work he is meant to do, work that good health makes possible." Americans, he added, have increasingly come to "think of health as something that can be bought rather than a state to be sought through an accommodation to the norms of nature."

This attitude stems to some extent from our pragmatic philosophy and way of life. But to no small degree it also is the product of the enormous influence exerted by the drug business, which within a generation has grown from a minor offshoot of chemical manufacturing into a major and booming industry, and of the extent to which the medical profession has allowed itself to fall under the sway of that business. Not nearly enough attention has been paid to the drastic alteration in the traditional relationship between the drug makers and the medical profession and the far-reaching effects this has had on the whole character of medical practice. Nor do most of us realize how profound is the influence that the pharmaceutical industry has come to exercise upon our health mores and the cost of medical care.

Up until only about two decades ago, the customary procedure was for the doctor to make up his own mind as to what medication would be best for the patient. The druggist then proceeded to compound the physician's prescription out of the relatively few chemical substances then available. Theoretically, the doctor still retains control over what he prescribes. But in actual practice, he has lost it. Instead of supplying the drugs that he thinks the patient should have, he is often indoctrinated by the big pharmaceutical companies through promotional methods similar to those that sell deodorants and laxatives.

Strictly speaking, the average physician no longer writes prescriptions. He merely orders certain prefabricated products, usually designating them by brand rather than by chemical name. Since the torrent of new medications makes it utterly impossible for him to check them all for their therapeutic qualities, he is primarily guided by what the drug manufacturers tell him. Although most of the pharmaceutical industry's "educational" activity is concentrated on the medical profession, a good deal of it spills over into the press, radio, and television. Thus, doctors are often also subjected to pressure from their patients for some new drugs that they may have read or heard about.

There are implications of the utmost seriousness in this reversal of roles of the medical profession and the drug manufacturers. How much reliance can we put on professional judgment when the doctor frequently surrenders some of his responsibility for the enlightened care of his patients and becomes the uncritical dispenser of medications of questionable value? There are few more alarming developments in modern medicine than the physician's growing dependence on the competitive methods of a commercial enterprise for some of the basic information and tools of his craft. What it amounts to is that we are increasingly being forced to entrust our health and welfare to a private business that, above all else, is interested in profits.

As in other areas of medical care, some of the issues raised by the phenomenal growth of the drug industry are the inevitable price of scientific progress. But a good many of the problems are rooted in the existing organization of medical practice and in the alacrity with which many physicians have succumbed to commercial promotion.

The array of new drugs has enabled the doctor to do infinitely more for his patients than he once could. But in many instances, the new medications are potentially as hazardous as they are beneficial, requiring great skill and discrimination in their use. They are now being developed and marketed at such a rapid rate that often they have been in wide use for some time before all their potential hazards have been discovered. They are, for the most part, composed of highly complex chemical compounds whose structure and properties can be clearly understood only by those with advanced training in the basic sciences. The average physician has thus inevitably become dependent on the claims made by the drug makers for their products.

Informed opinion is that much of the spectacular rise in the use of drugs in recent years has resulted not so much from clearly demonstrated medical need as from the impact of frenetic pharmaceutical advertising upon busy and gullible doctors. And excessive promotional expenditures and profit margins have made drugs far costlier than they should be.

The emergence of the pharmaceutical industry as a major force in the health care picture is increasingly confronting the medical profession with dismaying problems of conscience and ethics in which all of us have a momentous stake. When doctors are misled by flamboyant drug advertising, the patients are the real victims. Can the medical profession be depended upon to protect its members and their patients from exploitation? The profligate use of many products of questionable therapeutic utility raises serious doubts on that score. To what extent should the profession permit commercial promotion to infiltrate its educational literature? All too often, it is difficult to tell nowadays where education leaves off and advertising, not uncommonly disguised as scientific investigation, begins.

How far can the drug makers be allowed to go in taking over the bulk of the doctor's postgraduate education? One of those who strongly feel that we have already gone altogether too far in this direction is Dr. Charles D. May, the editor of *Pediatrics*, who recently warned in a challenging article in the *Journal of Medical Education* that the assumption by the drug industry of an aggressive role in the "education" of the medical profession is threatening "the traditional independence of physicians and the welfare of the public." Dr. May asked, "Is the public likely to benefit if practicing physicians and medical educators must perform their duties amidst the clamor and striving of merchants seeking to increase the sales of drugs by conscripting 'education' in the service of promotion? Is it prudent for physicians to become greatly dependent upon pharmaceutical manufacturers for support of scientific journals and medical societies, for entertainment, and now also for a large part of their education? Do all concerned realize the hazard of arousing the wrath of the people by an unwholesome entanglement of doctors with the makers and sellers of drugs?"

Dr. Walter Modell has denounced the sales ballyhoo of the big drug companies as "critical threats to the teaching and practice of medicine" and has charged that the market is being flooded with far too many inadequately evaluated products and extravagant claims as to their efficacy. "Since more than one drug cannot be best for the same indication," he has said, "we simply don't have enough diseases to go around. At the moment, the most helpful contribution is the new drug to counteract the untoward effects of other new drugs; we now have several of these." Adverse reactions to medications have "increased at a staggering rate," he reported, because "of lack of experience with many different and entirely new active drugs and because of inability to master the full implications of these agents as rapidly as they are marketed."

Dr. Martin Cherkasky, director of Montefiore Hospital in New York, has asserted that the barrage of exaggerated promotional claims with which physicians are bombarded seriously interferes with their ability to render good medical care. Millions of dollars could be saved annually for hundreds of thousands of sick people now "savagely burdened" by high drug costs, he has said, if doctors were more selective in their choice of medications and prescribed by chemical instead of by brand name, so that patients could take advantage of cheaper preparations that are just as good.

Thus far there has been no sign that the medical profession is taking these admonitions to heart and awakening to the peril of being largely guided in its prescribing by the people who sell the drugs rather than by those who have only the patient's welfare at heart. The bulk of the profession's postgraduate education remains in the hands of the pharmaceutical industry's high-pressure promoters. This state of affairs, Dr. Joseph Garland, editor of the *New England Journal of Medicine*, has cautioned, may turn medicine into "a junior partner to the big business of pharmaceutical manufacturing, with its large-scale exploitation of potent and consequently dangerous drugs."

An enlightening and distressing case history illustrative of the extent to which doctors have surrendered responsibility to the hucksters is provided by the meteoric rise of the tranquilizing drugs, which have rapidly gone to the forefront of pharmaceutical best sellers and brought their makers a multimillion-dollar bonanza. Within a few years after their introduction into the market in 1953, the tranquilizers had soared to an annual rate of more than $200 million in sales, vying with some of the antibiotics as the drug industry's biggest sellers. By 1957, the annual total of prescriptions for the various brands of tranquilizers had skyrocketed to more than forty million, and they accounted for four of the ten leading prescription items sold by druggists. Tranquilizer compounds are currently being marketed under some seventy different trade names. In the course of a year, Americans are consuming more than three billion tablets of Miltown and Equanil, the two most popular meprobamates, which are milder relaxants than the tranquilizers but act in a somewhat similar manner in relieving tension.

Many thoughtful physicians have expressed grave concern over the misuse and overuse of the tranquilizers without regard to their indication or an understanding of what they can and cannot do and what their harmful side effects might be. Two major considerations must be borne in mind here. One of them is the propriety of using tranquilizers as a sort of panacea for the multitude of minor anxieties that we encounter in our daily lives. The other consideration is the chemical properties and long-range physiological effects of drugs that investigators have discovered are sometimes not so harmless as they have been represented to be. On both counts, the extent of their consumption on prescription by inadequately informed practitioners has been reckless.

The frenzied popularity of these so-called aspirins of the soul has underscored the fact that millions of Americans are anxiety-ridden, jittery, and in need of a crutch to keep going. But is it advisable for people who are not sick in the ordinary sense of the term to try to get rid of their tensions, which up to a point are a perfectly normal reaction to stress and a stimulant to peak performance under pressure? Is it wise to seek to achieve a synthetic peace of mind by gulping pills? Is it desirable to resort so widely to compounds that reduce only the symptoms of anxiety without doing anything to solve the underlying problems causing the symptoms? Can drugs really replace self-knowledge in one's striving for a sane and well-ordered life?

Experts have time and again emphasized that although tranquilizing drugs are potentially a tool of great value, their use is fully as sensitive and skilled a procedure as the use of insulin for diabetics, of anticonvulsants for epileptics, and of digitalis and anticoagulants for cardiac patients. They have cautioned that before general practitioners prescribe tranquilizers for mental or emotional conditions, they should consult with a psychiatrist on the diagnosis and indication for treatment. Tranquilizing pills cannot serve as an alternative to psychiatric therapy, and they may sometimes lower the patient's tensions to the point where he becomes oblivious to the realities of life.

Not long after the tranquilizer fad got rolling, the Committee on Research, Therapy, and Public Information of the American Psychiatric Association expressed its apprehension about the widespread resort to such medications "for the relief of common anxiety, emotional upsets, nervousness and the routine tensions of everyday living." The committee warned that the "casual use of the drugs in this manner is medically unsound and constitutes a public danger." Shortly thereafter, the FDA issued a cautionary reminder to doctors that reserpine, one of the two major tranquilizer compounds, "is not the innocuous substance it was first thought to be, that there are contraindications, and that the safe level for long-term outpatient maintenance is lower than the originally recommended dosage schedule." The agency reported that reserpine has been found to produce "severe depression in a significant number of individuals, and has precipitated a very considerable number of suicidal attempts, some of them successful." But these and other warnings have been widely disregarded by physicians, who have continued to dispense tons of the psychiatric drugs with the utmost abandon. Despite mounting reports of adverse reactions, tranquilizer sales in the United States have more than tripled since 1955.

Very frequently, the patients themselves are apt to insist on getting serenity pills for whatever ails them. But just as often the busy doctor is likely to prescribe them when he is confronted with a vague diagnosis or with a patient whom he regards as neurotic. All too often in today's medical practice, unfortunately, patients trek from one physician to another, constantly searching for understanding and help and getting instead prescriptions for all sorts of drugs. Excessive medication would not be such a disquieting problem if doctors would only take more time to listen and to try to comprehend their patients' needs.

The tranquilizers provide important clues to the chemistry of the brain and have proved of great value in mental hospitals, where they have calmed agitated patients and helped to produce a more hopeful atmosphere. But their use outside an institutional environment, without an opportunity for close supervision of those who take them, remains beset by uncertainties and potential hazards. Some of them can cause severe side effects, including liver damage, intestinal hemorrhage, jaundice, blood-cell changes, a fall in blood pressure, and skin rashes. Others can boomerang the user into dangerous depressions or cause addiction. Still others appear to slow reflexes and to interfere with the ability to maintain sustained attention. When given in small office dosages, many of them are not much more effective than the older and milder sedatives at one-twentieth the cost.

The first tranquilizers turned out to be such a gold mine that drug companies left behind in the competitive race rushed into the market with a whole series of new variants and an avalanche of promotional literature designed to befuddle doctors and lay-men alike. Mass-circulation magazines soon blossomed out with dazzling accounts of the miracle pills for the mind. Even greater was the drumfire of propaganda concentrated on those who do the prescribing and choose the brands. In addition to many pages of advertising, medical journals began to publish glowing reports of clinical investigators that were often based on a few inconclu-sive preliminary tests. Doctors' mailboxes were stuffed with free samples and elaborately illustrated pamphlets purporting to con-dense a great deal of scientific material but actually consisting for the most part in questionable testimonials and references to re-ports never published or not fit to be published. Along with their samples and promotional ballyhoo, some of the pharmaceutical firms sent gift-wrapped pillows and slipper socks for the doctor's "personal peace and comfort."

Whatever questions there may be about the toxicity and other harmful properties of many of the tranquilizers, there is none about the comfort and prosperity that they have brought to the drug makers. One of the big drug companies specializing in the tranquilizer field reported a spectacular 31 per cent return on invested capital in 1961.

III

That the consumer has a vital financial as well as health-conservation stake in the marketing and consumption of drugs can be readily seen from a few statistics. Sales of drugs, including both prescription and over-the-counter items, are now running at the rate of $3.9 billion a year, which is considerably more than double the 1952 figure and is an increase of about $500 million since 1960 alone. The most dramatic expansion has occurred in the prescription field. Since 1929, expenditures for prescription drugs have jumped more than tenfold, from $250 million to $2.8 billion, reflecting a continued rise in consumption as well as in prices. In the past twenty years, the average price per prescrip-tion has climbed from ninety-nine cents to $3.22, which is a far steeper boost than the increase in the overall cost of living. The magnitude of the upswing in the average use of drugs is shown by the fact that although the population of the United States has increased by 40 per cent since 1940, the volume of prescriptions for pharmaceuticals has in the same period quadrupled. Between 1950 and 1960, per capita expenditures for drugs went up from $10 to $19.

Prescribed medications now absorb about twenty cents out of every dollar spent by Americans for health care and a much higher proportion in cases of prolonged illness. Family drug bills of $200 to $300 a year are not uncommon these days, and they sometimes run into the thousands of dollars. Men and women over the age of sixty-five have per capita drug expenditures of $42 a year, or more than twice the average for all ages. The costs of drugs not only are beginning to approach doctors' fees and hospital charges in importance but constitute the largest out-of-pocket item in the nation's medical care budget, since they are usually not covered by out-of-hospital health insurance.

A material increase in the use of drugs was to have been fully expected with the revolutionary changes in the pharmacopoeia and the prolific emergence of new and more effective preparations that have made immense contributions to better health and longer life. The antibiotics, sulfas, hormones, metabolic agents, diuretics, anticoagulants, blood-pressure depressants, and a number of other medicinals have proved of inestimable value. But some of the nation's most eminent authorities have repeatedly voiced concern over the widespread resort to medications of doubtful therapeutic worth, the frequently improper use of the antibiotics and some other drugs, and the general tendency to substitute hasty prescribing for the time-consuming procedures required for careful diagnosis.

Spokesmen for the pharmaceutical industry often boast that some 40 per cent of the medications now available could not have been filled as recently as five years ago and that more than 70 per cent of the current drug expenditures are for products that are less than ten years old. Novelty in itself, however, is no guarantee of efficacy. In fact, much of the unnecessary use of drugs, as well as their excessive cost, stems from the continued flood tide of new preparations and their frantic promotion.

New drugs are now accepted more rapidly—and also become

obsolete much more rapidly—than in the past. To promote a new product, a company not infrequently spends as much as half a million dollars on a fanfare of medical journal and direct mail advertising aimed at hitting every practicing physician in the country. A barrage of press releases touting the latest wonder drug is simultaneously showered on newspapers, magazines, and the radio and television networks. Such lavish saturation promotion is not only wasteful but dangerous on several counts. It needlessly adds to the cost of drugs and persuades many doctors to prescribe—and many patients to want—new medications simply because they are new and not because they are necessarily better than older and cheaper preparations. Since the average new drug now has a life expectancy of only two to five years, the pressure is great to rush into the market in the hope of a successful run before it is too late. This militates against adequate evaluation before drugs are released for general use and contributes to the confusion of those who do the prescribing. While some highly useful drugs have been produced under this haphazard and clamorous system, there is urgent need for a more rational and economical way of going about it.

Dr. Walter Modell recently came up with the awesome finding that there are now on the market no fewer than 150,000 pharmaceutical preparations. New medications, he said, are often introduced not because they are superior to existing drugs but "to horn in on a market which has been created by someone else's discovery." He denounced as "structural roulette" the prevailing game of making a minor change in the molecule of a competitor's drug, to get around patent restrictions, and rushing the resultant analogue into production.

A number of other clinical and pharmacological specialists agree that only a minute fraction of the spate of products marketed in recent years represents real advances in therapy and that most of them are the result of "molecule manipulation" to gain competitive advantages and to exploit the penchant of doctors and patients alike for newfangled remedies.

Dr. A. Dale Console, former medical director for a leading pharmaceutical firm, told the Kefauver subcommittee that the drug industry "is unique in that it can make exploitation appear a noble purpose" and has a simple maxim: "If you can't convince them, confuse them." Some of the new products poured into the market are worthless, he declared, while others have "a greater potential for harm than for good."

Contributing to the steadily mounting size of the drug bill, in addition to the needless duplication of brands in drugstore inventories, are the pharmaceutical industry's unconscionably high profit margins and excessive advertising and promotion expenditures, high retail markups, the use of proprietary rather than chemical names in prescribing, and the marketing of useless or dangerous patent medicines.

The industry's stock argument is that drugs are expensive because of the huge sums poured into research to make available to the public the latest fruits of scientific knowledge in the development of new products. That this argument is meretricious can easily be gauged by comparing the drug makers' research costs with their promotional spending and profits. The annual research outlay of about $280 million by the pharmaceutical manufacturers does represent the allotment of a higher proportion of sales income for this purpose than in most industries. But aside from the fact that much of the drug industry's research is "me too" development and of highly questionable character, it spends nearly $3 for promotion for every $1 spent on research. Its profit margins are way out of line. According to the Kefauver subcommittee, the drug industry has a rate of return on investment that is the highest of any manufacturing industry and nearly double the average for all manufacturing.

Senator Kefauver's investigating group estimated that the pharmaceutical industry spends $750 million a year—or nearly $4,500 for every physician in private practice—for various forms of advertising designed to persuade doctors to prescribe the trade brands of particular companies. This astronomical sum goes for a far-flung and enticing variety of promotional activities and gimmicks for wooing the medical profession and, to a more limited degree, also the patients. These include the army of detail men busily engaged in "educating" physicians, medical journal and direct mail advertising, a prodigal distribution of free samples, elaborate exhibits, subsidized trade and paramedical publications, public relations activities, the sponsorship of special conferences and of closed-circuit televised clinics, mass mailings of free phonograph records combining a pitch for the latest antibiotic or tranquilizer with a performance by an outstanding musician, and wining and dining, golf and bowling tournaments, and other free entertainment for doctors.

"Few, if any, industries in the American economy spend as small a proportion of their sales receipts to produce the goods they sell as does the pharmaceutical industry," said the final report of the Kefauver subcommittee. The report provided an enlightening analysis of the operations of the twenty-two leading drug companies that account for the bulk of the industry's output. Taken together, these firms spent only 32.1 per cent of their sales receipts on actual production costs. Of the rest, 24.8 per cent went for selling activities, 10.9 per cent for "general and administrative" expenditures, and 6.3 per cent for research. The twenty-two companies had combined profits of 25.8 per cent of sales before taxes and net profits of 13 per cent. The pretax profits of six of the firms ranged from 30 to 44 per cent of sales. Individual percentages of receipts spent for sales promotion ranged from a low of 18.1 to a high of 40.5 per cent of sales.

Dependable estimates are that the drug industry's profits on net worth, after taxes, are running at between 21 and 22 per cent. For a number of years, drug company securities have shown impressive strength on the stock market, with the firms dispensing increased and extra dividends like vitamin pills. Tips on new drugs that are about to be released occasionally appear in financial publications before being reported in medical journals and have been know to produce sharp spurts in Wall Street quotations. Over an eleven-year period, one firm paid dividends at a rate totaling $16,480 on a $10,000 investment, and the value of that amount of its stock soared to $137,200. An original investment of $10,000 in 1949 in another big company, which is one of the principal manufacturers of tranquilizers, would have paid in ten years the whopping total of $254,000 in dividends and capital increment.

The spread between the production costs of drugs and their retail prices is probably greater than in any other large-scale industry. Pills that cost the manufacturer one or two cents to make may cost the consumer as much as thirty cents each. The Kefauver subcommittee reported that a cortisone preparation used in treating arthritis that cost $1.57 for a bottle of one hundred tablets to produce was being sold to retail druggists for $17.90 and to the consumer for $29.83. The subcommittee also figured out that a diabetic taking a patented oral insulin tablet was spending $150 a year for an amount of medication manufactured at a cost of about $14, including the royalty paid to the patent holder.

In the face of such price gouging, Federal government agencies, which spend millions of dollars a year on drugs, have started buying pharmaceuticals abroad at hugh savings. The Veterans Administration, for instance, is buying tranquilizers from a Danish company at $3.84 per bottle of five hundred pills. The lowest wholesale price quoted in the United States was $19.25. The Defense Department recently reported that over a period of two and a half years, it had purchased $6.8 million worth of foreign drugs, which would have cost $17.4 million if they had been bought from domestic firms.

Although there are some six thousand companies making or distributing drugs to drugstores, hospitals, and physicians, the twenty largest concerns share 90 per cent of the business. Domination of the market by these firms stems from patent controls and the vast amounts they spend on promotion. This militates against the smaller companies, even in the case of nonpatented preparations, and largely eliminates the opportunity for price competition.

The patent system, with its arrangements for cross-licensing by the bigger concerns, ensures the exclusive exploitation of new drugs by the giants in the industry and insulates them against any attempted price cutting by smaller competitors. The effect of the patent system is clearly demonstrated in the price differential between penicillin and most of the other antibiotics. The price of penicillin, which is not protected by patent, has dropped sharply from its original high level. No such decline has developed in the cost of the other leading antibiotics, whose formulas are jealously hoarded by the patent holders and their licensees. Senator Kefauver's valiant attempts to crack the patent system were fiercely—and so far successfully—resisted by the drug lobby in a last-ditch defense of the industry's strongest bastion of monopoly prices.

But within the framework of the protective devices provided

by the patent system, the pharmaceutical industry is in savage competition, and the manufacturers race furiously to beat one another in bringing out new products. The competitive efforts are rarely aimed at price reductions, however. Their main purpose is to come up with some new twist, usually a minor modification in the molecular structure of an already available drug, that would capture doctors' prescription pads—for a few months, at any rate. This kind of competition puts a tremendous premium on hitting the market first with a new medication, often before it has been adequately tested, and fosters the "getting into the act" school of drug development and the superfluous duplication of virtually equivalent products.

Some thirty-five different antihistaminic drugs are being sold at present, all having practically identical actions but different names and dosages. Similar excesses are prevalent in regard to the antibiotics, the tranquilizers, and other groups. Contributing to the busy physician's pharmacological befuddlement is the general lack of any resemblance between individual trade names and active ingredients and the staggering multiplication of dosage sizes, tablets, capsules, ampules, vials, suppositories, syrups, ointments, lotions, and powders. Manufacturers not only are copying their competitors' products but also are duplicating their own products by marketing a bewildering variety of dosage forms.

A leading pharmaceutical manufacturer declared not long ago that the drug industry lives in the shadow of its own obsolescence. "If we don't try constantly to obsolete existing products," he said, "our competitors will. Competitive items can be expected to invade any new product's market in from thirty to ninety days after its initial introduction. This means we must promote new products rapidly if any reasonable sales volume is to be realized before they are superseded." Since the industry depends to a large extent on quick product turnover and labors under a compulsion to bring out new models every season, both its research and its promotion are geared to crash operation.

Instead of being principally directed toward the discovery of new compounds, much of the energy of pharmaceutical research is frittered away on modifications designed to compete with drugs already on the market. This sort of development is aimed at the immediate payoff rather than at basic scientific investigation that may not bear fruit until the distant future. "Extraordinarily few important new drugs have been originated by American drug houses," Dr. Frederick H. Meyers, professor of pharmacology at the University of California, has said. "Most of the major discoveries have been made either in other countries or by independent, nondrug company investigators here in the United States." To a considerable degree, the drug companies are the beneficiaries of research financed by the Federal government, universities, and private foundations.

The pressure to beat the competitor at his own game has led to mammoth advertising budgets. In 1940, the prescription drug industry was spending only a paltry $15 million on advertising. The outlay for the industry's medical journal and direct mail advertising alone has since soared to more than $125 million a year. Some of the biggest pharmaceutical companies are now spending fully one-third of their sales dollar for various forms of promotional gimmicks. By way of contrast, automobile manufacturers, who are certainly not averse to advertising their new models, spend less than 2 per cent of their income on advertising.

On top of the hectic advertising campaigns, doctors are besieged by the glib salesmen of competing firms, each claiming superiority for his company's products. Several firms maintain staffs of as many as one thousand detail men each. Since getting in to see busy doctors is not an easy matter these days and usually entails considerable waiting, one drug concern has estimated that the interviews of its detail men with physicians cost an average of more than a dollar a minute. But the drug makers are obviously finding that these costly visits pay off.

A glowing tribute to the "educational" contribution of the drug industry's sales force was paid some time ago by Dr. Austin Smith, president of the Pharmaceutical Manufacturers Association, in a statement published in the AMA *Journal*, of which he is a former editor. "Detail men form an indispensable link between the doctor and new knowledge that can help or save a patient," declared Dr. Smith. "In a few minutes the detail man can acquaint the doctor with the capacities and the limitations of a new drug."

This encomium drew a withering reply in a letter to the AMA *Journal* from Dr. George E. Moore, director of the Roswell Park Memorial Institute in Buffalo and a prominent surgeon and researcher. "Most detail men do not have an adequate background for evaluating therapeutic agents," Dr. Moore wrote. "What is the source of their information? Are they capable of sorting out the pertinent and statistically meaningful results of animal studies and preliminary human trials of a new drug? How can they know enough about the subtle differences in the structure of similar compounds that are being sold by rival companies? The busy practitioner grasps this weak crutch because of the difficulty of finding and evaluating medical reports scattered through a dozen journals."

The drug promoter has a remarkably free hand in seeking to influence the medical profession. The act spelling out the authority of the Federal Trade Commission, the agency charged with policing the advertising of goods in interstate commerce, contains this provision: "No advertisement of a drug shall be deemed to be false if it is disseminated only to members of the medical profession, contains no false representation of a material fact, and includes, or is accompanied in each instance by truthful disclosure of, the formula showing quantitatively each ingredient of such drug." This gives the advertiser loopholes a mile wide. To all intents and purposes, few holds are barred so long as the targets of the promotion are the doctors, even though, in the final analysis, it is the patients who may be bamboozled and perhaps even permanently harmed by the unforeseen adverse effects of insufficiently tested medications.

With the pharmaceutical industry's ballyhoo artists thus left largely to their own devices, the sky is often the limit. When Senator Kefauver produced at one of the hearings before his subcommittee examples of what he described as "misleading and gross" advertisements in medical journals for tranquilizers, appetite killers, and weight reducers, Dr. Ernest B. Howard, the assistant executive vice-president of the AMA, commented that it would be entirely unreasonable to require advertisers to tell "the whole truth and nothing but the truth." Medical journals glitter with flamboyant multicolored spreads and glossy double-page dramas of how a new drug has calmed the emotionally agitated patient, relieved the gnarled arthritic, or curbed the appetite of a compulsive eater. The picturesque advertisements usually appeal to emotion rather than to intelligent judgment. They use all sorts of innuendo to imply that the particular medication is the one and only and probably long-awaited panacea. Innumerable ingenious devices have been contrived to give promotional material an air of authenticity. Quotations are frequently used out of context, and the handpicked bibliographies include references to reports that have never been published or have appeared in publications of questionable integrity. Advertisements not uncommonly exaggerate the claims of therapeutic benefits; understate toxicity, complications, and side effects; and fail to mention altogether reports of tests that show the drugs to be of dubious value. Occasionally, they announce that additional clinical studies are now in progress and that the results will soon be reported. This has been likened by one observer "to the situation of Alice in Wonderland —the verdict first and then the trial."

"Never have so few been deluged with so much as the medical profession has with advertising claims for drugs," the *New England Journal of Medicine* has said editorially. "Evidently, drug manufacturers are finding it successful since the volume is steadily increasing as are the demands for time by detail men to further their claims. All this constitutes a unique situation where the busy physician eager to obtain and employ the most useful drugs for use in his practice is overwhelmed with such a plethora of agents, claims and counterclaims that he is completely confused regarding the true situation concerning therapeutic agents. . . . Thoughtful physicians have been much disturbed for a long time by the looseness of advertising claims, the lack of true information and the blatant approach that advertisers have been following."

Some of the worst excesses of the "hard sell" technique have been evident in the pushing of antibiotic combinations, which many authorities have condemned as worthless and frequently dangerous, and of tranquilizers. A number of distinguished physicians have exhorted their colleagues not to fall prey to the psychological warfare of high-powered sales promotion and to disregard the unduly enthusiastic and sometimes misleading claims regarding the benefits of multiple mixtures of antibiotics. The chairman of a special study group of the New York Academy of Medicine denounced the promotional literature for the tranquilizers as "extravagant and distorted" and designed to encourage "indiscriminate use" of these drugs.

A favorite gimmick is the "expert" testimonial, which is obtained by giving research grants to physicians and by sponsoring well-publicized symposia and is more often than not a sham. Dr. Maxwell Finland, who is a widely respected researcher, has charged that some drug companies use "stables of testimonial givers who, for some consideration or merely because they don't know any better," will attest to the merits of any new product.

An instance of out-and-out deception in a promotional brochure mailed to physicians by a leading pharmaceutical firm was brought to light several years ago by John Lear, the science editor of the *Saturday Review*. Lear was intrigued by what appeared to be a reproduction of the professional cards of eight doctors scattered across the country, cards representing a number of specialities, strung beneath a banner of bold type across the top of an advertisement reading: "Every day . . . everywhere . . . more and more physicians find Sigmamycin the antibiotic therapy of choice." Persistent efforts by telegraph, telephone, and letters to reach the eight doctors named as presumed endorsers of the drug finally established that none of them existed. As a result of this exposé, the company was charged by the Federal Trade Commission with attempting to mislead physicians. Its defense was that the advertisement had not intended to create the impression that the drug was endorsed by any specific physician and had merely depicted simulated doctors' business cards "to indicate in a symbolic way the various medical fields in which Sigmamycin might be employed."

No doctor can possibly find the time to read all, or even a substantial part, of the huge quantities of flashy direct mail advertising with which he is deluged. But the drug makers' method is to keep laying it on. Like all advertisers, they cherish the hope that eventually the harassed physician will break down and take a look at some of the material with which he is being snowed under. Dr. Solomon Garb of Albany Medical College reported after a three-year study of drug advertising that "the majority of mailed ads were unreliable to the extent that a physician trusting them could be seriously misled." But the cost of this outpouring of sales spiels is part of the price that patients pay for their medication.

Another serious and costly feature of the "blitz" technique of marketing new pharmaceuticals is the profusion of unsolicited drug samples with which doctors are showered—on the apparent principle that a pill in the hand will sooner or later by put into somebody's mouth. To introduce a broad-spectrum antibiotic, one company some years ago shipped out ten carloads of samples to more than 140,000 physicians at a reported cost of about $2 million. Although some doctors freely substitute drug samples for thought in their practice, others discard at least some of them as rubbish. Official concern over this situation was once expressed by the Post Office Department, which pointed out the danger involved in the indiscriminate discarding of undesired drug samples in waste receptacles that are often picked over by children and more professional scavengers.

A vivid picture of what the promotional material with which the medical profession is inundated is costing the public, not only as consumers of drugs but also as taxpayers, was given the Kefauver subcommittee by Dr. James E. Bowes, a gynecologist then in practice in Salt Lake City. Annoyed by the advertising pressures to which he was being subjected, Dr. Bowes began to count and weigh from time to time the gaudy brochures and bulky samples flooding his office. Then, he told the Senators, he decided to be more methodical. For a period of two months, he said, "I weighed every piece of mail on a postal scale, noting the company, the bulk rate of postage paid, and the corresponding third-class rate that you or I would have to pay if we were doing the mailing. I noted the drug samples received and calculated the wholesale cost of each pill, powder and liquid they contained. The results soon began to look fantastic."

Taking his own drug advertising mail as typical and applying this to the some 170,000 physicians in private practice in the United States, Dr. Bowes arrived at the conclusion that "it would take two railroad mail cars, 110 large mail trucks and 800 postmen to deliver the daily load of drug circulars and samples to doctors if mailed to one single city. Then, after being delivered, it would take over twenty-five trash trucks to haul it away, to be burned on a dump pile whose blaze would be seen for fifty miles around."

Dr. Bowes figured out that the material mailed by pharmaceutical firms to doctors came to a total of more than twenty-four thousand tons in the course of a year. He calculated that the more than $12.5 million spent annually by the drug makers for advertising postage at bulk mail rates was more than $5.5 million lower than the third-class rates that ordinary citizens would have to pay and represented at least that much of a contribution to the big postal deficit that the taxpayers have to meet. The sum expended by the drug manufacturers just on postage for advertisements and samples, he said, "would build three large hospitals per year. Probably fifty hospitals could be added to this figure if we had the amount of money that the pharmaceutical houses throw into the doctors' wastebaskets."

To give the subcommittee an idea of the cost of some promotional campaigns, Dr. Bowes cited the case of one firm that sent him a four-pound package of assorted samples. The postage alone amounted to $1.05, and he figured the wholesale cost of the drugs at $18.99. Extrapolating from this figure, Dr. Bowes concluded that the wholesale cost of the drugs sent out to the nation's medical practitioners in this single mailing came to more than $3 million and the postage to more than $170,000.

Aside from the intensive barrage of medical journal and direct mail advertising focused on the prescribing physician, the patient pays heavily for a multitude of other promotional contrivances. The drug makers spend millions of dollars every year to build prestige and to influence the doctor's choice of one particular drug out of a field of perhaps a dozen with the same pharmacological action by sponsoring exhibits and otherwise underwriting the costs of medical meetings, making educational films, staging plant tours, providing closed-circuit television coverage of medical events, and a wide variety of other schemes. Meetings of medical organizations often entail considerable expenses, including the costs of mailings, programs, stenographic aid, and special facilities for the press. The problem is usually solved by tapping the sources of drug promotion, frequently not without detriment to the character of the affair.

A number of authorities have questioned the educational value of many medical meetings, ranging in scope from the gatherings of small county societies to such great conventions as the annual sessions of the AMA attended by thousands. "At the large meetings, there are reunions, dinners, banquets, organized activity for the wives, and less and less emphasis on strictly scientific portions of the program," Dr. William Bennett Bean has said. "In fact, to get to the lecture hall, it may be necessary to run a gauntlet through a maze of commercial exhibits. Each exhibitor is expected to bring back evidence of attention in the form of names of physicians who have registered at his booth. Society officers and those conducting meetings urge everyone to register at each exhibit, and they remind the audience that the society is beholden to the exhibitors for money to hold the meeting. The emphasis on strictly professional and scientific activities dwindles in comparison with the commercial aspects. Thus the medical meeting is expanding in its functions and risks becoming a partially tax-deductible holiday for the wife and family, an opportunity for a collection of bushels of samples and reams of brochures, as well as the entertainment and sight-seeing trips."

The emergence of the drug industry as the patron of medical journals not only raises far-reaching moral issues but has enormously complicated the doctor's frustrating problem of trying to keep up to date with scientific developments. The steady expansion of ethical drug advertising has led to a great boom for medical periodicals, which are getting ever fatter and more numerous. With a fantastic total of some four thousand medical journals now competing for the profession's time, the sheer bulk of reading matter has become a hindrance rather than a help in the physician's unending struggle to keep abreast of progress in his field. The continuous proliferation of knowledge in itself makes it more and more indigestible. The spur of advertising revenue— along with the itch to get into print for prestige purposes, regardless of whether the author has anything new to contribute—adds immeasurably to the confusion.

Competent observers feel that lush support has inflated the number of journals far beyond need and that the plethora of space between the advertisements encourages the acceptance of inferior articles and has led to a serious deterioration in the quality of medical publications. Dr. C. Lee Buxton, chairman of the Department of Obstetrics and Gynecology at the Yale School of Medicine, has charged that many journals are cluttered with reports on research that are "worthless, nonscientific, and even, on occasion, fictitious." Aside from the dubious value of many articles, the prevailing poor level of professional writing constitutes a formidable barrier to communication. Much of medical writing is graceless and dull and tends to defeat the very purpose of communication, which is to convey information clearly. It is hardly surprising that the average busy physician, desperate for shortcuts through the forbidding jungle of academic verbosity, is tempted to bypass altogether the professional literature and to get most of his information from drug company mail advertising and from the skillfully edited and attractive digests put out directly or subsidized by pharmaceutical firms.

Periodicals operated with an eye toward moneymaking sometimes become diverted from their proper function as vehicles of reliable information and free and pointed criticism. Some medical journals are notorious for their subservience to the drug industry. Urgently needed is an overhauling of the legitimate medical literature by adopting more rigorous standards for the scientific validity of technical papers, by improving the literature's techniques of communication, and by reducing its dependence on drug revenue through more stringent controls on advertising copy.

"Most lamentable," Dr. Charles D. May has written, "is the lack of concern for the authenticity of material in the advertising pages in medical journals, which almost outweigh the editorial text in bulk and influence. Few journals show signs of a determined effort to reject misleading advertisements, and in none are the standards of acceptance high enough."

Even a publication of such unquestioned integrity as the *New England Journal of Medicine* has had trouble devising proper criteria for pharmaceutical advertising. Some years ago the *Journal* relinquished its association with the AMA's Cooperative Advertising Bureau, established to solicit advertisements for the publications of the various state medical societies, in order to be free to frame its own policies. The Boston periodical has pledged itself to limit its advertising to products that "are reasonably safe when properly used, that make no claims that cannot be substantiated and that are presented, if not always conservatively, at least with respect for the reader's intelligence." It has conceded editorially, however, that the latter yardstick "offers difficulties because of the relative incompatibility between such respect and modern advertising techniques." After the publication of one of its editorials criticizing the widespread use of antibiotic combinations, the *Journal* printed a letter from a physician reproving it for carrying in the same issue "three advertising spreads extolling the virtues of the very combinations that the editorial decries."

The problem of editorial responsibility for the character of the advertising in the medical journals is certainly not an easy one. But with the tremendous growth of the pharmaceutical industry and the gravely adverse effects of the hectic promotion of its products, many thoughtful physicians are becoming uncomfortably aware of their profession's ethical obligations in the matter. Drug advertising that in any way misleads doctors has a potential for harm not present in most other industries. "Because misinformation and mistakes about drugs can affect health and life," Dr. Harry F. Dowling told the Kefauver subcommittee, "advertising of drugs cannot be allowed to fall to the level of other advertising." When physicians become as dependent on confusing drug promotion as they now are, some controls on the quality of that promotion are imperative in the public interest.

In addition to their heavy subsidization of the professional journals, most of the large drug companies publish house organs that are sent free to doctors. Drug and medical equipment advertising also finances a number of slick and highly successful periodicals that are likewise mailed free to practicing physicians. An outstanding example of this type of publication is the biweekly *Medical Economics*, which usually carries well over a hundred pages of glossy advertising. This lively magazine specializes in keeping its readers up to date on some of the socioeconomic developments in medicine and in counseling them on how to make more money in their practice and through outside investments. Other giveaway periodicals combine digests of scientific information with news and advertising. All of them parade under the guise of objectivity but rarely bite the hand that feeds them.

Another expensive promotional device is institutional advertising, which does not directly plug any product but is designed to build up a favorable public image of a company. Some of the bigger drug firms spend large sums on such advertising in magazines of national circulation and through special television shows. Their institutional advertising usually concentrates on extolling not only the contributions of the pharmaceutical industry but also the virtues of the medical profession. The advertisers thus cater in one shot to their direct as well as indirect customers.

Although the manufacturers of ethical medications depend primarily on the prescribing physicians in their dealings with the consumers, they often also carry the attack directly to the public. A number of big public relations firms employed by drug companies provide science writers with a stream of helpful background material—along with discreet plugs for their clients' products. The sole objective of these agencies, which operate under such cover names as "medical news services" or "medical information bureaus," is to get free publicity about drugs into newspapers and magazines and on radio and television, on the theory that if people read or hear about new preparations, they will demand them from their doctors. Because of ignorance and a bent toward sensationalism, reporting in the lay press not uncommonly overrates the beneficial properties of new drugs. This is apt to subject doctors to pressures from patients eager for the latest remedy on the basis of information gleaned from their morning newspaper or the current *Reader's Digest*. The tranquilizers and antihistamines owe a great deal of their unwarranted popularity to this kind of enthusiastic reporting, and so do some of the antibiotics.

The sales technique of launching new prescription products through the mass-communication media runs contrary to the tradition that the promotion of ethical drugs should be limited to the medical profession. It therefore has to be used judiciously and with the aid of various subterfuges. In a particularly unsavory episode a few years ago, a leading pharmaceutical firm was caught red-handed in a barefaced lie. The company sent out a letter to physicians advising them that a new and more effective tranquilizer would soon be available; it deprecated premature publicity in the lay press, blaming "busy reporters" who had been snooping around for information that was none of their business. Several indignant science writers thereupon made public the text of a telegram dated eight days earlier in which the same company had invited them and a number of their colleagues to attend a grand unveiling of the new drug at a staff meeting in a local hospital. "You will see actual cases of delirium tremens, drug addicts and psychotics in the process of therapy on a tour of wards following the staff conference," the invitation said. "You will also see an uncensored sound and color motion picture of the hospital's experience thus far with the drug."

While a modicum of finesse is generally used in the promotion of ethical drugs, all discretion is tossed to the winds in the peddling of patent medicines sold without prescription. These preparations advertised directly to the public for self-medication offer a rich field for the blandishments of quacks and spielers. The whole sordid area of patent medicine advertising—in newspapers, magazines, and over the air—affects not only the pocketbook but also the health of an incalculable number of people. "Radio became a raucous voice plugging sedatives, headache powders, vitamins and numerous other medicinals," the *New England Journal of Medicine* has said. "After radio came television, which has brought the ancient medicine show to life. Just as credulous grandfathers of the present generation found the Indian medicine man and old Doc Jones and his cure for rheumatism convincing, so do their grandchildren find 'tired blood,' 'relieves headache twice as fast,' 'like a doctor's prescription' and other ridiculous statements, claims, half-truths and the associated entertainment convincing to an incredible degree. Unfortunately, the same factors are operating in the modern version as with the old Doc Jones show, but where the previous generation shelled out two bits to a dollar for a bottle, the grandchildren frequently shell out $5 and not infrequently come back for more and continue to do so for months."

A substantial portion of the more than $1 billion a year that Americans are now spending on patent medicines is thrown away on worthless nostrums ranging all the way from more potent aspirins to remedies for developing the bust, for growing hair or making it "permanently" vanish, and for curing every ill from hemorrhoids to cancer. The AMA's Council on Food and Nutrition said recently that much of the $350 million being paid out annually for vitamins in a waste and could far more profitably be spent on food. Spending for laxatives alone is estimated to be more than $150 million a year. Competent opinion is that frequent resort to elimination aids not only is unnecessary but is actually harmful. The sale of phony weight reducers grosses about $100 million yearly. Men and women suffering from arthritis are spending more than $250 million a year on uranium-ore pads, super aspirin, herb roots, and other remedies that are of little use or none whatsoever. Equally dubious is the medical value of the widely touted varieties of improved aspirin, for which more than $70 million is being spent a year. Many studies have shown that there is little difference between the action of ordinary and buffered aspirin. The tragedy, moreover, is that many of those bilked are least able to afford it. The less people spend on medical care, the higher is the proportion of their income going for self-medication.

In both the prescription drug and patent medicine fields, but particularly in the former, the consumer has to contend with a string of frustrations. Here, as Senator Kefauver pointed out, "he who orders does not buy; and he who buys does not order." The consumer not only is in no position to judge the effectiveness and safety of a drug but also is limited to the product prescribed by the doctor. He cannot shop around for the same product under a different name at a lower price. When it comes to drugs, the consumer is truly captive to a degree not as extensive in regard to any other necessity for which he has to spend his money. The basic issue is whether he should be left so completely to the tender mercies of an industry that has made vital contributions to our health and welfare but also has a sizable fringe of profiteers and charlatans.

IV

Many of the drugs now at the command of physicians have miraculous properties for controlling disease processes and saving lives. But the very potency of the new compounds makes it imperative that they be used intelligently and with the utmost discrimination. Expert opinion is that the required discernment is, unfortunately, all too often lacking in today's medical practice.

Powerful drugs are often tricky and can have unforeseen and dangerous side effects. They pose the risk of cumulative toxicity and allergic reactions and of altering the human body's natural resistance and sensitivity to both drugs and germs. All drugs are inherently toxic. The important consideration is the margin of safety in relation to a drug's effectiveness. The chemistry of medicine has been advancing so rapidly that the dividing line between successful therapy and the resulting complications can be very narrow, and it may take years for the pertinent evidence to accumulate. The rising incidence of adverse reactions, which one leading authority recently described as "alarming," is therefore hardly surprising when drugs are rushed into the market before their properties have been fully established and when strident promotion encourages doctors to accept new products uncritically.

The careless and often unjustified use of drugs has contributed immensely to the problem of man-made disease. "Untoward reactions to medication have increased at a staggering rate," according to Dr. Walter Modell, because of lack of experience with many of the new preparations and the widespread tendency toward overuse of some of them. In one large hospital in New York City, it was found that patients whose illnesses were directly attributable to improper drug therapy accounted for 50 out of 1,000 consecutive admissions.

Some of the worst excesses involve the unbridled use of the antibiotics, which now represent about one-quarter of the overall volume of prescriptions. The antibiotics fully deserve to be called "wonder drugs" and have contributed mightily to the conquest of some of mankind's greatest plagues. But they are not the cure-alls they are often billed to be and can produce serious reactions. They should not be used, as they frequently are, for every sniffle, ache, or fever. They should not be prescribed without a specific diagnosis or given for viral infections and other conditions for which they are worthless. Such unwarranted use not only is a waste of money but can be extremely dangerous. Aside from the hazard of possible severe side effects, indiscriminate dosing with antibiotics may mask the symptoms of serious disease, sensitize the patient so that he would be unable to benefit from the drugs in a later emergency, and encourage the growth of resistant strains of bacteria. The increasing frequency of outbreaks of staphylococcal and other perilous infections in hospitals in recent years is directly linked to the excessive use of antibiotics.

Only a relatively small proportion of the infections of the upper respiratory tract that millions of people develop every year respond to antibiotic treatment. It takes a simple laboratory test to determine whether an antibiotic will do any good. But frequently, neither the busy physician nor the patient is willing to wait for the test results, and antibiotics are given promiscuously for influenza and viral pneumonia and even for grippe and head colds. In the winter months, when viral infections flourish, it is not unusual nowadays for overworked doctors to prescribe antibiotics over the telephone without even seeing the patient. The often unnecessary resort to penicillin, in particular, is based on the ill-founded belief that it can do little harm and may be helpful in preventing complicating infections. Actually, the rate of adverse responses to penicillin is placed by some authorities at as high as 10 per cent.

So broad is the range of toxic and allergic reactions that some of the antibiotics have been found to cause that it is becoming increasingly evident that one patient's wonder drug can turn out to be another patient's, or even the same one's, poison. An individual allergic to an antibiotic may react only mildly to a first course of treatment but may suffer severely when he takes the drug a second time. The medical literature is replete with reports of the dire results of the unselective administration of such major antibiotics as penicillin, streptomycin, chlortetracycline, chloramphenicol, and oxytetracycline. The effects of hypersensitivity to penicillin have been known to range all the way from skin rashes and hives to severe shock, including a large number with fatal outcomes. It is estimated that about one thousand deaths a year are caused in the United States by sensitivity to penicillin. Prolonged use of chloramphenicol can injure bone marrow and result in a deadly type of anemia. Streptomycin may produce dizziness, affect equlibrium, and impair hearing. Chlortetracycline may cause a severe rash and fungus infection in the mouth. Both this popular drug and oxytetracycline can be responsible for serious intestinal irritation causing nausea and diarrhea.

The requirement for making at least a tentative diagnosis before prescribing and for establishing, first of all, whether the infection is susceptible of antibiotic therapy and then for picking the proper drug for the bacterial agent involved would seem to be so elementary that it need hardly be emphasized at too great length even to first-year medical students. And yet both the *New*

England Journal of Medicine and *Postgraduate Medicine*, another outstanding professional publication, have felt it necessary to rebuke their readers by calling their attention to these rudimentary procedures. In doing so, the *New England Journal of Medicine* commented that they are "indeed a far cry from present practice." Writing in *Postgraduate Medicine*, Dr. C. Henry Kempe, chairman of the Department of Pediatrics in the University of Colorado Medical School, gave his colleagues a beginner's lesson in medicine by reminding them that "fever is only a symptom" and can signify many diseases other than bacterial infections. By failing to distinguish between one fever and another and by using antibiotics indiscriminately "as forms of better aspirin" to bring down the temperature, he cautioned, doctors stand in danger of forgetting how to tell common sicknesses apart.

Equally sharp criticism has been leveled by leading authorities at the dozens of preparations that combine antibiotics or mix them with other compounds. The theory is that the therapeutic effects are thereby enchanced and that the emergence of resistant bacterial strains to one antibiotic is fought by another. But more often than not, these multiple drugs reflect the highly competitive nature of the drug business rather than real therapeutic need. Informed opinion is that they do not permit the doctor to prescribe the exact dosage of the one or more drugs most suitable for a specific case and are often dangerous.

The *New England Journal of Medicine* has for several years waged a tenacious battle against antibiotic combinations, deploring the ease with which many physicians succumb to the blandishments of sales promotion and welcome an easy substitute for the careful use of clinical judgment. Fixed mixtures, it has repeatedly emphasized, usurp the doctor's role and "encourage 'shotgun therapy,' which discourages the study and observation of the patient." Furthermore, it has warned, instead of broadening the spectrum of antibacterial action, one ingredient in the combination may interfere with the operation of the other so that they will neutralize or even antagonize each other and actually stimulate the development of resistant microbial strains. Package combinations, the *Journal* has said editorially, "should be approached with the greatest caution and skepticism. For, as every tradesman knows, 'package deals' are generally offered by a seller primarily to boost the sales of unmarketable or poorly accepted products."

"A minimum and absolute requirement in the utilization of a mixture is to know what it contains," the *Journal of the Canadian Medical Association* observed recently. "To stress this point may appear to insult the practicing physician, but experience has shown such caution to be necessary."

Among other frequently misused drugs are hormonal preparations, notably cortisone, and the medications for bringing down high blood pressure. Hormonal preparations designed to restore impaired metabolic functions are uniformly powerful and can destroy bone marrow, lower resistance to infection, and have other grave effects. Some physicians nevertheless prescribe them freely for joint complaints and other conditions without definitive diagnosis or treatment with more conservative measures. Adverse reactions to cortisone may range from swelling of the face or easy bruising of the skin to severe mental disorders or the unchecked spread of infection, which can sometimes be fatal. Hypertensive drugs can also have a variety of detrimental effects, and their overuse has been criticized by a number of authorities, including Dr. Irvine H. Page, a distinguished pioneer in blood-pressure research.

Doctors also are continually confronted with the danger of causing drug addiction. In this category are the morphine derivatives, which can set up dependence even after a relatively small number of doses, and the barbiturates. Addiction to barbiturates has become a major problem, and they are now second only to carbon monoxide as a means of suicide.

The antihistamine drugs, while less deleterious in their physical effects, provide another telling example of how frenetic promotion can prevail upon Americans to part with many millions of their hard-earned dollars. Launched with a fanfare of sensational advertising and extravagant publicity in the press, the antihistamines were originally touted as remedies for the common cold and proved to be a veritable bonanza for some of the drug companies. Although they are helpful in relieving allergies, they are worthless for nose and throat infections, and their continued wide use is far in excess of their value.

The basic trouble is that the torrent of drugs and their fanciful promotion have increasingly deprived doctors of their ability to judge the content, mechanism, potential toxicity, and other effects of new preparations but have, at the same time, encouraged them to substitute medication for diagnosis. Aside from the need for a more critical approach to the drugs they employ, physicians should also display a greater concern for the patient's pocketbook than many of them now do. A lesser gullibility for ballyhoo and a greater familiarity with generic names would sometimes enable them to prescribe much less expensive and as good or nearly as good alternative medications.

The profusion of new drugs and combinations and the frequent delays in the publication of reliable reports regarding their properties and effects make it extremely difficult even for the full-time pharmacologist to keep abreast of developments. For the average practitioner, it is an utter impossibility to study and evaluate them properly. This inevitably makes him dependent on the integrity of the drug makers and may force him to decide about the merits of new treatments by trial and error on his patients. This procedure can be detrimental as well as expensive, but reliable opinion is that it has unfortunately become quite common. Medications with seriously toxic properties have caused considerable damage before adequate knowledge of their adverse effects was obtained. Other drugs with little more than placebo value have been widely used before the true picture became apparent.

Many authorities feel that doctors need better training in pharmacology and that more effective mechanisms should be devised to bring dependable information on drugs rapidly from investigators to physicians. Several years ago, a group of doctors concerned over the extent to which their colleagues were relying on pharmaceutical promotion began publishing *The Medical Letter on Drugs and Therapeutics*, a newsletter designed to offer reliable and timely information on new drugs. *The Medical Letter* is doing a creditable job, and the pointed reports of its consultants often differ markedly from those of the drug houses. But it lacks facilities to make full tests of its own and must depend on the available literature, which often lags far behind the advertising campaigns. Another serious handicap is that because of its relatively limited circulation, it cannot hope to compete with the massive repetition with which the promoters are hammering home their message.

Clearly needed is some adequately financed and disinterested agency that would assume the responsibility for keeping doctors up to date on the advantages and drawbacks of newly marketed drugs. But even more important is the need for greater assurance of the efficacy and safety of medications before they are approved for sale. Although the tightening of the drug laws in the wake of the thalidomide incident has materially improved the situation, the available controls still fall short of the necessary safeguards against the insufficient testing of new products and the cumulative ill effects that they may produce. Even less adequate is the cumbersome and poorly coordinated machinery for keeping tabs on drug promotion in order to restrain its more flagrant abuses.

George P. Larrick, the United States Commissioner of Food and Drugs, testified before the Kefauver subcommittee in 1961 that worthless medications were getting on the market because his agency lacked the power to keep them off. He insisted, however, that there were ample legal controls against the marketing of dangerous drugs. That this was too sanguine an appraisal of the situation was promptly demonstrated within a year's time by the withdrawal of a number of widely used preparations that turned out to have serious side effects and by the thalidomide episode.

One of the most disquieting lessons of the thalidomide affair was that only the devotion and courage of a single FDA medical officer apparently stood between countless Americans and official approval of the sale of the German-developed drug in this country. Dr. Frances Kelsey resisted a steady barrage of telephone calls, letters, personal visits, and appeals over her head to her FDA superiors and single-handedly stood off the promoters of thalidomide until the drug's role in the deformities of numerous babies became known. If there had been a further delay in the discovery of the disastrous effects of thalidomide, Dr. Kelsy might have been overruled—as at least one of her predecessors had been, under pharmaceutical company pressures—to give the go-ahead signal for distribution of the drug. One of those who feels that "it could have happened here" is Dr. Helen B. Taussig, famed Johns Hopkins pediatrician, who two decades ago did the basic research and suggested the operative approach for turning "blue babies" into pink and active youngsters and who in the spring of 1962 first alerted the American medical community to the danger of thalidomide.

It still remains to be seen to what extent the legislation en-acted in the wake of the thalidomide affair will be successful in correcting the serious weaknesses in animal and human testing procedures for new drugs and in overcoming the inherent flaws of a system in which manufacturers depend on profits by getting the jump on competitors and by marketing cures that not infre-quently are of questionable value.

Even with the most stringent controls, laboratory experi-mentation and brief clinical trials of new medications can never be foolproof. The experience with the antibiotics over the past twenty years has shown that it takes prolonged use to establish the full frequency, range, and severity of the toxic, allergic, and other side effects of a drug. The record of pharmacological re-search and promotion is brimful of dubious practices and unjus-tified enthusiasms. "No one," Dr. William Bennett Bean has said, "has worked on the necrology of last year's sure cures, whose costly advertising brochures gather dust. Where are the cures of yesteryear? A study of abandoned drugs may seem a little foolish when so many new ones are arriving daily. But each failure is costly and wasteful—in time, money, hope, and perhaps in health."

Many competent critics have charged that the Food and Drug Administration is too weak and poorly staffed for its broad evalu-ative and policing tasks. In 1962, a study committee named by the Department of Health, Education, and Welfare recommended sweeping reorganization of the agency and the replacement of its top personnel with people with more adequate scientific training. The FDA's staff has since been beefed up, but it still falls far short of the number and caliber of personnel needed to carry the tremendous work load imposed by the agency's broadened re-sponsibilities. Instead of conducting tests of its own, the FDA has usually permitted the marketing of new drugs on the basis of clinical tests reported by manufacturers, which are often of doubt-ful worth. It is naturally in the manufacturer's interest to present his side of the story as persuasively as possible. Although the func-tion of the regulatory agency is to protect the consumer's inter-est, there is ample evidence that it has frequently been feeble in doing so, both because of a skimpy budget and because of an excessive tendency to fraternize with the commercial interests it is supposed to police.

The FDA's staff has been so limited that drug manufacturing plants have been inspected on an average of only once in five and a half years. There is far more rigorous inspection of meat-packing houses. Up to less than a decade ago, the agency had the job of assuring Americans of a safe supply of food, drugs, and cosmetics on an annual budget of only about $5 million. A series of increases has by now boosted its budget to about $50 million, which is still totally inadequate for its constantly expanding duties, which now involve attempting to police $110 billion worth of foods, drugs, cosmetics, and hazardous household chemical aids marketed in the course of a year.

The FDA's ties with the drug industry have sometimes been far too close for comfort, and some of its personnel have occasionally used it as a stepping-stone to more lucrative jobs with pharmaceutical firms. The chief of the FDA's antibiotics division was forced to resign several years ago after it was brought out by an enterprising magazine editor that he had collected more than $250,000 in fees for editing promotion journals for the very drugs he was supposed to police. A former FDA medical officer, who quit her job in disgust in 1960, told the Kefauver subcommittee that the agency had become "in many of its activities merely a service bureau" for the pharmaceutical industry. She testified there had been cases in which orders came "from above" to certify new drugs on the ground that the drug companies themselves were the best judges of their safety. She also quoted the FDA's medical director as saying to her that "I will not have my policy of friendliness with the industry interfered with."

Legal controls over drug promotion are grossly inadequate, and whatever statutory authority does exist is split up between the FDA, the Federal Trade Commission, and the Post Office Department and has rarely been enforced with any great vigor. Because of their limited powers and staffs and a general reluctance to tangle with the big drug companies, government agencies have over the years failed to proceed forcefully against mendacious or misleading pharmaceutical advertising.

The greater authority that the FDA has recently been given will be useless without a much bigger staff and a leadership animated by a deep and consistent concern for the public interest. And much more far-reaching measures than have yet been devised will eventually have to be taken to deal effectively with the paramount role that the drug industry has come to play in the field of medical care and with the enormous influence it now has on the medical profession and, through it, on the consumers of its products. How much longer can we allow our doctors to remain so totally dependent for some of their most essential tools on a business that is primarily interested in profits? It is incredible that we should go on tolerating a situation in which, as one pharmacological expert said not long ago, stronger safeguards are provided for dog and cat food than for the medicines used for human beings.

CHAPTER ELEVEN

Organized Medicine Fights
for the *Status Quo*

I

ABOUT a dozen years ago, the official publication of the biggest state medical society in the United States ran an editorial so brutally callous that it is hard to believe that it purported to speak for a profession whose members are, as a rule, diligent and responsible citizens and probably second to none in their concern for the welfare of their fellow men.

A lengthy editorial comment appearing in the *New York State Journal of Medicine* said that the majority of people are kept well because they cannot afford to be ill. The editorial said this was a harsh view of the matter and admitted a certain number of cases of such diseases as cancer and tuberculosis may go undetected. But then it raised the question of whether it might not be more desirable to have a few people perish rather than have the majority running to seek medical care at every possible opportunity, to be sick often in an effort to get their money's worth. They would find out, the editorial continued, that the medical services people think they are getting for nothing, though actually every tax payer is contributing, would be worth nothing.

A somewhat less Neanderthal but equally reactionary philosophy was proclaimed several years later by the AMA House of Delegates in a resolution stating that "any system of medicine that offers complete coverage and relieves the recipient of making any direct contribution for his own medical care (i.e., paying the doctor separately for each service) will lower his sense of responsibility for his own health and that of his family and will eventually depreciate the quality of medical services he receives."

Neither the AMA nor the medical journals are likely to be quite as outspoken these days in espousing the grim doctrine of the survival of the fittest and the potency of the almighty dollar.

But they have yet to come around wholeheartedly to the view that every human being has a right to a life of dignity. They still have to acknowledge and act upon the principle of adequate medical care as a basic human privilege.

Although the doctor's self-sufficiency has been gradually undermined by the march of science and social organization, the medical profession continues to adhere to an uncompromising creed of competition and rugged individualism. Stripped of its bombast, this ideology applies to medical care the same philosophy of the virtues of the open market that is regarded as appropriate for any other profit-making enterprise. Under this doctrine, self-reliance is developed and success achieved by the solitary individual only through the competitive process. Disease, according to this principle, thus becomes merely another form of struggle for existence. When such a doctrine is carried to its ludicrous extremes, illness in those who cannot afford it is equated with laziness, cussedness, and malingering.

It is this antediluvian view of society and of medicine's own responsibilities within it, so deeply at odds with the profession's great humanitarian tradition, that is responsible for its split personality, its quixotic tilting at windmills, and the masking of its inner conflicts by an incongruous combination of pretentious posturing and querulous self-pity. This curious dichotomy extends, to a large degree, to the rest of us, too. The average man is inevitably confused by the doctor's dual role as healer and businessman, as humanitarian and huckster, and by his collective stance. He is apt to have, for instance, two sharply contradictory impressions of the AMA: one of an austere scientific body devoted to the protection of the public and dedicated to upholding the ideals of a noble profession, the other of a monopoly that ruthlessly keeps its members in line and has a remarkable bent for defining the social good in terms of its own self-interest and for resisting innovation until the last possible moment. The irony is that there is considerable validity to both images. The AMA can point with pride to many positive accomplishments in furthering the cause of good medicine. But its persistent refusal to face the facts of life provides its detractors with ample grounds for censure.

The AMA was founded more than a century ago by a group

of conscientious physicians determined to combat the rank commercialism that then threatened to bring the entire profession into disrepute. Since then, it has done a commendable job in helping to improve the standards of medical education and to raise the level of medical practice. It still performs highly important functions in disseminating scientific information through its various publications, in exposing quacks and the peddling of nostrums, and in engaging in other valuable professional activities.

But having grown old and rich and powerful, the AMA now devotes much of its energy and resources to the defense of the profession's economic interests. The emphasis in its activities has to a large extent shifted from scientific matters to public relations and lobbying. It has refused to acknowledge the need for adjustments dictated by profound changes in medical science and in the setting of its practice and has bitterly opposed virtually every proposal for extending better medical care to more people. Consistently in the backwash of social forces, it has waged negative campaigns marked by foggy emotionalism and a striking absence of rational discussion of the issues. Since it is doomed to fighting a losing battle, it has time and again had to eat its words and support the beneficial measures that it had formerly opposed. But as is notably the case with voluntary health insurance, which it once denounced as impractical and socialistic, it has done so only in the hope of heading off still more sweeping changes.

There is little question that a considerable number of physicians do not agree with many of organized medicine's policies. But few have dared to express their disagreements openly. Medical societies are notoriously intolerant of dissent, and potential rebels are well aware of the dire consequences of heresy. Here and there, the old guard is challenged, but there is no two-party system in the AMA and its component state and county organizations. The minority lacks leverage, and the ruling hierarchy has little difficulty in keeping discontent beneath the surface. Medical opinion is easily molded, since doctors are an unusually clannish group, tend to associate almost exclusively with one another, have few interests outside medicine, and are often ignorant about relevant social and economic developments. For many of them, medicine is a stepping-stone not only to affluence but also to

social advancement; and after a long and penurious apprenticeship, they dread anything that may endanger their lucrative
status. Whatever heterodoxy exists within the medical profession
is usually confined to the conversational level. Interestingly
enough, however, many doctors are not averse to criticizing not
only their conservative leadership but also the rank and file of
their colleagues when assured of anonymity.

A sizable proportion of the opinions expressed in a random-
sampling study of what its own members think of it made by the
AMA several years ago added up to the view that organized
medicine should face up to changing social and economic conditions instead of invariably fighting a rearguard action. Typical
comments were: "The AMA collects dues and generates public
antagonism toward medicine"; "We cannot stay the social revolution, but we can enter the fight to shape it in the image of our
concepts"; "Let's offer a positive solution for such national problems as old-age medical care, indigent care, and so on, instead of
merely being against some idea that somebody else has thought
up"; "We continue to fight yesterday's battles and hesitate about
tomorrow's."

The same poll brought out that doctors have an even poorer
opinion of the performance of their own profession than do outsiders. Four out of every five doctors questioned agreed that
patients do not get as much time as they would like. In addition,
58 per cent conceded that most doctors try to cover up the
mistakes of their colleagues, 36 per cent agreed that physicians
have the idea that they are always right, and 23 per cent said
that the profession is not as dedicated to selfless service as it
should be.

But despite the rising unrest in its ranks, the leadership of
organized medicine stubbornly refuses to modify its standpat
views. The fantastic lengths to which its increasing identification
with ultraconservatism has carried it are tellingly demonstrated
by its tenacious resistance to the extension of the provisions of
the social security law to physicians. By now, the overwhelming
majority of Americans, including the leaders of both political
parties, regard the social security system, with its retirement and
disability benefits, as a logical part of the economic underpinning
for the later years of life. But for organized medicine, social

security always has been, and still is, a threat to the nation's moral fiber and "a foot in the door toward socialism." The medical profession remains the only one that has to this day refused to accept coverage under the law.

Whether or not physicians ever decide to avail themselves of social security protection in their old age and to extend such protection to their families in the case of premature death is their own business. But their dogged position that social security insurance is a dangerous encroachment on personal liberty cannot help striking laymen as preposterous. Social security is here to stay, no matter what the medical profession decides to do about it. The profession's stand on this point not only emphasizes the backwardness of its social thinking but is an outstanding example of biting off your nose to spite your face.

Opinion with regard to social security is by no means unanimous among doctors, and there have been increasing demands that the AMA reverse its policy and allow its members to be included in the system. But the House of Delegates has steadfastly refused to do so and has insisted that "American physicians always have stood on the principle of security through personal initiative." Resolutions requesting a nationwide poll among physicians to determine their views on the subject have been voted down on the ground that under the AMA constitution, its policies are determined by members of the House of Delegates "and not by popular vote." Although polls conducted by a number of state medical societies have produced substantial majorities in favor of accepting coverage, the House of Delegates has repeatedly taken the position that its own members "are sufficiently well-informed to represent adequately the views of the physicians of America on this question." Under the AMA concept of democracy, delegates elected by the members of state societies do not necessarily have to be guided by the views of their constituents. On a number of occasions, representatives of states in which doctors have gone heavily on record in favor of joining the social security program have voted the other way in the House of Delegates. The governing body of organized medicine not only is jealously protecting what it considers its sole prerogative of setting policy but is obstinately clinging to its own private Shangri-La of socioeconomics.

II

In order to try to understand why the medical profession's collective behavior is so much more shortsighted and self-seeking than the conduct of individual doctors, many of whom are conscientiously caring for the sick and giving freely of themselves, we must take a closer look at the anatomy of organized medicine —its organizational structure, the character of its leadership, and the manner in which it controls and intimidates its membership.

At the base of the pyramidal edifice of the organized profession are more than two thousand county and district medical societies, which regulate its conduct and enforce its rules at the grass-roots level. Above the local organizations are the state societies, whose authority is more general and extends to broader policy matters. At the apex of the structure is the AMA, the profession's top policy maker and spokesman, with a membership of about two hundred thousand physicians, a large bureaucracy, and an operating budget of $23 million in 1964. Membership at the county level is virtually compulsory for doctors in private practice; without it, they are usually unable to obtain hospital-staff appointments or the approval of the governing boards that pass on the qualifications of specialists. Such membership generally carries with it automatic enlistment in the state societies, although not necessarily in the AMA. But the great majority of private practitioners also belong to the national organization and pay dues, which have recently been raised from $25 a year to $45 a year to finance expansion of its activities—particularly its program "to portray faithfully the image of the medical profession." This is a nice euphemism for lobbying against anything that threatens the profession's income and other prerogatives.

Theoretically, the AMA is the creature of its local and state bodies and thus subject to their control. The county and district organizations elect representatives to the state societies, and these in turn name representatives on a proportional basis to the AMA's policy-making body, the House of Delegates. Actually, the national organization is an oligarchy dominated by a small clique.

One of the oldest and most formidable pressure groups in the United States, the AMA has for many years had a remarkable continuity of leadership and has exerted a potent influence in the marketplace of opinion. This has been due to its ample treasury and even more so to the cohesiveness produced by similarities in outlook among its members and by the threat of severe sanctions against recalcitrants. The lack of direct democratic controls and the apathy of the average physician ensure domination by a self-perpetuating faction and the powerful bureaucracy.

The basic structure of organized medicine is such that democratic rule ends, to all intents and purposes, on the county level. There is no effective forum for the expression of minority opinion, and no mechanisms are available to assure dissenters of any kind of representation. A semblance of democratic procedures exists in the local societies, where members vote directly for county or district officers and representatives to the House of Delegates of their state society. From this point on, representation becomes increasingly indirect. Those named to the House of Delegates elect the state officers and the state representatives to the top national assembly. The latter elects the president and other AMA officers and the governing board of trustees.

Even on the local level, it is easy for a small group to wield influence totally out of proportion to its numerical strength and to remain entrenched in power. Busy practitioners have little time to devote to medical politics and are content to leave such matters in the hands of their older and more successful colleagues. An attendance of more than one-fourth of the membership at business meetings is reported to be rare. On top of this is a nominating process that permits easy manipulation and the perpetuation of control in the hands of a tight little group. The president's authority to appoint a nominating committee that puts up a slate of officers and delegates gives the incumbents a dominant influence in deciding who will succeed them. Under this setup, the line of succession is tidily arranged, and only those who have proven their reliability are allowed to work their way upward. It is common for representatives to the state and national Houses of Delegates to be reelected year after year and for officers to progress from county to state and then to national posts as they acquire seniority. The medical politicians serve long apprenticeships on the lower rungs and are well insulated from any dissenting viewpoints by the time that they have reached the summit of the organizational pyramid, the august AMA House of Delegates.

The men who climb highest in the political arena of medicine are usually well-established specialists who can afford to give a lot of time to politicking while their practice is carried on by younger associates. Being older and set in their ways and having achieved professional prominence and financial success, they have every reason to be satisfied with the *status quo* and to resist any change in it. The fact that most of their colleagues are naturally conservative makes it all the easier to put up a solid front against the readjustments in the organization of medical care that the times so urgently call for.

In contrast to the normal political process, there is no campaigning for medical society offices in the real sense of that term, and members have the choice of the single slate brought forward by the rigged nominating committees. Counternominations from the floor are unheard of. Controversial issues are rarely discussed at medical meetings, and the men chosen to represent the membership in the state and national Houses of Delegates go there without binding instructions from their constituents. Poor attendance at meetings and the general reluctance to step out of line produce an atmosphere of serene conformity. If a contentious subject does come up, it is promptly buried in a committee for "further study."

The AMA House of Delegates is heavily weighted with small-town specialists, who find it easier to spare the necessary time than do their colleagues in the more competitive setting of the bigger cities, and a recent survey showed that the average member is fifty-nine years old. A conservative observer not long ago described the views of the majority of delegates as "right of center," which is probably an understatement. In theory, control of policy is vested exclusively in the House of Delegates. But since this body meets only twice a year and has little authority over the budget, many policy and administrative decisions are necessarily left to the fifteen-member board of trustees and the top-echelon bureaucracy.

In a rare display of independence at its session in the summer of 1962, the House of Delegates upset a tradition that an AMA president must first have served in a series of lower offices in the hierarchy and chose instead as president-elect Dr. Edward R. Annis, the flashy forty-nine-year-old Miami surgeon who had become the profession's most articulate spokesman against the proposed medical care program for the aged financed through the social security system. In turning down the choice of the organization's elder statesmen, the delegates actually appeared to move still further to the right in favor of a more rigid and aggressive policy.

One of the distressing aspects of the AMA's activities is the steady decline in the quality of its leadership. At one time, it numbered among its top officers distinguished physicians widely respected for their contributions to medical science. But the best minds in medicine have increasingly shown a distaste for the cockpit of medical politics, largely leaving the field to mediocrity.

The AMA's permanent salaried staff, which no one-year president can dislodge, inevitably wields great power. In overall charge of the more than seven hundred employees at the association's headquarters in Chicago and its office in Washington, which is one of the capital's most affluent lobbies, is Dr. Francis L. J. Blasingame, a former Texas surgeon, who is executive vice-president. Dr. Blasingame has in the past few years streamlined the administrative structure and tightened the chain of command. Another potent figure is Dr. Ernest B. Howard, who as assistant executive vice-president masterminds the AMA's lobbying activities.

The most important vehicle for disseminating the official gospel and organized medicine's biggest money-maker is the weekly AMA *Journal*, which has the largest circulation of any medical publication and is one of the most profitable magazines in the country. Aside from the wide assortment of scientific articles it publishes, many of them written in dry-as-dust style, the *Journal* faithfully reports the proceedings of the AMA's annual meetings and of its various councils. Some of the *Journal*'s profits are used to subsidize several other AMA publications operated at a deficit. Fattened by drug advertising, the *Journal* has grown heftier over the years, and advertising pages now account for about half of its bulk. But the reading matter is still sufficiently voluminous, as one observer has remarked, "to keep a really busy man from any risk of contamination by other literature." In a further effort to mold opinion, the AMA *News*—a much more concise and informal weekly publication, with a tabloid format, launched a few years ago—is sent to all physicians and to the press.

An AMA study committee reported several years ago that many doctors are intensely interested in the socioeconomic problems of medicine and recommended that the association's publications be opened "to a free and open discussion" of such matters. "We must restore to our members," it said, "the feeling of belonging. We must not stifle constructive criticism." But to this day, dissenting opinion gets an invariably cool reception in the pages of the AMA *Journal*, and both sides of an issue are rarely presented with any degree of adequacy. In 1962, the *Journal* refused to run a paid advertisement of the Physicians' Committee for Health Care for the Aged Through Social Security in favor of the Administration's program. The reason given was that the advertisement did "not conform to our standards."

The AMA not only operates one of Washington's biggest-spending lobbies but is reputed to be the envy of other pressure groups because of the skillful use it often makes of the personal physicians of members of Congress. As soon as word gets around that a Congressman is inclined to vote against the AMA line, the news is flashed to Chicago and relayed from there through the legislator's state and county medical society to his personal physician. This doctor promptly telephones or wires the Congressman, and his plea is likely to carry considerable weight, particularly with small-town and rural members of Congress.

The AMA has recently embarked on a course of even more direct political action, which promises to plunge doctors still deeper into politics. Since the Federal corrupt practices law prohibits the association from contributing directly to the campaign expenditures of any candidate for national office, the AMA has sponsored the formation of the American Medical Political Action Committee (AMPAC) to support friendly candidates—especially those pledged to combat the Administration's plan for health care for the aged. The House of Delegates has urged all physicians, their wives, and "interested friends" to join AMPAC chapters in their states. The term "interested friends," it was later explained, covers such "allied groups" as dentists, pharmacists, and officials of medical supply companies. Forty-six state chapters have been organized at the last count, with "sustaining membership" dues starting at a minimum of $99 a year. Thus armed with a respectable kitty, the AMA's new political organ went into action for the first time in the 1962 elections under the slogan that its outcome holds "the key to the preservation of medicine." Its efforts were concentrated in some fifty Congressional districts, and, except in the South, backing was generally given to Republican candidates. In the 1964 elections, AMPAC, headed by an ardent Goldwater supporter, spent more than $600,000 on its favorite candidates in about 150 Congressional contests. The results were bitterly disappointing to the AMA.

Aside from the implications of organized medicine's growing identification with extreme conservatism, there is the issue of whether doctors have any business entering political campaigns as a mass pressure group. Open electioneering has a tendency to spill over into doctors' waiting rooms, which have already become distribution points for propaganda on behalf of the established order. Some AMPAC chapters are reported to have urged physicians to use their personal influence with their patients in an effort to swing votes. Mixing politics with the practice of medicine is a dubious procedure and can only further impair the profession's standing with the public.

Still fresh in the minds of many people is the notorious propaganda "blitz" staged by the AMA in 1949–1951 against the legislation for a national health insurance system backed by the Truman Administration. Financed by a $7 million war chest raised through two special assessments of $25 on every member and additional funds obtained from insurance companies, banks, utilities, and other sympathizers, the campaign conducted by the California husband-and-wife public relations team of Clem Whitaker and Leona Baxter will go down as one of the most massive and disingenuous proselytizing assaults in American history. All the stops were pulled out in a naked appeal to emotion. Rational discussion of the issues was evaded, and advantage was taken throughout of the doctor's role as one who deals with frightened people at what may be critical moments of their lives. Physicians' offices, well stocked with literature warning of the horrors of government medicine and proclaiming that "the voluntary way is the American way," became the bulwarks of the crusade. Color reproductions of Sir Luke Fildes' touching painting of a doctor's solemn vigil at the bedside of a desperately ill little girl—a scene totally irrelevant to the conditions of current medical practice—were distributed by the hundreds of thousands for display in physicians' waiting rooms and in drugstore windows with the exhortation to "keep politics out of this picture!" Campaign headquarters in Chicago turned out a torrent of canned speeches, endorsements, editorials, and letters for transmittal as personal appeals to members of Congress. The technique was to reiterate ceaselessly the same theme from as many ostensibly independent sources as possible. In a single climactic two-week period, more than $3 million was spent on a blizzard of newspaper, magazine, and radio advertising attacking "socialized medicine." Whitaker and Baxter alone collected $325,000 in fees.

On the face of it, the crusade was a huge success. The compulsory insurance legislation was thoroughly beaten. But in large part, this was accomplished only because organized medicine had come around to the alternative of voluntary health insurance that it had once denounced as socialistic. Moreover, the day of reckoning has been merely postponed, and the medical profession is still carrying the burden of the resentments kindled by the tactics of the professional manipulators of public opinion in achieving their Pyrrhic victory. Long-overdue reforms cannot be held at bay forever just by being labeled un-American and by trying to endow the existing system of medical care with the halo of free enterprise and personal liberty. No flag-waving and high-minded sloganeering, no gimmicks to hoodwink the public can substitute for a positive solution or can make people go on believing what their experience disproves. Public relations pyrotechnics are in the long run worthless without a realistic assessment of human needs and concern for meeting them.

Regardless of whether or not he belongs to the AMA, every prospective or practicing physician is subject to its sway and profoundly affected by its decrees. The medical school he attends has to have the AMA's sanction. The hospital where he serves his internship or residency must have its approval for graduate training. His license to practice medicine is issued under rules influenced by the AMA. There is hardly a facet of his practice where the authority of the AMA and its component societies is not felt, directly or indirectly. In many respects, the authority of the states in medical affairs has virtually been delegated to organized medicine. Medical societies have acquired what amounts to a quasi-legal status in the health field by being allowed to set standards of medical education, hospital training, and practice, which are either incorporated into law or implicitly recognized by administrative agencies. The enforcement of existing statutes and proposals for new public health legislation are often materially influenced by medical organizations. State and local health departments usually work in close collaboration with medical societies, which are always on the lookout to protect the profession's interests against what they regard as government encroachment. Organized medicine controls qualifications for admission to the profession and dominates state licensing boards. In many states, it also holds a veto power over the formation of new health insurance plans under laws specifically requiring medical society approval for any such projects. No other private group commands such power within its area of interest and enjoys such unique freedom from public control.

No doctor in private practice can afford to antagonize a medical society or to stay out of the fold altogether. If he does not play the game according to the official guild rules, he is likely to wind up with few patients or none at all. Lack of hospital-staff privileges, which are usually contingent upon medical society membership, severely handicaps any physician and is ruinous to one who wants to practice surgery. In addition, many doctors, and especially surgeons, depend on patient referrals from other physicians. They will not get them if they are not in good standing with their medical societies. Nor will they be able to buy expensive malpractice insurance at the lower premiums that medical societies obtain by getting a master policy for their members.

Nonconformists are subject to powerful sanctions bearing directly upon their economic welfare. Expulsion or suspension from membership is not the only disciplinary weapon wielded by medical societies. There are a variety of informal pressures that are equally effective. A physician's reputation is a fragile commodity and can be easily impaired by the ill will of his colleagues.

Professional ostracism can have a disastrous effect on a doctor's practice. A practitioner subject to disciplinary action by his medical society is tried and judged by colleagues who may have an economic interest in proscribing his presumably offensive conduct. He has little redress outside the framework of the organized profession. In the case of a physician who has been expelled or suspended, even reinstatement may be of little use in undoing the damage to his means of livelihood. If a doctor is *persona non grata* with the "home club," he also is unable to get any other physicians to take the witness stand in his behalf if he should become a defendant in a malpractice suit.

The medical code of ethics, ostensibly designed solely to hold doctors to high standards of personal and professional conduct, has not infrequently been used to penalize dissenters from the official party line. In its name, disciplinary measures have been imposed upon physicians who have joined group-practice plans or who have otherwise strayed from the path of orthodoxy. The wife of a Buffalo, New York, radiologist who came out publicly for the Administration's medical care for the aged program complained to President Kennedy in the fall of 1962 that her husband had been blacklisted to the brink of bankruptcy.

The medical profession's extraordinary cohesiveness is not wholly the result of intimidation, however. There is probably no other calling in which there is such a strong sense of guild loyalty. Dissenters sometimes remain silent not only out of fear but also because they believe that the interest of the profession is best served by presenting a united front to the public.

Organized medicine has occasionally even resorted to economic reprisals against laymen who have aroused its ire. A classic example is the boycott of the products of the Borden Company, a leading dairy firm, organized by several medical societies in the New York City metropolitan area in the 1930's. The blacklist was ordered to force the Milbank Fund, a philanthropic foundation, to reverse its stand in favor of compulsory health insurance. The Borden Company figured in the picture because Albert G. Milbank, its board chairman, also was president and the principal financial backer of the Milbank Fund. The boycott was not called off until Mr. Milbank had abjectly recanted and the fund's secretary had been discharged.

The problems of medical care and practice have always been assumed by doctors to be beyond the comprehension of laymen. In fact, the organized profession not only fails to recognize the stake the layman has in medicine but tends sometimes to use the term "layman" as if it were synonymous with the term "moron." Out of the totally unwarranted assumption that only the medical profession knows what is good medicine for the public and what its economic arrangements should be has grown the conviction that the interposition of a third party, such as a lay-controlled insurance organization, can lead only to a deterioration of services. A cardinal principle of organized medicine is that any health program must be under its complete and unsupervised control. The doctor knows best, not only how to treat the patient but also how he himself should be employed and what he should be paid. Somehow it seems never to have occurred to the profession that while to the doctor the provision of medical care means the earning of his living, to the patient it means his health and often even the preservation of his life, to say nothing of the substantial effect on his pocketbook, and that he is entitled to have something to say about it.

Robert M. Cunningham, editor of the magazine *Modern Hospital* and a knowledgeable observer of the medical scene, once said: "Lay interference is a fundamental principle of American life. It is the principle of lay interference that puts civilians in charge of our military services, even in war times; it is the principle of lay interference that makes teachers and educational administrators responsive to the demands of boards of education; it is the principle of lay interference that gives the electorate final authority over all public officials, from the municipal clerk to the President. A doctor who objects to lay interference as such is asking that the medical profession be given the status of an untouchable priesthood, and the priesthood concept violates a basic tradition of American democracy."

III

Despite the professional window dressing, medical societies are essentially trade organizations whose principal function is to help their members make more money. That they have been eminently successful in this task can be readily seen from the profession's affluence and the fact that it is doing better than any other occupation except corporation management. The average doctor is riding a wave of prosperity. His earnings have doubled in the past decade and have increased nearly fivefold in the last twenty years. Illuminating is the income differential between physicians and college professors. In 1940, both medical practitioners and university teachers averaged $4,200 a year. Since then, the average earnings of professors have risen to about $9,000, while those of doctors have soared to a net of more than $20,000. Specialists have a median net annual income of about $25,000, and general surgeons average $27,900. Neurosurgeons head the list with net earnings of $34,700, plastic surgeons come next with incomes of $33,700, and orthopedic surgeons are in third place with an average of $32,700. One out of every five physicians now has net earnings of $32,000, and quite a few doctors clear $50,000 or more.

The classified advertising columns of the AMA *Journal* often make interesting reading. Job offers in one issue not long ago included one for a general practitioner in a small community in northern New York to replace a man who had grossed $35,000 to $50,000 yearly but had left to specialize; another for a pathologist in a Pennsylvania hospital to take the place of a retiring physician who had been averaging $32,000 a year; and a third for an eye specialist "in $30,000 to $40,000 class" sought for a partnership in Texas.

For a variety of reasons, the incomes of physicians have risen far more than is indicated by the increase in their fees alone. The growing demand for medical care has increasingly put a premium on the services of scarce professional personnel. Scientific advances, the employment of technical and clerical aides, improvements in transportation, and other developments have enabled the average doctor to see twice as many patients daily as he did a decade or two ago. Health insurance and the general prosperity have materially raised collections on bills. In the 1930's, practitioners were able to collect only about three-fourths of what patients owed them. Now the collection ratio is often 90 to 100 per cent. In contrast with some other enterprises, the medical profession's increased productivity and expanded services have not been reflected in lower prices for the consumer. They have instead largely resulted only in higher incomes for the producers.

Among the reasons commonly given by doctors in justification of their high-income level are the extreme length and costliness of their training, their heavy responsibilities, and the long hours they put in. They point out that medical education is far longer and much more expensive than that of any other profession and that the average physician does not start earning a livelihood until he is in his thirties and then usually goes through some lean years before he hits his stride. This, the argument runs, fully entitles him to an income sufficient to repay his investment and to pay for a comparable education for his children. It is, moreover, impossible to place any price tag, some doctors are quick to add, on the skills that can save lives. While a good deal of this apologia for high medical fees and incomes makes sense, few physicians ever take note of the fact that their education has been heavily subsidized. Medical school tuition charges are high and require great financial sacrifices. But more than four-fifths of the costs of medical education are met out of public and philanthropic funds. The defense of high incomes as compensation for a great investment in an education is thus far from airtight.

Much more pertinent is the rarely mentioned fact that the medical economy has a number of built-in characteristics that are peculiarly conducive to an unrestrained rise in prices. It is a sellers' market in which there is virtually no price competition, the consumer has very little to say about what he will be charged, and the suppliers not only are in control of prices but, to a considerable extent, also determine the need for their own services. Under such a setup, the consumer almost completely lacks the leverage he exercises in other sectors of the economy. This has further been aggravated by the mounting shortage of health manpower. Although the ordinary mechanisms of the marketplace are rarely operative in the field of medical care, the effects of the law of supply and demand are being increasingly felt. The biggest reason why doctors are making so much money these days is that there are not enough of them to go around. Failure to expand the ranks of the medical profession to meet the demand will inevitably keep pushing up the prices of medical services.

Frequently implicit in the defense of high medical charges is the contention that they are necessary to provide incentives for good work. This is a shameful argument for a profession supposedly motivated only by altruism. It is a sign of the corrupting influence of lucre on what has traditionally been a calling dedicated to service. Making too much money can prove to be fully as debasing to a profession as not making enough. The temptation to charge exorbitant fees sometimes becomes irresistible under a system in which opulence tends to be the essential status symbol. Under such a system, the guardianship of the great traditions of medicine is largely left to the top medical centers, where physicians usually work on a salary.

Whatever the rights and wrongs of medical and hospital charges, there is no question about the widespread feeling that they are frequently excessive. It must be remembered, first of all, that there is a considerable element of irrationality in the public attitude toward medical and hospital bills and that people do not approach them with quite the same logic that they apply in paying for other goods and services. The prices for men's haircuts, movie tickets, public transportation, automobile repairs, and numerous other items have risen even faster than have medical fees. But none of them arouses the same resentments that charges for the doctor's ministrations do. Similarly, a physician called to the scene of an accident often becomes the object of scorn when he wants to get paid, even though the tow truckers and garagemen always get their price. It is not so much the size of the doctor's fee itself that the patient sometimes objects to as the feeling that he is being charged for his misfortune. Not knowing in advance what the bill will come to magnifies his sense of helplessness and is another common source of irritation.

Medical and hospital bills usually come at a time of strain and anxiety and are likely to be measured by the standards of public service associated with doctors and hospitals. A man who is willing to swallow his indignation about a barbershop that charges all that the traffic will bear is unwilling to extend the same indulgence of commercial practices to the medical profession. The average person is inclined to take the doctor at his word when he says that he is practicing medicine for humanitarian reasons, and the layman is therefore surprised and hurt when he gets a big bill.

Very often he associates the bill with the physician's ostentatious manner of living and feels that his adversity has been exploited.

It is frequently pointed out that families of moderate means manage to find money for tobacco, liquor, television, and cars but complain about inability to pay for medical and dental care. What we have to reckon with here is the fact that people tend to choose certain and immediate pleasures instead of saving against the uncertain and wishfully distant expense of health care. About 6 per cent of what Americans are spending for personal needs now goes for medical care. This, on the face of it, does not appear to be an unreasonable proportion. It is less than half of what we spend for housing or transportation and is only slightly higher than the expenditures for activities that the U.S. Department of Commerce lumps together under the heading of "recreation" and that do not include liquor and tobacco.

But an outstanding characteristic of medical costs is that they are unpredictable and can be castastrophic. They can quickly wipe out a family's savings and plunge it deeply into debt. This is true not only of dreaded cancer or heart disease. A fractured hip can keep a patient in the hospital for several months and run up a bill of $3,000 to $4,000. A gastric ulcer requiring surgery may involve charges of $1,500 to $2,000. Even if a family carries hospitalization and surgical insurance, it must share much of the cost. And on top of the medical and hospital bills, there is the loss of income when the patient is the family breadwinner and must go through a long period of convalescence.

By their very nature, sickness and its costs fall unevenly. Far from being spread according to ability to pay, the burden is actually heaviest on the low- and medium-income groups, who spend a much larger share of their earnings on medical care than do those in the upper-income level. About 75,000,000 families in the United States, including more than one-fifth of those with incomes below $5,000 who have children, go into debt every year for medical bills to the tune of more than $1 billion. More applications for loans are filed with small loan companies by people needing assistance in meeting medical, dental, and hospital expenses than for any other single purpose. Many people live in dread of what serious illness may cost them. But reluctance to spend the money for timely medical advice in the early stages of sickness not uncommonly increases the gravity and duration of disease as well as its ultimate costs.

More so than in any other field, the medical profession has been permitted to establish its own charges almost entirely without the restraining effects of competition and public regulation. In no other profession or business is the supplier given such latitude to base his fees on his own estimate of the value of his services and of the patient's ability to pay. This calls for rigid self-discipline, which, unfortunately, is not always exhibited. Some physicians, and this is particularly true of surgeons, have been know to charge extortionate fees. Ironically enough, high fees usually tend to enhance a doctor's reputation, even though there is little ground for assuming any direct relationship between a practitioner's income and his competence. Actually, the privilege of setting fees, which the medical profession so jealously arrogates to itself, is an economic rather than a medical function and is one in which the public is fully entitled to have a voice. One of the principal reasons for the profession's deep distaste for health insurance is that it is increasingly providing a mechanism for negotiating the level of medical charges. The trend is inescapably toward limitations on the doctor's unfettered right to charge what he pleases. The fee-setting prerogative is more and more being taken out of the unilateral province of physicians and becoming a matter of collective bargaining with organized groups of the insured.

With three out of every four Americans now covered by some form of health insurance, charity work is rapidly fading away as an important element in medical practice, and so is the traditional justification for the sliding scale of fees. But although the theory that doctors are entitled to soak the well-to-do to compensate them for a large amount of free work has largely outlived its usefulness, it continues to be widely applied and is responsible for some scandalously high bills. The whole subject of charity work, by the way, has long been encrusted with a good deal of emotionalism and obfuscation. It is perfectly true that many physicians have generously given of their time and skills to take care of patients who could pay very little or nothing at all. But free work is not just something the doctors have given as a favor to the community. Hospital ward and clinic services have been an invaluable asset in the training of physicians. They not only have provided doctors with essential experience but also have traditionally helped them to get started on their profitable careers through the opportunity for highly useful contacts with established practitioners.

The sharp decline in the ratio of charity patients is now having a twofold effect. It is creating a serious problem by depriving medical students and hospital interns and residents of valuable clinical material needed for their training, and it is upsetting the classical defense of high charges. The medical profession nevertheless prefers to cling to the theory of its own selective largess, especially since the paternalistic burden is now greatly eased by the guarantee of insurance fees. Steep surgical fees are particularly open to criticism. Before the advent of health insurance, such fees could be justified on the ground that many patients who could afford a few home or office visits found themselves unable to pay for surgery and were operated on without charge. But the unpaid-for operation is increasingly becoming a rarity. Instead of lowering their fees, however, many surgeons have, in effect, raised them. In a large proportion of cases, they collect twice, from the insurance program and from the patient himself.

Many physicians have long complained about what they regard as the gross disparity between surgical and medical charges. The surgeon's training is longer and his earning career may be shorter than that of the nonsurgeon. His day's work is sometimes more exhausting, both physically and emotionally. But it is questionable whether this justifies the wide discrepancy in financial rewards between them. To a far greater degree than in any other medical specialty, the surgeon is provided by the community, through the hospital, with the tools, equipment, and space he needs for his practice. He pays nothing for his instruments, the use of operating rooms, and the services of nurses and other hospital personnel. Yet it takes an internist treating a hospitalized coronary patient about four weeks of daily hospital visits to collect the equivalent of a surgeon's fee for a routine appendectomy, which, along with postoperative visits, usually accounts for no more than three or four hours of the surgeon's time. The dominant role played by surgeons in the hierarchy of medical politics undoubtedly has a lot to do with the preference consistently given in Blue Shield fee schedules to surgical charges over those for other medical services. But surgery has always commanded high fees because of its dramatic life-or-death quality, even though the judgment and skill required may be lower than those of the family doctor who has made the original diagnosis.

The abomination of fee splitting stems directly from this inequity in the compensation of physicians, which has always caused bad blood between surgeons and other members of the profession. Considering themselves the victims of discrimination, general practitioners are especially liable to demand kickbacks from the fees collected from patients whom they have referred to surgeons. This racket, which amounts to buying and selling the sick with their own money and which is reported to be prevalent in many communities, not only boosts the bill but sometimes induces general practitioners to send patients to incompetent surgeons from whom they get a cut. It also encourages needless surgery.

Acting for reasons that have not always been wholly altruistic, the American College of Surgeons has for years waged a determined battle against fee splitting and has become involved in bitter disputes with the American Academy of General Practice as well as the AMA. Although the controversy is usually confined to the high plane of medical ethics, its basis is purely economic. The surgeons naturally dislike splitting their fees with someone else. General practitioners, on the other hand, see no reason why the surgeons should get most of the money, particularly if it is guaranteed by insurance payments. In a recent heated exchange over the issue, a top officer of the Academy of General Practice accused the College of Surgeons of a "biased and vested" point of view. Since "it takes two to tango," he added caustically, surgeons are obviously not completely blameless in the matter.

The College of Surgeons some years ago went so far as to urge the Commissioner of Internal Revenue to see that kickbacks from one doctor to another be eliminated from the category of necessary business expenses eligible for income tax deductions, and the Federal agency was only too glad to acquiesce. At the same time, several local surgical societies promulgated a rule requiring their members to submit their professional records and accounts, including income tax returns, to an annual audit for a check on possible fee splitting. Even though this campaign was directed against practices to which nearly every medical organization stands officially opposed, it was met by outraged cries that the College of Surgeons was blackening the name of the profession by calling attention to the sins of the few. The AMA went on record against the idea of compulsory financial audits for physicians, and a number of medical societies formally lamented that the profession's dirty linen was needlessly being washed in public.

Dr. Loyal Davis, chief of surgery at a leading Chicago hospital, chairman of the department of surgery at Northwestern University Medical School, and later the president of the College of Surgeons, once came close to being kicked out of the Chicago Medical Society for saying at a press conference that fee splitting was on the increase in that city. Dr. Davis was found guilty of unethical conduct after a hearing at which the truth or falsity of his statement was not even discussed and the sole issue was the harm he had done to the profession's prestige. Only an outcry in the Chicago press saved him from expulsion.

The AMA House of Delegates recently reaffirmed that it is unethical for one doctor to give a rebate to another for referral of a patient. But at the same time, it gave its blessing to a more socially acceptable way of doing so by ruling that it was ethical for a referring physician—usually a family doctor—to assist a surgeon in the operating room and get paid for it. The effect of such an arrangement is that the patient has to pay anywhere from $25 to $50 in addition to what the surgeon gets—for assistance that could be given as well or better by an intern or a resident without extra charge. The College of Surgeons promptly accused the AMA of condoning fee splitting. The latter indignantly denied this and deplored "the public airing of disagreements between large segments of medicine which can only confuse and shake the confidence of the public in the medical profession and distort the true image of medicine which the American people should have."

Many authorities are convinced that the time has come to standardize and stabilize medical fees in order to eliminate gouging and to correct existing intraprofessional inequities. Since most people are covered by health insurance, the criterion of ability to pay is increasingly becoming a relatively minor question primarily concerning the very poorest and wealthiest fringes of society. If the upward spiral of fees continues, the net result will be that patients will have to pay out of their own pockets, over and above insurance benefits, almost as much as they used to pay when they were uninsured. In that case, the insurance protection will have lost most of its meaning. The public also wants some assurance that, aside from standard fees, the rise in the unit costs of medical and hospital services is unavoidable and that they are not just being pushed up by the growth of demand and by organizational inefficiencies.

Under the pressure of mounting public criticism and the threat of an imposition of fees by state regulatory action, a number of medical societies have been gradually moving in the past few years toward so-called relative-value schedules, in which fees are fixed according to unit points assigned to various medical procedures. Under this system, the value of each procedure in terms of time and skill required is related to certain basic services, such as a routine office call or blood count, and allotted a certain number of points. Each point is then given a dollar value reflecting the usual basic fee in the area, and the going rate for every procedure is established accordingly. Thus, for example, an appendectomy may be assigned a value of thirty units, which means that a physician who charges $5 for an office call would be entitled to $150 for removal of an appendix.

Assuming that it can be adequately enforced without outside policing, and this is a big assumption, the relative-value system provides a reasonable method for uniformity in measuring the worth of various types of medical services. But there are many barriers to its universal adoption. The medical profession is extremely sensitive to any encroachments on its privilege of setting its own fees and may be expected to fight to the last against any meaningful restraints upon it. Another problem is that it is difficult to measure the intangibles involved in many medical procedures and to attach an unequivocal dollar value to them. The whole system of charging a separate fee for every service, moreover, is inherently wide open to abuse.

Although about one-third of all active physicians are now working wholly or in part on salary, organized medicine continues to insist that good medical care can best be provided only when the patient is charged on a piecework basis. According to the official gospel, salaried employment limits the exercise of the doctor's independent judgment, impairs his professional standing, tends to make him perfunctory in his work, and has an adverse effect on his relationship with his patients. Only the fee-for-service method of compensation is supposed to encourage initiative, stimulate wholesome competition, and maintain high standards of care. This is plainly preposterous. It implies that some of the most distinguished clinicians, teachers, and researchers who are on full-time salary in the nation's great medical centers are not as devoted to their calling as are private practitioners. It does the medical profession an injustice by putting a price tag on dedication. In no other profession is salaried employment even remotely considered undesirable.

Actually, it is piecework remuneration that frequently not only is an engine of inflation but also offers financial incentives that may conflict with purely medical considerations and are sometimes corrupting. The commercial mores of an acquisitive society have left their mark upon the healing art. Under the conditions of private practice, all too often the doctor is the focus of a conflict of interests and is forced by the limitations of the patient's pocketbook to compromise and to settle for paltry palliatives that fall far short of what medical science is now able to do.

Time and again, the organized medical profession has displayed a peculiar propensity for self-righteousness and for confusing matters of self-interest with what should properly be a professional concern and responsibility for bringing the benefits of medical science within the reach of the greatest number of people. It has persistently refused to face up to the adjustments necessitated by scientific and economic developments and by the sweeping alterations in the nature of medical care and practice. It has stubbornly resisted any change whatever in the *status quo* and has modified its opposition, step by step, only under the inexorable pressure of events. Although its standpat policies have been camouflaged by the rhetoric of ethics, they have invariably been motivated by economics. In view of the skill and devotion of many doctors, it is all the more tragic that the profession's leadership has had such a dismaying record of obdurate obstructionism.

Organized medicine has spuriously sought to equate the financial relationship of doctor and patient with their personal relationship by contending that any change in the method of paying physicians would irreparably impair their rapport with their patients. This ardor for the mystique of doctor-patient affinity has been significantly missing, however, in the case of nonpaying patients. The medical profession has readily yielded to government agencies the responsibility for the health care of the indigent and for the institutional treatment of the mentally ill and of tubercular patients requiring long-term therapy. The tune is clearly different when there is no opportunity for fat fees.

The profession's concern for free enterprise in the medical economy has been particularly evident when public health programs appeared to threaten its own profitable prerogatives. The AMA House of Delegates once denounced legislation for Federal grants to the states for maternal and child welfare as "a form of bureaucratic interference with the sacred rights of the American home." When the Salk polio vaccine first became available, the profession's first reaction was to seek to protect the privilege of its members to collect fees. A number of medical societies promptly passed resolutions demanding that free inoculations be curtailed and that the vaccine be allowed to reach the public only through "regular channels."

The medical profession cannot escape its destiny. What it clearly needs is a profound reassessment of itself and of the proliferating challenges confronting it in an age of upheaval. "Seek something beyond the split-level ranch and the two-car garage," the late Dr. Thomas A. Dooley wrote a young colleague shortly before his death. "Become supremely aware of and intimately involved in the great issues of your day. The proud state of being a doctor is a joyful thing . . . a lofty one, and one filled with tremendous potential for good." The self-serving posture of organized medicine has far too long imperiled the profession's integrity and deprived it of the constructive leadership it could and should exert in seeking to apply the mighty potentialities of scientific progress as widely as possible.

CHAPTER TWELVE

Medicine's Widening Horizons
and Responsibilities

I

ONE of the paradoxes of the American medical scene is that although psychiatric concepts have deeply permeated medicine—and, indeed, all our culture—psychiatry itself remains relegated to the periphery and isolated from the mainstream of medical thought and practice. An examination of some of the reasons for this state of affairs should give us a clearer view not only of psychiatry but also of some aspects of medicine in general.

That the status of psychiatry and of its place within the context of medical practice is a matter of the utmost importance is all too obvious from a look at the statistics of the staggering load of mental and emotional illness. The some 720,000 patients now hospitalized in mental institutions occupy close to half of all the hospital beds in the United States. More than a quarter of a million persons are admitted every year to such institutions. In addition, about 400,000 persons are treated annually in mental health clinics, and thousands of others receive private psychiatric treatment. These are generally people suffering from the more severe psychoses or neuroses. It is authoritatively estimated that there are about nine million other Americans whose optimal functioning is impaired by less serious mental and emotional disorders and who could benefit from psychiatric care but do not get it. There are nearly four million alcoholics in this country, and relatively few of them receive psychiatric treatment for the emotional disturbances that are at the root of their addiction to liquor.

The magnitude of the mental health problem was amply documented during World War II, when 865,000 young men were rejected by Selective Service examiners for psychiatric reasons and 980,000 disability discharges from the Armed Forces, or 43 per cent of all such separations, were granted on similar grounds.

In 1962, an intensive survey of a midtown Manhattan area by a team of psychiatrists and social scientists came up with the startling conclusion that four out of every five of its residents suffer from some form of mental disturbance. Symptoms described as "marked, severe, and incapacitating" were found in 23.4 per cent of a cross section of the large neighborhood studied.

There has been a pronounced upward trend in the rate of mental hospitalization during the past three decades, and the incidence of mental disease is expected to keep on rising. One obvious factor is the extension of the average life-span and the steadily growing multitude of older people, who have a much higher ratio of mental ailments than the younger age groups do. Less clear, but undoubtedly considerable, is the role played by the vast social changes of our era and the strains they impose on emotional equilibrium. The traditional bulwarks of stability have been eroded in our society, and the causes of conflict and anxiety have multiplied. The sort of marginal individuals who managed to get along in the simpler rural setting of a generation or two ago find it much more difficult to deal with the competitive pressures of urban living. Family ties have become less cohesive and community roots less firm in our increasingly urbanized, industrialized, and secularized civilization. Both geographical and social mobility have sharply increased, intensifying the problems of adjustment to a rapidly changing environment. All along the line, there has been an upswing in the tensions likely to precipitate mental illness in those with a special vulnerability to it.

Increasing attention has also been focused in recent years on the psychosomatic elements of illness and on the profound reverberations that such emotions as anxiety, frustration, depression, and anger can have on the human organism. There has been a growing understanding of the mechanisms whereby the individual seeks to adapt himself to his environment and of how he uses a variety of psychological defenses, some of them on the conscious and others on the unconscious level of functioning, in an attempt to make the necessary adjustments. We have learned that the intangibles of human relationships are inextricably intertwined with organic pathology and as essential to an understanding of disease as test-tube reactions and microscopic studies of biopsies. More and more, we are beginning to understand the role of emotional factors in the genesis of disease and, conversely, the shattering effects of serious illness upon the individual's emotional integrity. It is becoming ever clearer that there is no such thing as a purely physical or purely emotional reaction; that patients are complicated and sentient beings, each with his unique complex of hopes and fears, loves and hostilities; and that when people come to the doctor, they usually look for a great deal more than just a body repair shop where they can have their valves ground or their motors retuned.

Our supply of psychiatrists is pathetically small in relation to need. There are only about 16,800 psychiatrists in the United States, or an average of one for every 12,000 persons. This clearly requires not only that the available psychiatrists be utilized as effectively as possible but also that there be a close rapport between them and the rest of the profession. It makes it incumbent upon all other physicians—and particularly general practitioners, pediatricians, and internists—to have a sympathetic understanding of psychiatric principles and to apply them in their practice. Good doctors practice psychiatry every time they see a patient, regardless of whether they are aware of it or not. Competent opinion is that many mental hospital admissions and readmissions could be averted with proper and timely medical attention. Even more so than the psychiatrist, the family doctor is in an ideal position to perform a psychotherapeutic function. He sees the patient early in the disease process and within his normal setting and is thus in the best position to evaluate the bearing that his personality makeup and conflicts may have on his illness. He has the further advantage of the naturalness of the situation. His inquiries are less disturbing and do not carry the stigma so often attached in our culture to anything associated with mental disease.

Unfortunately, the medical profession still shares with the public many misconceptions and prejudices about psychiatry and psychiatrists. All too prevalent among doctors is an aloofness, if not outright antagonism, toward the emotional elements of disease and toward psychiatrists themselves. The old habits of rigidly separating body from mind die hard. Trained to concentrate on organic pathology, the average busy practitioner is apt to look with suspicion upon many of the insights emanating from psychiatric, psychological, and sociological research, if he has had an opportunity to hear of them at all.

Seriously aggravating the situation is the state of psychiatry itself—its imprecision and the schisms within its ranks, its tendency toward unscientific empiricism and metaphysical theorizing sometimes bordering on downright mumbo jumbo, its penchant for the use of mythological thinking and of mystery and fable instead of the spadework of logical deduction, its addiction to florid and obfuscating jargon, its failure to keep pace with much of the progress of medical science and many of its techniques, and the common segregation of psychiatrists from their medical colleagues, partly due to professional hostility and divorce from the fraternity of hospital staffs but perhaps even more so to their own clannishness and lack of touch with the main currents of medicine.

It is both ironic and tragic that just as some physicians tend to ignore the psychological components of illness, so are psychiatrists often apt to be guilty of a reverse distortion in their preoccupation with personality function. Many of them have, in effect, turned their backs on neurology, the science of the physiology of the nervous system and of its diseases, and are attempting to treat the psyche almost as if it were separate and apart from its organic environment. Their equipment is limited to the pen, pad, and couch. They rarely look for a possible physiological explanation of the patient's distress or even take the trouble to do a physical examination. The lack of precision and of measurable criteria in their diagnostic and treatment approach often smacks of pseudoscience. This is not wholly the fault of the psychiatrists. They have to deal with elusive phenomena defying exact scientific measurement. The terrain of their special interest is still largely unexplored. The thinking areas of the brain and the pathways leading to them from the nervous system are yet to be fully mapped. Although there are many lacunae in medical knowledge, our understanding of most of the body's physiological processes is infinitely firmer than that of the origin, development, and treatment of mental disorders.

Of all the enigmas confronting man, none seems so unfathomable as the mystery of the caverns of his own mind—how the fantastically complex machine that is the human brain functions normally and what happens to this prodigiously delicate mechanism to cause the terrible disorganization of thought and behavior that is mental illness. In all medicine, there is nothing quite so intricate. In no other ailment is there such a complicated range of elements—involving the biology of the brain, the psychology of the mind, and the effect of social environment on both—that appear to contribute to it. In trying to tackle the riddle of human personality and to establish precisely how it cracks under stress, one authority has said, medical research is confronted with a "highly complex and most individualized psychochemical system which reflects the totality of constitution plus the storehouse of past experience mingling in the arena of present awareness."

Even this dark domain is gradually being illuminated. Patient probing on many fronts, integrating a variety of disciplines ranging all the way from biochemistry to sociology, is producing intriguing leads toward a broad concept of the causes and mechanisms of mental disease that involves organic as well as environmental factors. The consensus of some of the keenest investigators is that research will ultimately establish that psychosis has its genesis in a combination of psychological stresses and some sort of malfunctioning of the metabolism of the brain. Elucidation of what precisely goes wrong with the chemistry of the mind would represent an enormous forward step. It would save psychiatry from the morass of arcane specualtion and bring it back into the fold of scientific medicine. It would greatly improve the prospects for the prevention and cure of mental disorders.

It is important to remember that the father of modern psychiatry never lost sight of the strong likelihood that physiological factors play an important role in mental illness. Sigmund Freud once said that "behind every psychoanalyst stands the man with a syringe." What he meant was that the method of psychotherapy that he himself had devised—whereby the psychiatrist attempts to resolve the patient's deeply buried anxieties by talking them out and bringing them to the surface—was not a technique that would work in every case. He felt that although psychotherapy could be effective in treating the neuroses, the milder mental disturbances, other methods were needed to help psychotics. Up to a few years ago, medicine had nothing to put into the psychiatric syringe. A variety of recent research developments are beginning to lay the groundwork for a possible chemical antidote to abnormalities in the functioning of the brain.

What Freud did, largely as a reaction to the narrowly organic concept of mental disease that prevailed during most of the nineteenth century, was to emphasize the profound influence of early experience and of environmental stress upon personality and behavior. Freud's teachings underscore the great importance of subconscious frustrations and hostilities shaped in the formative years by unsatisfactory parent-child relationships and the role that these feelings play in mental breakdown. He believed that the inner conflicts originating in childhood often lead to a failure of adaptation and to maladjustment in adult life. His great discovery was that everyone of us is, in effect, two persons and that our subconscious personality has a tremendous effect on everything we do and think. The Freudian method of psychotherapy seeks to uncover the hidden part of the patient's makeup that gets in the way of his normal functioning. As the patient gains an insight into the unconscious forces at the root of his difficulties, his ability to cope with his own problems is greatly enhanced.

Few people now dispute the overall validity of Freud's theories. The trouble is that some of his disciples have gone far beyond the teachings of their master and have built up an almost exclusively psychological hypothesis of the origin of mental disease. In doing so, they have tended to overlook the fact that thought and behavior are dependent upon biological processes and to ignore the plausibility that organic mechanisms are no less involved in mental disorder than are the effects of upbringing and environment.

The elaboration of Freud's ideas has over the years spawned a plethora of schools of thought and cults within psychiatry, each of them dedicated to the virtues of its own techniques and scorning the others as heretical. The main source of dissension is the split between the psychogenic and organic orientations. Those who espouse the theory that most mental disorders are primarily psychological favor the analytic approach, in which the patient is supposed to "work through" his personal problems by being helped to perceive his own conscious and unconscious motivations. The organic school, on the other hand, tends to combine such purely medical techniques as the use of drugs and shock treatments with so-called directive or supportive psychotherapy, in which the psychiatrist seeks to change the patient's attitudes and behavior through advice, admonition, and reassurance.

In less technical language, these two contending factions have sometimes been described as the ivory-tower and red-brick schools of psychiatry. The reason for this designation is that historically the schism stems from the progressive divergence between academic psychiatry—as taught and practiced in medical school hospitals, psychiatric institutes, and private mental hospitals—and the harsh realities of the big overcrowded, understaffed, and isolated state mental hospitals. Academic psychiatry has tended to adhere to a psychoanalytically based orientation derived from the study and treatment of a small number of neurotic patients rather than from observation of hospitalized psychotics. The pitifully inadequate psychiatric staffs in the state hospitals have never been able to afford any such luxury. The sheer pressure of numbers has forced them to adopt a more direct organic approach. In actual practice, this has usually meant scrimpy treatment for most mental hospital patients. Ironically, however, the weight of recent research appears to lean toward the theory, if not the practice, of the organic school.

The psychogenic faction, which is made up of psychoanalysts and some other psychiatrists in private practice, is not large numerically, but its leaders are among the most articulate spokesmen for psychiatry and wield great influence. Their basic tenet is that the healthy functioning of the personality can best be restored by laying bare the origin of the patient's predicament and developing within him an understanding of the psychological forces responsible for it. Physiological methods of diagnosis and treatment are rarely employed by psychogenic psychiatrists.

The red-brick school, so known because its proponents are concentrated on the staffs of the state mental hospitals, contends that since there can be no twisted thought without some twisted process in the brain, mental illness usually requires both medical and psychological treatment. Another major argument of the organic group is that psychotherapy cannot possibly cope with the huge burden of mental disease. In the first place, there is the difficulty of communication between the psychiatrist and the severely psychotic patient, who usually speaks in incomprehensible gibberish, if he talks at all. Secondly, psychotherapy, especially psychoanalysis, is immensely time-consuming and costly. Dr. Winfred Overholser, for many years superintendent of St. Elizabeths Hospital in Washington, estimated that the average psychoanalyst cannot expect to see more than about 250 patients in a lifetime of practice. We can never get enough psychiatrists or patients able to afford the expense to tackle the problem with psychotherapy alone.

Although all psychiatrists and most psychoanalysts are MD's, the graduate education of the two principal orientations is quite different. The psychogenic practitioners undergo psychoanalytic training, during which they are themselves analyzed, and their interest in clinical medicine tends to decline after they leave medical school. In fact, their purely medical skills are likely to atrophy from sheer disuse as the years go by and from failure to keep in touch with new developments in the fundamentals of general medicine. Psychiatrists leaning toward the organic approach have a stronger affinity to clinical medicine and are more liable to have some graduate training in the biological sciences and in neurology. But in their case, too, the pressures of psychiatric practice are often apt to lead to a neglect of basic medical competence.

In a remarkably pointed and candid presidential address at the 1961 annual meeting of the American Psychiatric Association, Dr. Robert H. Felix, former director of the National Institute of Mental Health and now dean of the medical school of St. Louis University, expressed alarm over the isolation of psychiatry from the rest of medicine and told his colleagues that "we must always be physicians first and psychiatrists second. It is not enough that we be physicians in name only." Steadily expanding knowledge and responsibilities, Dr. Felix said, will require of psychiatrists "not merely a broad scientific and medical background but also current knowledge concerning many aspects of medicine which will become more and more essential for the proper management of clinical problems. This means that not now or ever can we allow our medical skills to atrophy, if we are to keep abreast of our field as it develops and thereby give our patients that to which they are entitled—the best that can be obtained."

No one can be a good psychiatrist, Dr. Felix asserted, without being "a good physician first and always," which means continual professional improvement and "retaining and using a variety of basic medical skills which any patient has a right to expect of any physician, regardless of his specialty. To restrict medical thinking and awareness exclusively to one special field is to become a technician, and a physician is much more than a technician. . . . If psychiatry is a medical specialty concerned with the prevention, diagnosis and treatment of mental and emotional disorders, how can psychiatrists allow their basic medical skills to fall into disuse —to rust to the point that they are unusable on demand?" he asked. "If one deals only with the psychological and social phenomena of those who present themselves for relief, if one thinks not in terms of the whole individual, if one is not always on the alert for manifestations of malfunction in any organ system, if one is no longer competent properly to identify such pathology and effectively to deal with it either himself or by wise referral, how does one qualify to employ a medical procedure? How does the psychiatrist differ from the nonmedical practitioner of psychological or sociological procedures? The latter is, at least, not expected by his client or by society in general to possess medical skills."

The advent of the tranquilizing drugs and other recent research developments have deepened the dichotomy between the psychogenic and organic schools and lent additional emphasis to the wisdom of Dr. Felix's plea that psychiatrists should not consider themselves exempt from the maxim "Physician first, specialist second." There is little question that the whole field of psychiatry is in a state of transition and that more and more attention will be paid to the physiological basis of mental illness. Although the tranquilizing drugs are often being flagrantly overused in nonhospital practice, they furnish striking confirmation of the view that mental disorder involves a biological disturbance. These drugs do not cure mental disease. Nor does their soothing effect last when the medication is discontinued. But the fact that they can block off even temporarily the intensity of distorted emotions clearly points to an abnormality in the chemistry of the brain.

Understandably, the tranquilizers got a cool reception from

the psychiatrists of the psychogenic persuasion but received early and vociferous acclaim in the state mental hospitals. By proving effective in calming overactive and aggressive psychotic patients, and particularly the frenzied agitation of schizophrenics, the new drugs brought a welcome degree of tranquility to the disturbed wards. But this has by no means been an unmixed blessing. For the tranquilizers can, at most, treat the symptoms and not the underlying causes of mental disease, whether these be organic or psychological or both. In many cases, they are merely adjuncts to psychotherapy, which the understaffed state hospitals are unable to provide on the scale required to meet the need. It is true that the tranquilizing drugs have made possible a stepping up of mental hospital discharges and have reversed a long-standing trend by helping to bring about an actual decline in the resident population during the past few years. But by increasing the amenability of thousands of patients to psychotherapy, they have also underscored the critical need for many more psychiatrists and for additional ancillary personnel to take advantage of the new treatment opportunities.

Along with the tranquilizers, the hallucinogenic drugs also have provided clues to the possible organic mechanisms of mental illness. Just as the tranquilizers turn off psychotic symptoms, so the hallucinogenic compounds do the opposite through their ability to produce temporary psychotic behavior in normal people. The very fact that they can do so through their chemical effect on the brain is another indication that mental derangement is basically a physiological phenomenon. It also suggests that the body itself may sometimes produce a chemical, similar to the hallucinogens, that causes mental disease. A natural chemical substance known as serotonin has been figuring prominently in some of the recent investigations. The possibility that this chemical may keep us sane and that mental disorder may be connected with a deficiency in its supply or with some defect that upsets its function appears to be indicated by a number of research findings. It has been discovered that at least one hallucinogenic drug blocks the action of serotonin in the brain, whereas some of the tranquilizers work in reverse and apparently achieve their calming effect by releasing this chemical from its inactive state. Some scientists believe that serotonin acts on the multitude of switching points that control the transmission of impulses to and from the brain through the pathways of the nerves. Impairment of the normal function of serotonin may thus upset the brain's communications system and produce a distortion of the messages it sends out and receives. Regardless of whether the breakdown in the serotonin mechanism is a primary cause of mental disorder or merely a subsidiary development, it is certainly highly suggestive.

Other significant indications of a probable link between mental disturbance and some physiological deficiency come from research work on suspected chemical peculiarities in the blood of schizophrenics and the greater incidence of tumors of the brain and of the pituitary gland—the latter can severely upset the body's hormone balance—among psychotic patients. Studies of identical twins extending over a period of more than thirty years have shown that mental disorders occur most frequently in families with what appears to be a constitutional vulnerability to such diseases. None of this rules out the importance of such psychological elements as damaging emotional experiences during childhood and other environmental stresses. But it strongly points to an interplay of physiological and emotional forces in the enigma of mental illness.

Whatever answers research finally comes up with, it is plain that all too few people are now being reached by psychiatrists and that the practice of psychiatry, more so than any other branch of medicine, is peculiarly a part of the class and caste system in the United States. To a truly shocking degree, income status is directly related to the kind of psychiatric treatment that Americans get. Private psychiatric care is so expensive that only the well-to-do can afford it. This is particularly true of care in private mental hospitals, where the charges are apt to run from $10,000 a year up. Sooner or later, the vast majority of mental patients end up in state hospitals. But the burden of the great bulk of psychotics is shouldered by little more than one-third of the limited supply of psychiatrists. Nearly two-thirds of the psychiatrists are in private practice, and they usually treat only neurotics and want no part of psychotics. Moreover, being in extremely short supply, they tend to select their patients on the basis of social and intellectual standing and compatibility, to say nothing of ability to pay.

It is perfectly obvious that if the hundreds of thousands of people suffering from mental and emotional ailments and now denied the proper care are truly to benefit from what psychiatry has to offer, we shall need many more psychiatrists, shorter and more economical methods of psychotherapy will have to be developed, and paramedical personnel will increasingly have to be brought into the picture. Since individual psychotherapy can hardly do the job, a promising technique that must be vigorously pursued is group psychotherapy, in which groups of patients under the guidance of trained therapists discuss their problems and try to work them out through mutual analysis and the release of pent-up anxieties and hostilities. Many authorities also feel that lay psychotherapists should be allowed to take over part of the treatment load. Such therapists could be trained much more rapidly and at far lesser cost than it takes to turn out psychiatrists, who now frequently jettison their medical knowledge anyway as time goes on.

No precise methods for the prevention of mental disease will be available so long as its etiology remains obscure. But enough is already clear to indicate that the best preventive approach lies in the avoidance of stress so great that it passes beyond the individual's capacity to deal with it and eventually lowers his ability to withstand breakdown. Animal experiments have demonstrated that long-continued severe stress causes the impairment of certain hormone-producing glands and lowers the threshold for the appearance of illness. Studies of the effect of isolation of infants have shown that inborn capacities deteriorate if they are not stimulated. The capacities of young children to learn, to react emotionally, and to love must be constantly exercised if they are not to atrophy and lead to a lifetime of immature behavior. The best opportunities for healthy development lie in educating people for sound parent-child relationships and in seeking to eliminate as much as possible the causes of needless anxiety in our culture.

Psychiatry has gone a long way toward humanizing biology by reexamining man's conduct and uncovering some of its determinants. It has provided challenging insights into the labyrinthine pathways of human behavior and given renewed emphasis to the truism that although the brain is subject to the body's ills, it also is—as the repository of thought, emotion, and imagination—more than merely another bodily organ. By learning how to listen, a quality so often conspicuously absent in today's medical practice, psychiatrists have once again demonstrated the comfort that troubled people can find in sharing their hopes and fears. Psychiatry cannot in itself give meaning to people's lives. But when adequately utilized, it can contribute immeasurably toward the attainment of loftier levels of human happiness and achievement.

II

Scientific progress and the sheer impossibility of providing enough medical and auxiliary personnel to cure everybody who is sick underscore the conclusion that the best hope for the future lies in a much more intensive application of preventive medicine. To reduce the issue to its simplest terms, two fundamental principles must be kept in mind: the best way to cut down medical costs is to prevent illness; and the best medicine is, in the long run, the cheapest medicine. Although these are self-evident premises, they are all too often ignored. Countless lives are needlessly lost or blighted and many millions of dollars are spent unnecessarily because of failure to follow elementary commonsense rules and because the prevailing system of medical practice militates against the systematic and intensive use of preventive measures.

Expert opinion is that there is a vast amount of preventable illness in the United States and that its toll of disability and premature death could be substantially reduced by timely and adequate medical care. We have yet to act upon the truism that the most humane and effective way to check the soaring costs of disease and its manifold handicaps is to do everything feasible to keep people healthy and, failing that, to detect and arrest sickness and to cure or rehabilitate those stricken by it as expeditiously as possible. This can be accomplished only through a system that encourages guidance in the basic principles of personal hygiene and provides the necessary facilities and services for prompt recourse to medical attention. It cannot be fully achieved when the pattern of payment for each separate service tends to defer treatment until illness becomes entrenched and when doctors are so busy, to a large extent with the end results of health neglect, that they have neither the time nor the inclination to use their influence to foster good health practices or to carry out the required preventive procedures.

More so than ever before, the doctor's function is not only to get sick people back on their feet but also to help healthy people stay well. Aside from being a healer, the personal physician must also be a teacher, both in directing his patients on how to avoid disease and in showing them how to live with their disabilities. By advising them on proper diet and other fundamental safeguards, by stressing the importance of periodic checkups, by detecting and treating trivial complaints before they become serious, he has it within his power to enable people to get more out of life through improved health and vigor. At the other end of the spectrum, as the problems of chronic illness grow more pressing and as the potentialities of rehabilitation are rapidly widening, he has much greater opportunities to render restorative services. Medicine is increasingly getting away from the old definition of health as merely the absence of disease. "As health is relative," the late Dr. Edward J. Stieglitz once said, "there is always room for improvement, even in those assumed to be well because of the absence of symptoms and signs of obvious disease. Apparently well people could be healthier."

There is little question that the promotion of health throughout life can be a paramount factor in the prevention of the chronic ailments and that the great challenge of keeping people fit as they grow older can best be met by being constantly on the alert against the precursors of future illness. And beyond the prevention and alleviation of disease is the goal of striving for maximum physical, mental, and social efficiency. Unfortunately, not only is the doctor's role as teacher often neglected in today's medical practice, but preventive measures are not given nearly the attention they deserve. The average solo practitioner finds no financial rewards in time-consuming preventive and rehabilitative efforts. Although the medical profession has given lip service to the concept of health promotion, it has done very little about it.

In the past, when the communicable diseases were the major cripplers and killers, measures for health maintenance involved only a limited degree of individual responsibility. The development of pure water supplies, pasteurization of milk, the sanitary disposal of sewage, and other environmental improvements were achieved through social action in which the individual may have participated as a citizen but was not otherwise directly responsible. But now the individual effort of an informed person will do more for his own health and that of his family than all the things that can be done through public health measures. It is the individual who must eat properly and avoid obesity, have enough exercise and relaxation, consult his physician promptly when he has any symptoms of ill health, and realize that it is just as important to seek advice from the doctor on how to keep well as it is to call upon him for help when illness strikes. The degree of individual initiative and cooperation required for the prevention and treatment of the chronic and psychosomatic ailments is wholly different from the specific sanitary controls that have dramatically reduced the threat of the epidemic contagious diseases.

It is therefore all the more distressing that for every hypochondriac, there are probably half a dozen people who for both economic and psychological reasons neglect their health. The tragic consequences of the unutilized potentialities of early cancer detection and treatment are but one example of the costs of laxity. As an unprecedented mobilization of research talent pursues the quest for the causes and cure of cancer, the best hope for immediate gains against the nation's second largest killer lies in wider use of existing diagnostic tools, which are frequently neglected by patients and physicians alike. Although we already have the scientific knowledge to save fully half of the 420,000 Americans who each year develop cancer, a spokesman for the American Cancer Society recently told a Congressional committee, only about one-third of them are saved, because of widespread failure to pay prompt attention to suspected symptoms of malignancy and because of the lack of a sufficient supply of doctors "to conduct the regular thorough physical examinations upon which the early diagnosis of cancer so largely depends."

A shockingly high proportion of previously undetected diseases, many of which are fully amenable to available treatment measures, has been time and again brought to light in mass physical screenings. Multiphasic examinations of 10,709 apparently healthy persons carried out at the Tulane University School of

Medicine in New Orleans, for instance, disclosed that fully 92 per cent of them suffered from some form of ill health and that 804 had heart conditions. Examination of 9,216 workers in a chemical industry showed that 26.3 per cent were twenty pounds or more overweight, 19.5 per cent had high blood pressure, a similar proportion were badly in need of dental attention, 10.4 per cent suffered from some degree of hearing loss, and 5.9 per cent needed correction of visual defects. In still another series of periodic health examinations covering a total of 16,465 industrial workers, it was found that only 13.6 per cent were "entirely healthy" and that 37.5 per cent had some "significant" disease, while the rest were suffering from less serious conditions. That such neglect is by no means confined to the lower- and middle-income groups was demonstrated by medical examinations given at the University of Pennsylvania to 1,513 business executives. At the first examination, 612 of these men were found to have ailments of which they had previously been unaware. Reexamination of 822 members of this group after a lapse of sixteen months yielded 386 additional diagnoses of newly detected disease.

Until they are driven to it by discomfort or other obvious symptoms of illness, many people prefer putting off going to the doctor principally because of the expense involved. This is, of course, the worst kind of false economy. But procrastination is a normal human trait, particularly when it comes to deferring something that does not appear to be immediately pressing and will mean an extra strain on a tight family budget. In addition, there is the anticipation of a painful experience, especially at the dentist's office, and there is the fear of bad news that one would rather postpone hearing. Sheer negligence is another frequent deterrent to obtaining needed medical attention. Many people cannot get around to finding the time to see a doctor unless they are confronted by obvious illness, and they consistently disregard some of the basic precepts of healthful living.

Overeating and lack of sufficient physical exercises are common American failings. Our frequently irrational attitudes toward health protection are exemplified by the prevalent reaction to the mounting evidence linking cigarette smoking with lung cancer and the overwhelming proof of the value of water fluoridation in preventing dental caries. Although study after study has shown that the person who smokes more than one package of cigarettes a day stands a ten to sixty times greater risk of developing lung cancer than the one who does not smoke at all, the consumption of cigarettes has been steadily rising in the United States. Only about one-quarter of the nation has thus far taken advantage of the benefits of fluoridation of public water supplies. Even though competent authorities agree that fluoridation is perfectly safe, its adoption has been resisted in many communities as a poison, a Communist plot, or a form of compulsory mass medication infringing upon sacred individual rights. Similar opposition was encountered years ago in regard to water chlorination, pasteurization of milk supplies, and immunizations against smallpox and diphtheria.

The early detection of disease calls not only for prompt attention when signs of ill health first appear but for periodic physical checkups before such symptoms develop. Such examinations at regular intervals may disclose a dangerous gain in weight, a slow but insidious rise in the blood pressure, or the signs of an imminent nervous breakdown under the pressure of prolonged stress. There are many hints of disease-in-the-making that, when caught in time, can avert disaster. Aside from being a means of discovering imminent trouble, periodic checkups also are a vitally important vehicle for guidance in health conservation. A careful analysis of a patient's personal and working habits will frequently reveal things that a physical examination alone cannot possibly show. If done in an unhurried manner and in atmosphere of mutual confidence, it affords a rare opportunity for teaching a patient how to live healthfully.

Competent opinion is that everyone should have a complete health inventory at least once a year. But here again, there are the barriers of cost, built-in hindrances to preventive procedures in the existing organization of medical practice, and the average person's inertia when it comes to his most precious asset—his health. Comprehensive physical examinations are time-consuming and expensive. Ideally, they should include a complete blood count, a blood-sugar test for hidden diabetes, a blood-sedimentation test to check on a variety of possible infections, a blood-cholesterol test to establish a possible tendency toward coronary disease, a urea nitrogen test of kidney function, a uric acid test for possible gout, a full rectal examination, an electrocardiogram, and a complete series of chest and gastrointestinal X rays. This runs into a good deal of time and money, which many people are unable to afford or reluctant to invest even if they have the means. This is only part of the difficulty, however. Not only is the public yet to be adequately educated as to the importance of periodic checkups, but the medical profession itself is still far from completely sold on the idea.

Trained primarily to treat disease, the average physician does not find it easy to change the framework of his services toward greater emphasis on the preventive approach. Many doctors lack the required competence as well as the equipment for truly exhaustive examinations. Treating illness after it develops, moreover, is much more lucrative than trying to prevent it or to seek it out. A doctor can give routine treatments to anywhere from five to ten patients in the time that it takes to do a thorough examination. While the charge for the latter is higher than for an ordinary office visit, it is rarely scaled to compensate the practitioner fully for his time. There are, furthermore, not nearly enough physicians to examine everybody and still have time left over for care of the sick. This alone means that a truly large-scale preventive effort will have to be deferred until we get a much greater pool of medical and auxiliary manpower.

A much more feasible and economical first step toward the timely detection of disease is made possible by the mass-screening technique, whereby large groups of people undergo quick tests for presumptive evidence of the presence of a variety of abnormalities and are referred to physicians for further examinations when the findings are positive. Such screening procedures can be carried out by paramedical personnel under medical supervision, permitting the physician to use his time for interpretation and more elaborate diagnostic studies. Fairly reliable screening tests that can be applied on a mass basis are now available for diabetes, tuberculosis, anemia, certain forms of cancer and heart disease, and vision and hearing defects. Mass screening is not an adequate substitute for a competent physician's individual attention, but it can lead to the discovery of a significant amount of disease and spur many people who would not otherwise do so to seek medical care. Yet even the use of this shortcut has been lagging because of lack of sufficient interest by the medical profession and public indifference.

That people do not generally practice what they theoretically consider to be desirable was strikingly demonstrated in a survey of public attitudes toward health care conducted a few years ago by the University of Chicago's National Opinion Research Center in cooperation with the Health Information Foundation. About 80 per cent of those questioned agreed that a person ought to see a doctor for a regular checkup even though he feels well. But only 29 per cent reported that they themselves get such examinations regularly. A smaller but still considerable discrepancy was brought to light when people were asked specifically whether such common symptoms as persistent headaches or cough, shortness of breath, and chronic backache warranted consulting a physician. Although a large majority replied in the affirmative, it developed that far fewer of those who had actually experienced any of these symptoms had followed their own advice. Interestingly enough, however, 62 per cent of those interviewed who had children reported that their youngsters were receiving regular checkups.

The precept that continuous health maintenance is fully as important as episodic treatment has gradually caught on in the pediatric and obstetric fields. Several studies have shown that pediatricians actually spend more than half of their day's work caring for well children, examining them periodically to make sure that everything is progressing normally, immunizing them against specific diseases, advising mothers about diet, and in many other ways helping parents to rear healthy children. Obstetricians have generally likewise adopted the concept of regular prenatal and postnatal care. But the rest of the medical profession and the majority of the public have yet to accept wholeheartedly the idea that what is good for children and expectant mothers is good for everybody.

The basic trouble, to no small degree, is that human beings choose to cling to the illusion of immortality. So long as we feel reasonably well, we would rather not look ahead into the perilous future. Subconsciously, we may prefer to remain in ignorance as long as possible about an elevation in the blood pressure, a trace of albumin in the urine, or calcification of the spine. Seeking medical attention with appropriate promptness requires a strong enough motivation to overcome the emotional resistance to such action and a greater degree of medical sophistication than most people possess. It also calls for a revision of the current notions about hypochondria and abuse of medical services. The advice to see the doctor early does not make explicit how early. It leaves it up to the individual to decide through self-diagnosis when he needs medical care to avoid the full effects of an incipient illness. Here guidance and education play a central role, not only for recognition of the value of preventive care but also in such matters as better understanding of normal human structure and function, wise nutrition habits, appropriate exercise, mental health, the advisability of avoiding prolonged and excessive fatigue, the need for a balance between work and play in the wise investment of leisure time, and appreciation of the effects of aging and the hazards of chronic disease in the later years. Much more attention must clearly be devoted to health education if we are to take advantage of the new vistas opening up for disease prevention and health promotion.

Inseparable from the prevention and treatment of disease are the various long-range therapy measures covered by the comprehensive term "rehabilitation" that are designed to mobilize the patient's organic and psychological forces to a level as close to normal functioning as possible with the faculties he has left. The very medical advances that have preserved so many lives have also led to a vast increase in the numbers of the disabled, not only among the elderly but also among children and those in the most productive years of life. Until not so long ago, the handicapped were the forgotten people, the objects of pity and charity for whom little or nothing could be done. But rapid progress in the rehabilitation field now makes possible the training of many of the disabled and their restoration to the dignity of self-support or at least of self-care. Rehabilitative techniques can teach a deaf child to speak and an amputee to walk again with prostheses. They can go a long way toward correcting the impairments left in the wake of acute or chronic illness. They can be equally effective in teaching a patient with coronary disease to live within his limitations and in helping an emotionally unstable individual to readjust himself to the demands of daily existence.

Involved in the rehabilitation process, in addition to doctors, are many other professional talents—including those of nurses, medical social workers, clinical psychologists, and physical and occupational therapists. But the primary responsibility rests with the physician who first encounters the disabled patient. In fact, rehabilitation, or its failure, actually begins when the original diagnosis is made and the treatment starts. The tragic reality is that untold suffering and a heavy drain on the economy could be averted if the rehabilitative skills we now know how to employ were fully applied. Because of lack of knowledge or interest on the part of many physicians and the critical shortage of competent personnel, disability is now often neglected in its early stages, when the patients are most amenable to retraining, and hundreds of thousands of the chronically ill and handicapped are denied the opportunity for more meaningful and productive lives.

"Future disability is not accidental and should be, to a large extent, predictable on the basis of present characteristics and mode of life," so that it "may be modified or avoided by personal or community application of physiological hygiene," Dr. Ancel Keys, the noted University of Minnesota physiologist, has said. Tending to support this sweeping statement are medicine's steady accumulation of new knowledge and tools and the ever-broadening understanding of the total character of human health and disease, in which body and mind, family, school, occupation, and other environmental elements are inextricably interlaced. We are gradually widening our comprehension of the mechanisms of resistance to disease and of the dynamics of adjustment to the environment. We are becoming aware that susceptibility to disease and disease itself are the outcome of a configuration of multiple causes rather than of simple cause-and-effect relationships. Illness, as Dr. Oliver Cope of Harvard Medical School has put it, is "not the entity. Studying only disease is like trying to understand how a grape got that way without studying the bunch, the vineyard, the soil, the climate. We have to understand disease as a cropping out as a result of circumstance."

As the medical and social sciences continue to delve into the convoluted complex of health and disease, we are beginning to understand that there is really no sharp boundary between the two. We are increasingly becoming aware that there are not only forces which precipitate disease but also those which predispose toward it and tend to prolong it; that there are few single causes in biology but instead, as one authority has said, complicated "situations and environments in which the probability of certain events is increased"; that man's mode of life and social relationships profoundly influence both his physical and his mental health; and that the threshold of disabling stress in any one individual is determined to a large degree not only by his genetic endowment but also by the bearing which his past experience has had on his capacities for adjustment and his special tolerances and vulnerabilities.

But for every answer we have, there are still at least a dozen unanswered questions. Even in the field of bacterial and viral disease, we have yet to establish the mechanisms that permit the microbial process to evolve from the dormant into the active state. The human body usually carries a variety of virulent microbes that normally remain latent. But under certain circumstances, these organisms become activated and flare up into disease. What apparently is most important is not so much the event of infection as the conditions that affect the body's ability to destroy the disease-producing bacteria or viruses, to prevent their multiplication, or to inhibit their toxic assaults.

Our understanding of what constitutes physiological normality and of how wide its range can be is still grossly inadequate, based as it largely is on the study of disease rather than of health. Like disease, health and adaptability cannot be fully considered in detachment from the environment in which the individual lives and works. In medicine's traditional preoccupation with repair and recovery, there has not been nearly enough emphasis on life's variability and on the vital role of environmental opportunity. In order to define the characteristics of the healthy and to devise a lexicon of health, the well rather than the sick must be the subjects of investigation.

How do the specific genetic and environmental factors differentiating one individual from another lead to the development of certain diseases? Why do some people escape heart disease even in extreme old age and others develop coronary ailments before the middle years? Why do some people have a greater susceptibility to cancer than others? Although biochemical factors are undoubtedly of paramount importance in the development of heart disease and cancer, the conviction is growing among scientists that multiple factors are at work in these insidious disorders, including lifelong hygienic practices, nutrition, occupation, and even the degree of emotional adjustment. It is not inconceivable that invaluable clues to the causes and mechanisms of heart disease and cancer—and possibly also some means of predicting and preventing them—might emerge from large-scale and long-term studies of predisease characteristics and modes of life.

Enormous scientific returns would also undoubtedly be derived from a similar broad approach to research on aging. Why are there such wide individual variations in the rate of aging, and what is the relative influence of genetic and environmental elements on these differences? Why do some men and women remain spry and alert in their eighties and others begin to show signs of physical and mental deterioration in middle age? Authoritative opinion is that the aging process itself and the diseases that often develop in older people are not necessarily the same thing. We have yet to explore the full dimensions of aging as an independent variable in an effort to understand the roles that time and continued exposure to the noxious influences of the environment play in it. The immensely complex questions range, as one scientist has said, all the way "from the dynamics of cell structure to the problems of adaptability under different psychosocial circumstances." But the lessons we may be able to draw from such research, in terms of better health and greater happiness, are truly dazzling.

The answers to these and other enigmas of human biology probably still lie in the far-distant future. But to an extent undreamed of only a few decades ago, medicine already has the knowledge and skills to protect man against perils that were once unavoidable and often deadly, to detect the effects of wear and tear upon his body, and to assure him—with the aid of the benefits accruing from better nutrition, housing, and education—of a much higher level of well-being and efficiency than his ancestors were generally able to obtain. The old-time plagues and pestilences have been wiped out, making possible a striking extension of average life expectancy and opening up new horizons for the flowering of human resources. New hazards to health have arisen, however, as by-products of our technological advances. As the menace of communicable and acute disease has been alleviated, the problems of the chronic and degenerative ailments and of mental illness have grown more formidable. With the new opportunities have come fresh challenges that we have barely begun to meet.

The fruits of available knowledge are still to be applied fully and brought within reach of the largest possible number of people. The medical profession's thinking is yet to be reoriented from heavy concentration on the treatment of illness to the prevention of disease and disability, even though doctors will more and more have to deal not only with patients who are sick or who think they are ill but also with those who want to stay well. We still have to devise new patterns of organization of medical services to meet constantly changing health problems.

On the basis of the advances of the past few decades, Dr. Caldwell B. Esselstyn wrote:

> One can look forward to the ability to control an increasing number of today's incurable diseases. To diabetes, pernicious anemia and the infectious diseases will be added many more as medical science learns an increasing amount about the fine structure of cells, thanks to the electron microscope, the mechanism of metabolic pathways governed by the enzyme, the structure of the large protein molecules, including viruses, the nature and interrelation of hormones, the clinical nature of genes, the mechanism of the replication of cells, the factor or factors that cause cells to multiply widely, the humoral and neural factors that cause hypertension and the mechanism and action of the antibiotics, and obtains a more fundamental understanding of neuroses and psychoses. These are but a few of the activities that will place the emphasis in medical practice of the future on the degenerative diseases, more and more attention on rehabilitation and psychiatry and a tremendous increase in the proportion of time spent in preventive medicine. There will be a gradual breaking down of the artificial barriers between private and public.

As medicine consolidates its defensive positions by progressively bringing the major killing diseases under control, it will increasingly be able to turn its attention toward the goal of a fuller life in which man can realize his utmost potentialities and achieve as successful an adjustment to his environment as his organic constitution permits. This, of course, not only is medicine's job but also calls for a broad offensive on all levels of social action. However, the role of the medical profession in this supreme undertaking is a very large one and demands its fullest integration with the other forces of progress in our society.

III

"Research" has become a magic word in American life, an open sesame to the Federal treasury and the substantial resources of a great variety of private agencies. Next to the fantastic sums now being spent on the incessant perfection of nuclear armaments and the preliminaries to the race to the moon, there is probably no other field in which there has been such a spectacular jump in spending in recent years as that of medical research. There can certainly be no quarrel with the need for mounting a concerted research attack on heart disease, cancer, and the other major maladies still plaguing mankind. But thoughtful observers are increasingly raising the issue of priorities. In view of the penurious state of American medical education and the growing shortage of professional health manpower, there is ample ground for asking whether we are not putting the cart before the horse.

Congress has for years proceeded on the dubious theory that the urgency for more medical research is far greater than the necessity for more medical care. In doing so, it has consistently ignored the obvious facts that the skills of physicians and related personnel are the pivotal elements in the prevention and treatment of disease, that the production of more and better doctors is the mainstay of medicine, and that there is little point in lavish appropriations for research without a similar concern for training the people who can furnish the medical care we are now capable of giving and who are competent to do the research that can improve health care still further.

Legislation for critically needed Federal aid for medical education to relieve the financial plight of the existing medical schools and to permit the establishment of a number of new ones has continued to languish in Congress. But so potent has become the political popularity of medical research that, instead of the usual practice of pruning the national budget, it is now an annual ritual for the House and Senate to vie in exceeding the President's budgetary request for the National Institutes of Health (NIH), the research arm of the U.S. Public Health Service. In 1962, the agency got $100 million more than the White House had asked for.

In the past twenty years, the annual NIH appropriation has skyrocketed from $3.5 million to more than $1 billion. Along with support from other government sources, Federal expenditures for medical research are now running at the rate of about $1.5 billion a year. This is supplemented by an annual outlay of $335 million from philanthropic foundations and voluntary health agencies. The overall figure is nearly eight times what we are spending for medical education. Aside from this gross disparity in the proportion of support, there is the question as to whether money is being pumped into medical research too fast to be used soundly. Nor has the impact of the flood of research grants on the universities and medical schools been wholly salutary.

Top NIH officials are reported to have privately expressed dismay at times at the casualness with which Congress has opened the purse strings. As their budgets have kept on climbing, they have been forced to beat the bushes for ways to spend the riches thrust upon them and have not infrequently found that there was more money than there were research ideas worth pursuing or competent researchers to do this job. The agency's appropriations have shot up so rapidly that it has had trouble maintaining adequate controls over the thousands of grants it has handed out, most of them to university and medical school researchers. Not only are the long-term awards, given for periods of up to eight years, often renewed automatically without sufficient follow-up, but there are reported to be serious doubts about the value of some of the research projects financed by Federal funds.

Dr. Philip H. Abelson, director of research at the Geophysical Laboratory of the Carnegie Institution of Washington and editor of the journal of the American Association for the Advancement of Science, commented recently that heavy governmental support for scientific research has attracted many people without adequate motivation or intellectual capacity to contribute anything important to science. Mediocre research has diluted the scientific literature, he said, and made valuable work more difficult to recognize. Similar concern over the effects of the prodigality of research funds was expressed not long ago by Dr. Maxwell Finland of Harvard Medical School. He told a Congressional committee that the financial support for medical research is seriously out of balance with the resources available for the training of doctors and was "draining off a large number of potentially good physicians and teachers" and at the same diluting the standards of research because of the lack of enough qualified investigators.

Teaching and research often go hand in hand and, if properly balanced, can materially improve the quality of instruction. The profusion of research grants has enabled the medical schools to expand their faculties, since investigation and teaching readily mesh in medical education. But the explosive increase in research work has sometimes also forced the schools to dip into their own budgets for additional outlays for plant and maintenance. Many medical schools that have large research programs sponsored by outside sources remain desperately in need of adequate support for their regular teaching activities. If a further decline in the availability of medical care and a deterioration of its quality are to be averted, the schools must be enabled to strengthen and expand their teaching capacity through large-scale Federal grants for general operating purposes and for the construction of new facilities. Funds must also be provided for scholarships to attract and aid able students.

"For the first time in the history of medical research," Dr. James A. Shannon, the NIH director, has said, "the limitation on progress is due more to shortage of manpower than money available." This problem is certain to become still more acute as the research effort keeps on growing, as it is quite likely to do, and the medical schools are increasingly falling behind the need to turn out enough doctors both to do some of the research and to meet the mounting demand for medical care by a rapidly expanding population. At the same time, the medical profession's high earnings make it all the more difficult to recruit enough physicians who are willing to give up remunerative private practice in order to become teachers and research workers.

Over and above these considerations, there is the very serious question as to whether medical research lends itself to the kind of crash approach that produced the atomic bomb. There is an obvious popular appeal in the clarion call for an all-out attack on "the dread diseases." But many people have a grossly exaggerated idea of what can be accomplished merely by the expenditure of millions in the solution of the immensely subtle riddles involved in the processes that produce heart disease, cancer, and a number of other ailments. Diseases do not readily fall into compartments. Nor does science normally achieve its practical results by aiming directly at them.

It is to be ardently hoped that we shall soon start moving to correct the flagrant imbalance between financial support for medical research and for medical education. But even if Congress finally sees the light, the process of expanding medical education facilities is inherently so slow that there is little prospect for a substantial enlargement of the supply of doctors and other health personnel in the near future. We cannot appropriate today and have any appreciable increase in the number of physicians within a year or two. No matter what is done, we can expect continuing shortages in the years to come. This outlook makes it all the more imperative that we give fully as much attention to the problems of raising the level of the available professional manpower and of its most efficient utilization as we do to the means of increasing it. Here we run into the focal point that, by failing to adopt new organizational arrangements dictated by scientific progress, the prevailing system of medical practice has become more and more extravagant in the use of personnel and facilities. The training of doctors is far too costly and there are not enough of them to go on permitting the waste of their talents.

As long as doctors continue to operate independently, even though they are no longer self-sufficient and are increasingly dependent upon the knowledge and skills of their colleagues, duplication of effort and inefficient use of equipment are inevitable. When patients are commonly referred from one physician's office to another's, there is an unavoidable repetition of effort, laboratory examinations, and records. Another frequent waste of trained manpower in our present scheme of medical care results from the fact that many young physicians are only partly occupied in the early stages of establishing themselves in practice. Aside from its other savings, the provision of medical services in health centers through group practice eliminates this problem by giving new graduates an opportunity to start using their skills fully as soon as they complete their hospital training.

It is extremely doubtful whether the challenge of utilizing professional services more effectively, in order to provide better medical care per man and per dollar, can be met within the existing framework of independent practice. Essential is an extensive reorganization of the patterns of practice to provide for the wider sharing of skills, facilities, equipment, and records and for easier communication between doctors. It is becoming ever more obvious that medicine cannot meet the needs of the 1960's and beyond if it continues to cling to nineteenth-century concepts of organization. We can get the most out of scarce professional manpower, not only by way of cutting overhead costs but also in the form of a higher quality of care, only through the economies of more rational organization, including better use of auxiliary personnel.

The answer to the cost-control problem in medicine, just as in industry, lies in the adoption of methods that make for greater productivity. This, obviously, cannot be attained by making doctors work still longer hours and cutting down further the time given each patient, a process that is already impairing the general quality of medical care. The only promising approach lies in the efficiency and economy of large-scale organization, which would permit more effective use of less costly auxiliary skills to augment the expensive capacities of physicians and allow them to apply their judgment where it is most urgently needed. The same forces that have brought about ever-greater teamwork among the various medical specialties also dictate broader cooperative arrangements with the paramedical occupations.

It is highly significant that in a number of Western European countries, high standards of medical care are being maintained with a lower ratio of doctors than in the United States and that their ratio of specialists, in particular, is considerably below ours.

Outstanding examples are Sweden and the Netherlands, which have managed to chalk up the best health records in the world with a much smaller proportion of physicians than in this country. This clearly indicates that there are ways of improving the utilization of professional services.

Greater efficiency and, frequently, a higher general level of competence have been achieved in a number of European countries through regional organization of hospitals and their staffing by salaried specialists. Sweden has demonstrated that a remarkably low record of infant mortality can be maintained by having nurse-midwives give virtually all prenatal care under the direction of obstetricians. Specially trained nurse-midwives, backed up by the family doctor and specialist, also provide the bulk of both prenatal and postnatal services in several other Western European countries with excellent health records. Advantage also has been taken in Europe of similar possibilities for economy in the pediatric field through more comprehensive use of nurses. Trained nurses are fully competent to administer inoculations and to perform many other chores, including the health education of mothers, now done by pediatricians, who have been trained for crises but currently devote much of their time to the routine.

Expert opinion is that much more can be done to cut costs through the whole spectrum of medical care by way of wider use of nurses, laboratory technicians, physical and occupational therapists, dietitians, medical social workers, and a variety of other assistants to save the time of doctors for the jobs that they alone can do. One of the main reasons for slow progress in ths direction has been the medical profession's touchiness about its traditional prerogatives and its reluctance to surrender its sole jurisdiction even over areas of practice that physicians are increasingly avoiding.

It is true that the division of labor in medicine can be carried too far and that the increasing use of intermediaries between doctors and patients has its dangers. One of the main objectives of the doctor's independent existence may be defeated, *The Lancet,* the British medical publication, recently observed, "if he leaves all dressings to the nurse, sympathy to the receptionist, messages to the secretary, and the solution of home problems to the social worker. Organization can be a menace to the personal care we are supposed to be organizing."

But organization is the inevitable result of technological progress. When properly managed, it can also help bridge the growing chasm between the harried physician and the patient who feels rejected when he is unable to get the attention he craves for. Nurses and other auxiliary aides can sssume more strategic positions on the health team not only by carrying out the doctor's orders and doing the things that he need not do himself but also by helping to meet the patient's emotional needs and transmitting his problems to the physician. They can take on vital new roles in the management of convalescence and rehabilitation within the healing matrix of the home. Through use of the language of homely common sense, they can perform a crucial function in the neglected field of health education.

Even more important and intricate than the need for better utilization of the more economical ancillary skills is the issue of the competence of doctors at a time of constant changes in the dimensions of medical science. Here, too, far-reaching organizational reforms are essential if more Americans are to get the kind of medical care that scientific progress has brought within our reach. The MD degree in itself does not qualify the new graduate for immediate practice as a physician. Before he can hang out his shingle, he must complete a period of training under guidance in an approved hospital. But this is only a beginning. So vast has medical knowledge become and so staggering the amount of factual information that a doctor may need that it is utterly impossible for a medical school to impart all of it. Undergraduate medical training merely provides a foundation for further education during the internship and residency periods and throughout professional life. The best that the medical school can do, besides teaching the student the fundamental principles of human physiology and some of the basic technical skills, is to try to inculcate within him the habits of scientific thinking and to impress upon him the importance of continuing to keep abreast of the advances of his rapidly evolving discipline.

The goal of all education is to motivate and equip men and women to continue to educate themselves. More so than in almost any other field, this is indispensable in medicine, which entails a lifetime of constant renewal of knowledge. Some physicians progress and mature through the stimulation of close daily association with their colleagues, by carefully following the pertinent literature, and by taking refresher courses from time to time. Others are unable or unwilling to take advantage of such opportunities, and their competence becomes static and thereby automatically declines. The doctor who fails to keep up with the growing store of accumulated knowledge practices throughout his career the kind of medicine that was in existence at the time he graduated from medical school, with only such modifications as he has been able to acquire from sporadic contacts with other physicians, from desultory reading of the medical journals, and even more so from the promotional literature put out by the drug companies. His patients are thus often deprived of the benefits of new developments in medicine.

The distressing reality is that the existing system of graduate and post graduate medical education, starting with the internship and residency training in the hospital, is often grossly deficient and that many physicians cease to learn after they are licensed and derive much of their inspiration from pharmaceutical salesmen. Most likely to fall behind is the busy general practitioner, whose need for continuing education is most acute but who has the least time and incentive to get it. For many doctors, the problem boils down to a choice between neglecting their practice—and income—and neglecting their homework. It can be readily surmised which alternative most of them choose.

As new therapies and techniques have continued to multiply, the medical schools have had increasing difficulties in trying to cram the necessary knowledge into the student's skull within the limited available period of time. The growing embarrassment of riches has more and more forced the schools to concentrate on basic principles and to rely upon internship and later training to teach young doctors the finer points of practicing medicine and upon the resolution of their alumni to maintain continuous progress thereafter. But the trouble is that while the medical schools are carrying out their own task tolerably well, they have little control over continuing education, with the result that the job is often done poorly, if at all. The main problem in medical education has to a large extent shifted from the student to the intern and resident and to the practitioner with his need to keep up to date. Here responsibility is now so diffused and often so poorly exercised that what the medical schools are trying to accomplish is in grave danger of being undone during hospital training and then in the hurly-burly of daily practice.

The crisis of graduate and postgraduate medical education is clearly evident in the steadily worsening internship and residency situation. Although internship is intrinsically a part of under-graduate medical education and should really be looked upon as the fifth year of medical school, it has often deteriorated into little more than a vehicle for providing understaffed hospitals with the low-paid services of apprentice physicians. Much of the same thing is true of a good deal of residency training. This goes a long way toward defeating what is perhaps the most critical phase of the whole educational process.

There are fine teaching hospitals in which the internship and residency periods are a fruitful educational experience and not only broaden the young doctor's competence but also strengthen his appreciation of high scientific and ethical standards of prac-tice. But there are many more hospitals, according to competent opinion, in which the overworked and undersupervised house staff is learning instead to purvey poor medicine. There are many hospitals that fail to meet adequate standards for intern and resi-dency training and are using fledgling physicians to provide the minimal needs of patient care in the absence of full-time salaried staffs. The student learns from day-to-day contact with sick people in the wards and outpatient clinics, and the kind of physi-cian that he will become is dependent upon the opportunities that he is given for learning and upon the quality of medical care rendered by those whom he observes. He is denied genuine train-ing when, as is now frequently the case, he is primarily used as a source of cheap labor and overwhelmed with routine chores as a helper for doctors in private practice.

There is an enormous spread between hospitals that are top-notch teaching institutions and those that barely satisfy minimal requirements. Properly staffed hospitals have fully equipped laboratories for the basic medical sciences and salaried experts who are available throughout the day as teachers and consultants. They have comprehensive educational programs that utilize the experience and skills of the full-time and visiting staffs. In the general run of hospitals, on the other hand, the training is largely confined to hurried rounds with busy practitioners and the opportunity to write histories and to do physical examinations. These hospitals now mostly depend upon inadequately trained foreign physicians and the weaker American students who have no alternative but to take the poorer internships and residencies. There is thus a radical and deepening cleavage between the quality of services patients are getting and the kind of doctors being turned out to take care of them in the future.

At the root of this alarming state of affairs are the growing shortage of doctors, the rapid expansion of hospital capacity, the surge toward specialization, and the inadequate standards of approval for internship and residency training. Internship programs, which are a prerequiste for medical licensure, are approved by the AMA Council on Medical Education and Hospitals. Residencies, required for specialty training, are sanctioned by the AMA and the specialty boards involved. As more and more hospital beds have been built, the pressure has steadily mounted for house staffs. The stampede toward specialization has at the same time required a rapid expansion of residency openings. But while the AMA has supinely kept on accrediting additional training spots with little regard for their qualification, the output of the nation's medical schools has failed to keep pace with the constantly increasing demand. The result has been that far more internships and residencies have been approved than can actually be filled.

What has happened may readily be seen from the fact that the some 13,000 internships for which hospitals are now approved are nearly double the annual total of graduates from American medical schools. The 32,620 residencies currently offered by hospitals are double the number available only a decade ago and are almost five times the size of the medical school graduating classes. The upshot of this exercise in irresponsibility, aside from the poor training that many young physicians get, is that part of the gulf is filled by foreign doctors and the rest is left gaping. About 2,000 internships and 5,000 residencies have for several years remained vacant.

So concerned have responsible leaders in the hospital field

become over the situation that one of them recently suggested that major responsibility for intern and resident training be vested in the medical schools. The proposal came from Dr. Russell A. Nelson, director of the Johns Hopkins Hospital and a former president of the American Hospital Association, who said the time was ripe for a thorough reorganization and upgrading of graduate medical training similar to the sweeping reforms in undergraduate education brought about as a result of the Flexner report more than fifty years ago.

Fully as deplorable is the state of much of what goes under the name of postgraduate education for practicing physicians. Although they are already overburdened by the multitude of their own curricular and financial problems, some of the medical schools and their affiliated hospitals are making a valiant effort to offer refresher courses, seminars, and institutes designed to direct the attention of doctors to new scientific developments. They also send out teams of faculty members to conduct review programs for local physicians in their own medical societies or at hospital-staff meetings. A great variety of clinics are available in the better hospitals to help doctors keep themselves competent in their specialties. Other refresher courses are often conducted by medical societies under drug company sponsorship. But just as there is a wide disparity in the capacity of hospitals to provide educational opportunities for interns and residents and in their devotion to this end, so are the postgraduate programs notably diverse and uneven. As the expansion of knowledge continues to accelerate, the gap is widening between what needs to be done in the field of postgraduate medical education and what is actually being done. Not only is there no integrated approach to the challenging task of helping doctors keep up to date, but the impediments to a really meaningful scheme of continuing education are great.

The doctor who gets his training in a good hospital works in a group-practice setting, where he is constantly exposed to the guidance of skillful teachers and the stimulating interplay of teamwork. He is schooled to high standards of medical workmanship and taught to study each patient with painstaking care. But when he goes into private practice, it is not always easy to maintain these standards under the pressures of a crowded waiting room and an endless round of hospital and house calls. The independent physician stands alone in the competitive race and is largely left to his own devices in keeping abreast of the times. This is particularly true of general practitioners who are isolated from the mainstream of medicine by the lack of hospital-staff affiliations. Overwork and fatigue often stand in the way of a selective reading of the great mass of professional literature and of taking advantage of the not always easily accessible educational opportunities. Many doctors cannot afford to take time off from their practices for refresher courses or even to attempt to keep up with the tremendous flow of scientific information.

Competing for the physician's time—besides patients and drug salesmen—is a veritable flood of new ideas in the rapidly changing and expanding body of medical knowledge. How virtually insurmountable the problem is becoming may be gathered from the estimate that some three hundred thousand articles are now being published in medical journals every year. Although the great bulk of this literature is of little value to the average practitioner, he must read some of it if he is to treat his patients more effectively. Their lives may sometimes depend on his possession of the latest medical information. But under the contingencies of solo practice, it is an enormously difficult struggle to keep ahead of the avalanche of new material and to discriminate between genuine scientific developments and the exaggerations frequently peddled by the pharmaceutical industry's vast enterprise of commercial exploitation.

The educational process is commonly forced to a standstill when patients come at all hours, the telephone keeps on ringing, days off are rare, and protracted absences for study at medical centers are expensive and difficult to arrange. Before long, as scientific inquisitiveness and perception are gradually blurred by time and the constraints of daily practice, the busy physician finds himself less and less uneasy about his inability to keep up with the progress of medicine. Professionally, he has been defeated by the prevailing system of medical practice.

There is general agreement among competent authorities that if the public is to be assured of the full benefits of scientific advances, concerted and vigorous action will have to be taken in the area of postgraduate medical education. But how can overworked and underinformed doctors be encouraged under the free-enterprise system of practice not to allow their professional competence to become rusty? What incentives can be offered them to continue their education, and what penalties can be imposed for their failure to do so? How this goal can be attained without the leverage of much more forceful controls than are now available is far from clear.

In 1962, after a lengthy exploration of the problem, a broadly representative study group came up with an ambitious proposal for establishment of a national "university without walls" with a faculty whose function it would be to develop "core curriculums" for continuing education in the various branches of medicine. These would include taped lectures and demonstrations to be telecast nationally and filmstrips and other teaching materials to be used in a systematic program of regional and local conferences and clinics in hospitals and at medical society meetings.

The report of the study committee, which had been organized by the AMA, with the cosponsorship of most of the nation's other leading medical organizations, minced no words about the critical need for keeping doctors up to date. It quoted the conclusion of the President's Conference on Heart Disease and Cancer that "the best medical education and training can become obsolete in five years unless the physician makes a very determined effort to continue his education" and conceded that "there is a serious gap between available knowledge and application in medical practice." But the best it could offer to assure wide participation in the proposed organized program of continuing education was "a variety of voluntary examinations" to allow doctors taking the courses to assess their own progress. "The physician," it carefully emphasized, "might elect to take the examinations or to ignore them." This is a far cry indeed from a system of group practice that spurs continued competence and has built-in mechanisms for checking on it or from the big stick of periodic re-examinations for renewal of licensure to force doctors to keep on their toes. A proposal for establishing minimum standards for postgraduate education was rejected in 1964 by the AMA House of Delegates.

All in all, there is no getting away from the fact that millions of Americans are now receiving second-class medical care and will continue to do so unless there is a broad reorganization of the existing system of unsupervised solo practice.

So perturbing has the situation become and so deep is the growing cleavage between many practicing physicians and the professional elite in the great teaching medical centers that a heated debate has been raging in academic circles in recent years on how to deal with what is referred to as "the dilemma of the two-culture split in medicine." As the better hospitals tend more and more toward staffing with board-certified specialists, some of them on a full-time salary basis, there is the danger of a virtually unbridgeable gap between the physicians competent to use the most intricate medical procedures and the general run of outside practitioners. Uncontrolled continuance of this trend will inevitably lead to a further stratification of the medical profession. It can result only in an accelerated retrogression in the quality of care given to a large proportion of patients by making it even more difficult to keep all doctors conversant with medical advances.

How can the gulf between medical research and practice be narrowed? Have the dimensions of medical science become too big for the average doctor to master? Since there are degrees of skills required in the treatment of various kinds of diseases, should there be a clearer division of function among medical practitioners? And to carry this idea to its logical conclusion, should there be different types of medical schools or of curriculums to produce several kinds of physicians?

One of those who think so is Dr. David Rutstein, head of the Department of Preventive Medicine at Harvard Medical School, who has called for a sweeping reorganization of the present system of medical education. "The educational needs of the specialist and scientist on the one hand and general physicians on the other grow farther and farther apart," Dr. Rutstein has said, "and it is increasingly difficult to include them within the compass of the medical curriculum." He has therefore proposed the introduction of two separate curriculums—one for general physicians and the other for specialists and medical scientists—as the best way for meeting the need for more doctors and for attaining a higher quality of medical competence. The curriculum for general physicians would concentrate on the practical aspects of medicine and be shorter than the present one, thus making it possible to turn out many more doctors. The longer curriculum would emphasize the broader scientific background needed by specialists, medical school teachers, and future researchers.

Dr. Rutstein is by no means alone. A number of other prominent medical educators have likewise faced up to the fact that every medical school cannot possibly do everything that every other one does and do it well, and they have urged that the curriculum he made more flexible to adapt it to the differentiated needs of various types of students. There have been suggestions that some schools, particularly those associated with state universities, be oriented to the training of doctors for general practice and that the schools affiliated with institutions with the highest standards of scholarship concentrate on the training of physicians and other scientists who will play leading roles in specialized medical care, teaching, and research.

All such proposals have evoked cries of dismay from the traditionalists in medicine. The rebuttal has been that any such formal differentiations would intensify the breach within the profession and, by lowering still further the status of the family physician, would deter able students from a career dedicated to personal care. The need, one authority has said, is for instilling more rather than less science into clinical medicine. Another has asserted that "society would be singularly ill served by the production of medical corpsmen in place of basic physicians resulting from a medical education and experience leaving them lifelong students of medicine." There is a great deal of merit to this argument. But the trouble is that it offers no solution to the perplexing problem of how doctors can be motivated and enabled to maintain and develop their competence.

As medical science and education have continued to grow in complexity, many medical schools have developed a hard core of full-time faculty members, not only in such basic science subjects as anatomy and physiology but also in clinical medicine, who combine research with responsibility for patient care in the wards and outpatient departments of teaching hospitals. This is much preferable to the system in vogue not so many years ago whereby most clinical teachers were recruited from the ranks of busy practitioners who had little time for their students or interest in them. Physicians who devote their main interest and energy to teaching and research are far more likely to inculcate in students a scientific point of view. The full-time principle has nevertheless encountered considerable opposition within the profession on the ground that teachers cut off from the practical urgencies of private practice are in danger of developing an "ivory tower" attitude toward the day-to-day problems of medical care. Whether this, if true, is good or bad is a debatable proposition. There is certainly no denying that the medical faculties provide the most outspoken critics of the profession's standpat leadership.

At its best, the task of the medical school goes far beyond the abstract teaching of the arts and skills of medicine. It also involves the demonstration of good medical care and its dispensation to the needy in the wards and clinics of the university hospitals. It seeks to widen the intellectual horizons of future physicians through a synthesis of education, research, and patient care. But the great challenge the medical schools still have to meet head on is the training of doctors who will accept the desirability and necessity of the bold innovations that the constantly changing profile of disease and of medical practice so urgently demands.

Anxious to keep their peace with the organized profession, the medical schools and their affiliated hospitals have generally remained aloof from the development of the big group-practice insurance plans, where the most significant metamorphosis of the organizational patterns of medical service is under way. Medical education and group-practice prepayment both stand to gain a great deal by pooling their resources. With many people who formerly went to the charity wards now able to afford private care, the schools are suffering from a drying up of the traditional sources of clinical teaching material. The group-practice plans offer not only a new reservoir of patients but also the opportunity for involvement in direct service programs that expose students to dealing with the total health maintenance needs of people rather than with patients just being treated for sporadic illness. Another advantage is that apprentice physicians can greatly benefit by working, from the start, not with compliant charity cases but with patients who are paying their own way and who must be treated with consideration for their dignity. Here the doctors of tomorrow could truly begin preparing themselves for the medicine of tomorrow.

IV

As part of their rising standard of living, Americans are now spending far more money on medical care than ever before and are certain to dig still deeper into their pockets for this purpose in the years to come. No item in the U.S. Bureau of Labor Statistics cost-of-living index has skyrocketed as much as have health care costs since World War II. In the 1949–1961 period, all items in the Consumer Price Index rose 28.3 per cent; but the overall grouping of medical services increased by 62.4 per cent, and hospital room rates shot upward 128 per cent. Physicians' fees have climbed 67 per cent in the past fifteen years. The result of this inflationary spiral, combined with greater per capita utilization of health services and rapid population growth, has been that the nation is now spending more than nine times as much for medical care as it did some thirty years ago. Medical services presently account for about 6 per cent of disposable income as compared with only 4.5 per cent as recently as 1950. Even when measured in terms of constant dollars adjusted to the rise in the general price level, the current per capita outlay for medical care is considerably more than twice what it was in 1929. Outside of the huge expenditures for health purposes out of tax funds, health care spending at present comes to an average of about $120 a year for every man, woman, and child in the United States.

There is every reason to believe that the upward cost trend will continue and that this will provoke increasing concern and more clamorous questions as to whether medicine costs more than it should and as to how we can pay the bill. Unquestionably, there are many legitimate reasons for rising medical prices. The chief "culprit," of course, is scientific progress. It not only has brought a profusion of new, elaborate, and expensive methods of prevention, diagnosis, and cure but also has kept alive millions of people who have some kind of chronic illness. A substantial portion of the bill goes for the care of these men and women who, if medical science had stood still, would have died long ago of one of the acute diseases that now are preventable or curable.

As the proportion of older people and the standards of medical care continue to rise, necessitating more and better trained personnel and still more intricate facilities and equipment, the problems of the financing of health services will be steadily aggravated. The burden of chronic illness is certain to keep on growing. More and more people are avidly accepting the idea that good health is purchasable. All of which means that both the unit price of medical services and the rate of consumption will go on rising. Seriously complicating this pattern is the fact that the supply of professional manpower has utterly failed to keep pace with the demand.

There is little doubt that, as the richest nation in the world, we can afford adequate health care. On the whole, there is no ground for being apologetic about the high costs of medical care. The benefits to be derived from these expenditures are immense, and there is no reason why we should not be able to allocate an ever-greater proportion of our national income to health services. The core of the problem is how the costs can be controlled and distributed so as to keep them within the reach of the great mass of people and how medical care can be made more widely available without losing its effective qualities. There is every indication that the public is prepared to pay the cost of progress— provided that it is necessary and reasonable. But there are also many indications of growing impatience with that portion of the cost which is questionable and suggests motives inimical to the public interest.

There are no easy answers and no ready restraints available for the dilemma of the medical care cost spiral. But much of the remedy clearly lies in a more sensible organization of health services and in unfettered experimentation with various approaches toward greater economy. It lies in more efficient utilization of personnel and the reduction of needless overhead costs, in better integration of facilities, in greater resort to preventive measures, in the removal of incentives for the overuse of expensive hospitalization and wider use of more economical services when they serve as well, and in all the other benefits that would accrue from the application of the methods of large-scale organization in the health field.

There are no cost-cutting panaceas. Regardless of the manner in which medical services are provided and paid for and regardless of the most effective scheme for sharing the risks, good health care is intrinsically expensive and is likely to be even more so in the future. But to a large degree, the orderly organizational pattern that alone can prevent runaway inflation depends on the wholehearted cooperation of the medical profession. To an extent unequalled in any other sphere, doctors control the nature, course, and cost of medical treatment and are often allowed to charge what they please. The utmost in restraint and greater flexibility and responsiveness to the imperatives of the profound changes in the character of the medical economy are therefore essential for the preservation of the private practice of medicine.

Americans are more and more coming to regard adequate medical services as a social necessity and right, not only as a means of survival but as an essential requirement for the richer fulfillment of the longer span of life. That this assumption is not too farfetched and not entirely alien to the medical profession's own traditions is amply attested by the pledge of the Hippocratic oath to render aid to all those who need it.

In one form or another, broader medical security is coming in this country. It is extremely shortsighted and, in the long run, futile for the medical profession to ignore the implications of this development and of the other far-reaching adjustments required by the march of science. Continuance of such an attitude can only endanger the role that the profession is justly entitled to play in devising sound plans for the future of medical practice. It can lead only to mounting public revulsion and, possibly, to ill-considered action in a field where rashness can be extremely costly, not only financially but also in terms of human life and happiness.

V

The foremost issue in the medical care field is not, as the organized medical profession keeps on insisting, a simple choice between the sterling virtues of independent private practice and the grave perils of "socialized medicine"—a fighting term laden with emotional connotations and loosely used to describe anything deviating from the traditional norm. The basic issue, in fact, is whether a reasonable middle ground can be found between the anarchy of unrestrained and wasteful individual enterprise and the possible stultifying effects of excessive governmental intrusion.

Singularly blind to the sweeping implications of the technological revolution and heedless of their craft's traditions of experimentation and innovation, the spokesmen for organized medicine have dogmatically limited the field to a fictitious option between solo practice and regimentation. They have attempted to endow the method of payment of a separate fee for each service with the halo of personal liberty and the sacrosanct affinity between doctor and patient. They have sought to elevate a conglomeration of vague contentions into immutable ethical principles and to use them as roadblocks to progress. They have labeled anything that threatens the *status quo* as socialistic and insisted that matters urgently concerning all of us be left to their sole discretion. Determined to hang on to their monopoly, they have consistently spoken with the voice of self-interest and continued to fight a bitter rearguard battle against the inexorable forces pressing for new adjustments.

Actually, no significant segment of public opinion is now favoring anything like a total government take-over of the medical economy. Nor is there much substance to the menacing specter of an all-powerful bureaucracy determined to extend its tentacles to the purely professional aspects of medical practice and thereby irreparably impair their quality. The choices we face in evolving a more balanced and efficient system of medical care are infinitely more complex and yet far more flexible than the clear-cut alternatives held out by those who view history in the artless terms of an unequivocal struggle between good and evil.

The opponents of any form of governmental participation or controls in the health care picture are unmindful of the fact that in medicine there is no such thing as a purely private concern and that private and social interests always have been and always will be inextricably associated with it. They ignore the broad coexistence in our political system of public and private programs for retirement and disability pensions, for compensation for occupational injury, and numerous other benefit plans. They disregard the reality that we already have a highly mixed medical economy, in which tax funds cover more than one-fourth of overall health care expenditures. They overlook the fact that the classic competitive individualism that they so ardently defend no longer really exists and that the meshing of voluntary and governmental activities in the public interest is fully within the American pluralistic tradition.

The real choice is not between an obsolescent laissez-faire scheme and outright governmental domination. It lies instead in an enlightened willingness to heed the imperatives of change and to seek to channel them into a constructive course. It involves further development along the lines of our tradition of collaboration between the private and public sectors of society. It calls for an approach that stresses experimentation, variety, and expedited gradualism as the best means of achieving both quality and economy in the provision of medical services.

We are not inevitably destined to follow the pattern adopted in Britain and a number of other countries with compulsory national health insurance systems. It is highly significant that although many of the proposals contained in the legislation for a national health insurance plan beaten in Congress about fifteen years ago have since been enacted into law and government financing of health activities has grown enormously, only a few extremists now favor outright public control of medical care. The foreign programs have generally arisen from different stages of social and economic development than ours, and the fact that we have abstained so long from emulating them indicates in itself that we are likely to follow a different course. This is largely contingent, however, upon the ability of the medical profession to overcome the stereotypes of the past and to readjust its thinking to the realities of the scientific and socioeconomic revolution. The shape of the future organization of medical care and practice in this country will to a material degree be determined by the vision, imagination, and leadership that the profession manages to apply to the problem of providing medical care more equitably and at a reasonable cost.

The doctors must take a new look at themselves and at the society in which they live and practice. They must recognize the deep and justified concern of millions of people over the spiraling costs of medical care and health insurance. They must become politically sophisticated enough to perceive the peril of being identified in the public mind with rapacious standpatism. They must come to understand that the crisis in medicine, as in many other fields, is the direct consequence of the vast adjustments that we all must make to the phenomenal advances in science and technology and that new challenges call for new perspectives.

There is no reason why natural differences cannot be resolved through negotiation and compromise instead of being left exclusively to the arbitrariness of political action. A system built mainly around voluntary health insurance has many advantages. It avoids excessive concentration of power, facilitates initiative and experiment, ensures a variety of approaches, and stimulates consumer vigilance. We have much to gain from building upon the foundations that have made possible the great medical progress of the past few decades. But we shall be able to conserve the best elements in the existing order only if we move forward. Medicine can remain a predominantly private enterprise only if it is operated at all times in the public interest.

The expansion and strengthening of health insurance are by all odds the first and strongest bids that can be made for the preservation of the voluntary system of medical care. It is important to bear in mind that it was not the multimillion-dollar public relations "blitz" staged by organized medicine but rather the offer of an alternative in the form of voluntary health insurance that averted the adoption of a compulsory program in the late 1940's. A corollary to an effective insurance scheme, even if it is largely operated under private auspices, is a wide degree of public regulation, which is the most feasible alternative to outright public operation. Broader governmental assistance in certain areas that are beyond the means of private initiative likewise appears inevitable. It is wholly within our political tradition to use tax funds to pay for certain services that private institutions are unable to provide. There is ample room within the far-flung complex of our health care services for exercise of the peculiar American talent for combining governmental, private, and philanthropic endeavors to meet social needs.

The basic choice, then, is between conservative and radical therapy. But a course of moderation requires, first of all, an objective approach and a reasoned discussion of the issues instead of emotional sloganeering.

There is room in a democratic society for different points of view and different ways of doing things. A fundamental ingredient of such tolerance, however, is free competition among reasonable alternatives through which patterns of progress can most effectively be hammered out. All too many barriers thrown up by medical intransigence unfortunately still stand in the way of untrammeled experimentation with the most efficacious methods of providing medical services. Acceptable solutions for the problem of how the best possible medical care can be put within the reach of the greatest possible number of people can be devised only through application of the same critical spirit that has been responsible for the remarkable advances of scientific medicine.

"Every profession and every social institution is the product of a particular time," August Heckscher, director of the Twentieth Century Fund and a particularly perceptive student of our culture, wrote not long ago in the *New England Journal of Medicine*. "Times change; a new constellation of forces comes into being, and yet the institution frequently lives on in more or less stubborn form. It has by this time developed around it a whole fabric of supporting theories and vested interests. . . . It becomes defensive and uncompromising, and things that had once been recognized as the product of their time and place are spoken of as if by some decree they had been given eternal validity. The prevailing structure of medical care—the doctor in solo practice dealing on a fee-for-service basis with the individual patient—is not part of the eternal order of things. It is a social convention, and like all social conventions it is subject to re-examination, to development, to change."

The medical profession's general ideology reflects, Mr. Heckscher observed, the nineteenth-century concept of ethics under which "one man was expected to bear what he must, whereas another was expected to take what he could get." While this callous attitude has been softened, he said, by an overlay of professional standards and at least a theoretical dedication to disinterested service, it has nevertheless remained a fact that in the traditional physician-patient relationship, "the doctor stood to profit in proportion as the disease he diagnosed was of particular gravity or in proportion as the cure was prolonged." George Bernard Shaw made the same point in *The Doctor's Dilemma* by noting that a physician stood to gain far more from operating than from deciding not to operate.

Another way of looking at the medical profession's travail from a historical perspective is to view it as the typical reaction of a privileged class to the process that is compelling it to come to terms with its Industrial Revolution. It is not stretching an analogy too far to say, one observer has commented, that the doctor is increasingly being forced into the "factory" represented by the hospital and other institutions for the organized provision of medical care and subjected to the requisite labor discipline. That he often resents it is hardly surprising.

How fatuous it is for organized medicine to go on clinging obdurately to the tenets of rugged individualism is readily apparent from a glance at some of the major trends on the American medical scene. As medical science has continued to bound forward, the technical complexity of health services has increasingly outstripped the old patterns of organization. The onetime self-sufficiency of the solo practitioner has been progressively weakened. What was once an intensely personalized activity has been transformed into a huge institutional complex with intricate and highly specialized skills and facilities and a multiplicity of supporting professional personnel. At the same time, there have been sweeping changes in the social and economic structure and in the standard of living and a growing public awareness of the advantages of modern health care.

The available mechanisms for dealing with a plethora of problems—the explosive growth of medical knowledge, the profound changes in the character of disease, the far-reaching shifts in the age distribution of the population, and the constantly rising level of expectations—are bursting at the seams. The mounting prevalence of chronic disease in itself has had a pervading influence on the nature of the physician's task. The focus of treatment no longer is confined to the patient but extends to his family and community and involves the understanding and support that he needs in order to function as effectively as possible within the framework of his disability.

Good medical care today usually requires far more than a solitary doctor with a few of his elementary tools. It requires broad interrelationships and a recognition of the fact that not all physicians are equally well trained or qualified. The maintenance of high standards calls for the same tight self-discipline that prevails on the staff organizations of the better hospitals or for some other form of quality controls. The quality of medical care is an elusive property in which personal considerations often play a paramount role. But objective standards for its measurement are now available, and their increasing application may be expected as consumers become more sophisticated and better organized. The supposed obligation of the consumer to choose doctors whose qualifications he is unable to judge will be appreciated less and less as the years go by.

The various levels of government already are providing medical care for large segments of the population, including veterans, the families of servicemen, the indigent, and most of the mentally ill. More than half of the nation's hospital beds are operated by governmental agencies. About half of the annual investment in health in the United States is now derived from taxation and insurance payments, and the proportion coming from these sources is certain to keep on growing. One authority has predicted that within another ten to fifteen years, probably as much as 90 per cent of all payments to physicians will come from health insurance and tax funds.

Under mounting public pressure, health insurance will gradually become more comprehensive in nature, extending its coverage to home and office care and to diagnostic procedures outside the hospital, and will be subject to increasing public regulation. This will be accompanied by a steady growth in the teamwork of group practice as more and more physicians bow to the inevitable and adopt cooperative techniques in the interest of higher quality and greater economy.

The emphasis in the medical practice of tomorrow will be increasingly on preventive and rehabilitative measures and on wider application of the skills of psychiatry. Much of the medical care will be given in outpatient community health centers and in nonprofit nursing homes equipped to provide intensive nursing and rehabilitative services. As medicine moves away from concentration on acute episodes of illness and toward concern with the positive maintenance of health, it will more and more become involved in problems of social structure and action and in the molding of popular attitudes and values through the instrumentalities of mass education.

The great potentialities of medicine cannot be fully realized without far-ranging reforms in the manner in which health services are rendered and paid for. We have yet to bridge the distressing gap between what we know and what we do. Fully as vital as the pouring of many millions of dollars into medical research is the reorganization of the mechanisms for delivery of the fruits of the harvest of new knowledge to the consumers.

The prospects for effective cost controls are not encouraging under a system in which there are no means of supervising private professional performance, no enforcible standards of quality, no methods of determining errors of omission or commission, and no machinery for preventing the waste of uncoordinated or unneeded services. The tide toward change cannot be stemmed by endless harping on the merits of free enterprise and by repeated falling back upon the mystical relationship of doctor and patient. To paraphrase Georges Clemenceau's memorable remark that war is too important to be left to the generals, the health of people is far too crucial to be left solely to the profession's benevolence.

As far back as 1926, the late George E. Vincent, then president of the Rockefeller Foundation, said: "It looks as if society means to insist upon a more effective organization of medical services for all groups of people, upon distribution of the costs of services over large numbers of families and individuals, and upon making prevention of disease a controlling purpose. Just how these ends will be gained only a very wise or a very foolish man would venture to predict. One thing seems fairly certain: in the end society will have its way." While much progress has been made since then, organized medicine has moved far too reluctantly in the face of pressing necessity. Instead of seizing the opportunity to lead toward the new order, it has fought a delaying action and has acquiesced to changes only when they appeared to be the inescapable alternative to still greater disasters. "The time has passed," as Dr. Gunnar Gundersen, a former AMA president, told his colleagues a few years ago, "for policies based on generalities, platitudes, and flag-waving. The time has passed for medical crankiness, complaint, arrogance, and pigheadedness. The time has passed when we can fight our battles simply by quoting George Washington, Thomas Jefferson, and the rest of the Founding Fathers." For the medical profession, it is truly the eleventh hour.

It is obviously much more palatable to preserve the *status quo* than to alter it, particularly when a profession is as affluent and as contented with its prerogatives as medicine generally is these days. But aside from the pecuniary motives, there are deeply rooted traditional relationships in medicine that are not readily amenable to change. The physician's lot in our society, moreover, is often replete with frustrations.

Ideally, the doctor must know a great deal more than medicine and be a well-rounded, broadly educated person, keenly sensitive to the kaleidoscopic panorama of our culture and its shifting values, aware of the impact of the social and spiritual environment upon the origin and course of disease, responsive to his profession's wider responsibilities in an era of tumultuous upheaval. To treat the whole man, he must be a whole man himself. It is hard enough to be such a paragon under the best of circumstances. The conditions of today's medical practice make the task all the more arduous.

The physician has to contend with conflicting images of his profession's role and with the excruciating responsibilities of a still inexact science. It is difficult for him to reconcile the realities of daily practice with the altruistic concept that monetary reward is a subordinate consideration to service. It is not easy for him to discard his protective armor of omniscience. Finding himself caught in a whirlwind of change, he wearily seeks refuge in the dream of the halcyon days when the practice of medicine was solely the doctor's domain and there was no intrusion by politicians, consumers' organizations, and the press into the privacy of medical care.

Despite mounting controversy and resentment, the doctor still stands on a pedestal. But his traditional posture of prestige and affection is becoming more and more shaky. No drumfire of persuasion in itself, no wiles of the professional manipulators of public opinion, can serve to bolster it. The only things that really count in molding the physician's public image are the manner in which he treats his patients, his competence and compassion, his recognition of the urgent need for making the economic burden of medical care more bearable, his awareness that the progress of medical science not only is steadily enlarging the arsenal of tools for healing but also calls for new patterns of thought and action.

The hour may be later than it seems. Like the rest of us, the medical profession must adjust its thinking to a constantly changing reality. If the profession is to have a hand in shaping what is to come, it must learn to roll with the punch and accept the inevitable. It must learn that the good of the public comes first and that of the doctors second.